Structural Mechanics and Analysis

A Macmillan Series in Civil Engineering—Gene Nordby, Editor

Computer Methods in Solid Mechanics by Joseph J. Gennaro

Structural Mechanics and Analysis by James Michalos and Edward N. Wilson

Open Channel Flow by F. M. Henderson

(Other titles in preparation)

Structural Mechanics and Analysis

JAMES MICHALOS

*Professor of Civil Engineering
and Chairman of the Department,
New York University*

EDWARD N. WILSON

*Associate Professor of Civil Engineering,
New York University*

The Macmillan Company, New York
Collier-Macmillan Limited, London

Preface

This book deals with principles of structural mechanics and their application to the analysis of structural systems and components. It is not a book on design, but the needs of the designer have been kept prominently in mind.

Design, and not analysis as such, is generally the engineer's goal. However, in order to plan and design the more and more complex systems with which he must deal, the engineer needs a thorough understanding of the principles of structural mechanics. There should be no mistaking the fact that analysis is not design, but neither should it be forgotten that they are closely related.

Structural analysis involves principles of statics, principles of geometry, and properties of materials. The forces (or stresses) and deflections in some structures can be completely defined by a consideration of statics and of properties of the material only. Such structures are called statically determinate, and they are treated in the first five chapters of the book. Chapters 1 and 2 deal with the determination of reactions, shears, moments, and forces in plane structures, including beams, cables, arches, and trusses of various types. The string polygon and the pressure line, used subsequently in Chapter 10, are introduced in Chapter 2 and applied to the solution of problems.

Chapter 3 is devoted to influence lines, and Müller-Breslau's principle is introduced and applied. The properties of the influence line are used to determine maximum effects due to moving loads, without recourse to formulas and special criteria. The types of structures considered are beams, girders, trusses, arch ribs, and arch trusses.

Three-dimensional trussed frameworks are treated in Chapter 4, and include compound and complex frameworks, domes, and towers. One of the problems solved in this chapter is subsequently resolved through use of matrix formulation in Chapter 9 in order to illustrate the potential of matrix methods used in conjunction with an electronic digital computer.

Chapter 5 deals with some approximate methods of analysis for statically indeterminate structures. Such methods can be important in preliminary design or in analysis when quick estimates are needed or when checking an "exact" analysis.

In Chapter 6 a thorough treatment is made of movements and rotations which may be of interest in themselves or which may be necessary in the analysis of statically indeterminate structures. The student must thoroughly understand this chapter before he can deal adequately with the remainder of the book. Emphasis is placed on the geometry involved and on the analogy of the computations of geometry to well-known computations of statics. The relationship of special techniques, such as the method of virtual work and Castigliano's method, to each other and to the real problem of geometry is demonstrated.

The analysis of statically indeterminate beams and frames is introduced in Chapter 7. It is now necessary to satisfy simultaneously the requirements of statics and geometry of the system, taking into account the properties of the materials. Similar requirements must be satisfied in dealing with other problems of steady state, such as electric or hydraulic networks. Classical and numerical methods of analysis are presented and thoroughly illustrated. Again, emphasis is placed on an over-all, unifying view. The methods of analysis presented are related to one or the other of two classifications. Either a solution satisfying the requirements of statics is assumed and the corresponding errors of geometry subsequently corrected, or a solution satisfying the requirements of geometry is assumed and errors in statics corrected. The effects of elastic supports and of support settlements are included. Influence lines are obtained by superposition of corrections on an assumed influence line.

Similar methods of analysis are used for statically indeterminate trusses in Chapter 8. Internally indeterminate trusses, continuous trusses, and trussed arches are included. Influence lines are again obtained by superimposing corrections on a statically possible influence line.

Matrix methods of analysis are introduced in Chapter 9. Strictly speaking, these are not methods of analysis but rather matrix formulation of known methods of analysis. Sections 9.1, 9.2, and 9.3 on properties of matrices, matrix inversion, and eigenvalues may be omitted if they have been covered in a mathematics course. If not, they are sufficient for following all applications in this book. Similarly, Section 9.4 on linear algebraic equations can be omitted. Emphasis in Sections 9.5, 9.6, and 9.7 is on a physical understanding of the relationship between a stiffness matrix and its inverse and between a flexibility matrix and its inverse. In Sections 9.8 and 9.9, matrix formulation is applied to the force method and to the displacement method of analysis. We do exactly what was done in Chapter 7, but solution of the equations is obtained by inversion of the flexibility or stiffness matrix of coefficients. The particular advantage of matrix formulation in connection with computer operations is highlighted. Matrix methods are subsequently used in Chapters 10, 12, and 13.

Methods of analysis for arches and rings are presented in Chapter 10. The pressure line, its use in approximate analysis, and the corresponding requirements of geometry are used to introduce the treatment. The force method of analysis is shown to yield equations identical to those obtained from a consideration of the geometrical requirements corresponding to the pressure line. The method of the elastic center and the column analogy are then developed, and the column analogy is used for the determination of effects of volume changes and for obtaining fixed-end moments and properties of flexural members. Influence lines are obtained by superposition, and matrix formulation of the displacement method of analysis is applied to continuous arches.

A straightforward treatment of plastic analysis for continuous beams and rigid frames of steel is presented in Chapter 11. Buckling of columns, and numerical methods (including matrix iteration) for determining buckling loads of columns and stress intensification of beam-columns and frameworks are included in Chapter 12. The determination of secondary stresses in trusses completes the chapter.

In Chapter 13 on structural dynamics, the usual theory of free and forced vibrations of systems with one degree of freedom is presented at the beginning. Numerical analysis of multi-degree-of-freedom systems is then introduced, and problems dealing with dynamic response to impulse-type (blast) loading are solved, making use of a digital computer.

The purpose of Chapter 14, dealing with the digital computer, is simply to give a background and an understanding of a digital computer and the programming process. Teaching of programming is beyond the scope of this book.

At New York University, Chapters 1 through 6 are covered in a 3-credit (semester) course in structural analysis; Chapters 7 through 11 are covered in a 3-credit, follow-up course in analysis; and Chapters 12 and 13 are included in a 2-credit course in structural mechanics.

Some final words are in order. In analysis, as elsewhere, no output is better than the input. Input involves not only loads, materials, and support conditions, about all of which there can be uncertainties, but also the mathematical model that is used in the analysis to simulate the actual structure made of real materials. The answers obtained are, strictly speaking, correct only for this model. This does not mean that great care should not be taken in analysis. It does mean, however, that the student must differentiate between precision and exactness. Precision is often necessary to obtain reasonably correct answers. Good judgment, which the student must try to develop to the limited degree possible at this stage of his development, is necessary to assess "exactness". In closing, it should be pointed out that these uncertainties are no less a problem in other engineering disciplines.

JAMES MICHALOS
EDWARD N. WILSON

New York City

Contents

CHAPTER 14

Structural Mechanics and Analysis

Chapter **1**

Principles of Plane Statics

In this chapter we consider the requirements of statical equilibrium and their application to the determination of external and internal resisting forces when loads are applied to simple structural elements. Attention is restricted to those cases in which all applied forces and resisting forces can be considered as acting in a single plane. The great majority of framed structures can be broken down into frames and elements whose forces lie in a plane.

1.1 Applied Forces

Structures and structural elements are subjected to applied external forces, or loads, which induce other external forces, called reactions. The loads may be dead loads, which are those resulting from the mass of the structure itself, or live loads, which are loads resulting from use or the existence of the structure and which are caused by humans, animals, vehicles, equipment, blasts, impact, water, snow, ice, wind, earthquake, and so forth.

Dead load (DL) can be computed precisely. Live load (LL) generally can be only estimated, with due regard to past experience and present and future developments. Some live loads are movable (equipment, furniture, goods) and some are moving loads (vehicles, wind, and such equipment as cranes). Moving live loads often result in an intensification of load effect that is generally, though not correctly, termed impact. This same intensification is caused by blast or other impulse loading and by suddenly applied or impact loading. Such dynamic effects are treated in Chapter 13.

Temperature change, shrinkage of certain materials, change in geometry due to stress, and movement of supports will induce stresses in certain structures. These conditions are treated in Chapters 6, 7, 8, and 10.

1.2 Equilibrium of Forces

It is assumed that the student is familiar with the principles of statics, and only a short review of the equilibrium of forces is included herein. Forces that lie in one plane—that is, coplanar forces—are of two general types. A concurrent coplanar force system is one in which the lines of action of all the forces intersect at one point. A general coplanar force system is one in which the lines of action do not intersect at one point. A special case of the latter system is a parallel coplanar force system, in which the lines of action are all parallel. A further restricted special case is that of two equal but opposite parallel forces, called a couple.

Any force of a coplanar force system can be resolved into two components along any arbitrary pair of directions, or any two forces can be represented by a resultant. This is illustrated in Figure 1-1, in which the parallelogram of forces is shown. The vectors $\overline{OB}$ and $\overline{OC}$ are equivalent in action to the vector $\overline{OA}$, which is the diagonal of the parallelogram.

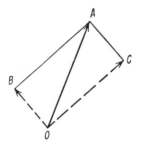

Figure 1-1.   Force Parallelogram

A system of forces acting on a body at rest or in constant motion is in a state of equilibrium when the resultant of all forces and moments is equal to zero. This requirement can be expressed conveniently by the following equations:

$$\sum F_x = 0; \qquad \sum F_y = 0; \qquad \sum M = 0 \qquad (1.1)$$

The subscripts x and y represent orthogonal axes along which force components are added. Moments are taken about an axis perpendicular to the xy-plane.

It is emphasized that Equations (1.1) are only a convenient means of expressing what is postulated by Newton's second law of motion. The same requirement can be stated by writing

$$\sum M_A = 0; \qquad \sum M_B = 0; \qquad \sum M_C = 0 \qquad (1.2)$$

in which the subscripts A, B, and C refer to three different moment origins in the plane. Furthermore, any combination of Equations (1.1) and (1.2) can be used, providing the three equations are independent.

1.3   Support Symbols and Reactions

Structures are able to develop resistance to loads through restraints supplied by supports. Types of supports are shown symbolically in Figure 1-2. In

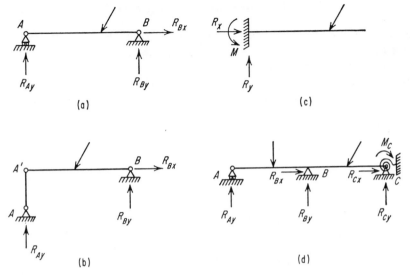

Figure 1-2. Types of Supports and Reactions

(a), (b), and (c) the reactions are statically determinate, since in each case there are three reaction components which can be determined by three equations of equilibrium. Vertical components of reaction are given a y subscript; horizontal components, an x subscript.

In (a) the left-hand support is shown on rollers to indicate that no horizontal component of reaction can be developed. This is an idealization, since some frictional resistance to free movement will always be present. The circle, or pin, at the end of the beam indicates that there is no resistance to rotation. If this is true at both ends, the beam is said to be simply supported. As a matter of convenience, the circles at the beam ends can be deleted if desired, and this is done throughout most of this book.

At end B the support is fixed against horizontal movement. Consequently, horizontal as well as vertical component of reaction can be developed at that end. In general we can say that the reaction at an end with rollers will act normal to the plane of the rollers and through the pin at the end of the member, whereas the reaction at an immovable support acts through the pin but at an unknown angle. Resolving this reaction into components is simply a matter of convenience.

In Figure 1-2(b) conditions are identical to those in (a) with the exception that the roller support at A has been replaced by a linkage AA'. The reaction at A is still vertical because it must pass through two pins that are in vertical alinement. The value is equal to that in (a).

The left end of the beam in Figure 1-2(c) is fixed against rotation as well as displacement. Therefore, in addition to vertical and horizontal components of reaction, a resisting moment is developed.

The beam of Figure 1-2(d) is continuous over support B and partially restrained against rotation at C. There are three more reaction components

3

than can be determined from three equations of equilibrium. Such structures, termed statically indeterminate, will be described further in Section 1.5 and treated comprehensively in Chapters 7, 8, 9, and 10. For the present we are interested in types of reactions. The one at C is different from those considered heretofore. The support is fixed against movement, but the end of the beam is neither fixed against rotation nor free to rotate. We have an intermediate condition which is indicated symbolically by a spring whose resistance to rotation, depending on its stiffness, can be anything from zero to infinity.

1.4   Computation of Reactions

A loaded beam with overhang is shown in Figure 1-3(a). A so-called free-body sketch of the entire beam is shown in (b). Such a sketch consists of all the forces, whether loads or reactions, acting on the beam. For convenience,

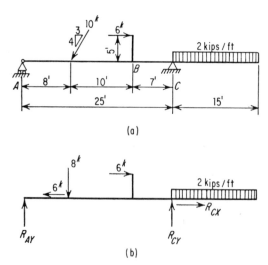

Figure 1-3.   Beam Reactions

the load of 10 kilopounds (1 kilopound = 1000 lb; abbreviated as "kip" or "k") has been resolved into its components, with the horizontal component acting along the longitudinal centroidal axis of the beam.

It should be clearly understood at this point that we can write any three equations expressing equilibrium, provided they are independent, and can solve for the three reaction components. In general, however, this will require the solution of simultaneous linear equations. On the other hand, we can be selective in choosing the three equations so that each involves only one unknown if solved in proper sequence.

For the beam under consideration, first take moments about the simple support at C. Thus, calling a moment (force × distance) positive if it tends to produce clockwise rotation about the moment center,

$$\sum M_C = R_{Ay} \times 25 + 6 \times 0 - 8 \times 17 + 6 \times 5 + 2 \times 15 \times \tfrac{15}{2} = 0$$

$$R_{Ay} = \tfrac{136 - 30 - 225}{25} = -4.76^k \downarrow$$

The negative sign indicates that the reaction acts opposite to the way it was assumed—that is, downward in this case. Note that the moment of the uniform load about C has been accounted for by finding the resultant load ($2 \times 15 = 30$) and multiplying this by the distance to its line of action ($\tfrac{15}{2}$).

In the same manner, we can determined R_{Cy} directly by taking moments about the pin at A, because R_{Cx} will produce zero moment and thus drop out.

$$\sum M_A = 6 \times 0 + 8 \times 8 + 6 \times 5 - R_{Cy} \times 25 + R_{Cx} \times 0 + 2 \times 15 \times 32.5 = 0$$

$$R_{Cy} = \tfrac{64 + 30 + 975}{25} = \underline{42.76^k \uparrow}$$

To obtain R_{Cx}:

$$\sum F_x = -6 + 6 + R_{Cx} = 0$$

$$R_{Cx} = \underline{0}$$

The reader will observe that R_{Cy} could have been obtained directly by summing forces in the y-direction, since we already had determined the magnitude and direction of R_{Ay}. Any error in R_{Ay} would then have been reflected in the value obtained for R_{Cy}. It is safer to compute independently by eliminating previously determined values. In a beam this is done by using two moment equations to determine the vertical reaction components and $\Sigma F_x = 0$ to determine the horizontal reaction component. An equation expressing $\Sigma F_y = 0$ can then be used to furnish a check for the vertical components of reaction. For example, in Figure 1-3:

$$\sum F_y = 4.76 - 8 + 42.76 - 2 \times 15$$

$$\sum F_y = 0 \qquad Check$$

The beam and loads in Figure 1-4 are identical to those in Figure 1-3, with

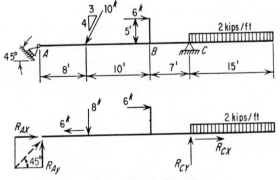

Figure 1-4.   Beam Reactions

the exception that the reaction at A must now act at an angle of 45°, as shown by the broken arrow. This means that we now have a horizontal component of reaction, R_{Ax}, which, by geometry, must be equal to the vertical component, R_{Ay}.

The values of R_{Ay} and R_{Cy} are computed exactly as before and are identical to those obtained for the beam of Figure 1-3. Then

$$\sum F_x = R_{Ax} - 6 + 6 + R_{Cx} = 0$$

But

$$R_{Ax} = R_{Ay} = \underline{-4.76^k} \leftarrow$$

and, therefore,

$$\sum F_x = -4.76 - 6 + 6 + R_{Cx} = 0$$

$$R_{Cx} = \underline{4.76^k} \rightarrow$$

If the structure in Figure 1-5(a) is considered as a whole, there are four unknown reaction components, one each at A, F, E, and D. This is one more than can be obtained directly from three equations of statical equilibrium. However, if we look at the supports in direct contact with the truss, we see they furnish three reactions with known directions and points of application. These consist of a vertical reaction at A and reactions in the directions FB and CB at B.

A free-body sketch of the truss is shown in Figure 1-5(b). The inclined reactions at B have been replaced by their vertical and horizontal components; and, as we know the directions of the reactions, their components are related to each other as shown, leaving us with a total of three independent unknown reaction components. Then

$$\sum M_B = R_A \times 120 - 9 \times 30 - 12 \times 80 = 0$$

$$R_A = \tfrac{270 \times 960}{120} = \underline{10.25^k} \uparrow$$

Any other moment equation or a summation of forces in either the x- or y-direction will result in an equation with two independent unknowns, R_{Fy} and R_{Cy}. To obtain the individual values, it is necessary to solve two equations simultaneously. This can be done in the following manner.

$$\sum F_x = -\tfrac{4}{3}R_{Cy} + R_{Fy} - 9 = 0$$

$$\tfrac{4}{3}R_{Cy} = R_{Fy} - 9$$

$$R_{Cy} = \tfrac{3}{4}R_{Fy} - \tfrac{27}{4}$$

$$\sum M_A = -(R_{Fy} + R_{Cy})120 + 12 \times 40 - 9 \times 30 = 0$$

$$R_{Fy} + R_{Cy} = \tfrac{480 - 270}{120} = 1.75$$

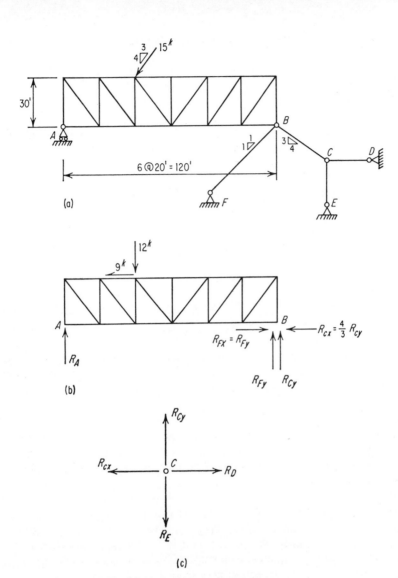

$$R_{FX} = R_{Fy}$$

$$R_{cx} = \tfrac{4}{3}\,R_{cy}$$

(b)

(c)

Figure 1-5. Truss Reactions

Substituting for R_{Cy} in terms of R_{Fy} from above,

$$R_{Fy} + \tfrac{3}{4}R_{Fy} - \tfrac{27}{4} = 1.75$$

$$1.75R_{Fy} = 1.75 + 6.75$$

$$R_{Fy} = \tfrac{8.50}{1.75} = \underline{4.86^k} \uparrow$$

Then, from

$$R_{Fy} + R_{Cy} = 1.75$$

we get

$$R_{Cy} = 1.75 - 4.86$$

$$\underline{R_{Cy} = -3.11^k \downarrow}$$

As a check,

$$\sum F_y = R_A - 12 + R_{Fy} + R_{Cy} = 0$$

$$\sum F_y = 10.25 - 12 + 4.86 - 3.11 = 0 \qquad Check$$

The horizontal components at B can now be found from their relationship to the vertical components as follows:

$$R_{Fx} = R_{Fy}$$

$$\underline{R_{Fx} = 4.86^k \rightarrow}$$

$$R_{Cx} = \tfrac{4}{3}R_{Cy}$$

$$= \tfrac{4}{3}(-3.11)$$

$$\underline{R_{Cx} = -4.14^k \rightarrow}$$

The reactions at D and E can be determined with reference to the free-body sketch in Figure 1-5(c), in which the reactions R_{Cy} and R_{Cx}, determined in (b), are now shown in their true directions at C.

$$\sum F_y = R_{Cy} - R_E = 0$$

$$\underline{R_E = R_{Cy} = 3.11^k \downarrow}$$

$$\sum F_x = -R_{Cx} + R_D = 0$$

$$\underline{R_D = R_{Cx} = 4.14^k \rightarrow}$$

The student should observe that the reaction components R_{Cx} and R_{Cy} in Figure 1-5(b) were assumed in the wrong direction, and this is shown by the negative values obtained. Although it makes no difference as to what directions are assumed, the student should attempt in each case to make the correct "guess" as a means of developing his "feel" for structural action.

1.5   Stability and Determinacy

We have seen that structures with three available reaction components are statically determinate with respect to the reactions—that is, the reactions can be determined from a consideration of equilibrium alone. This presupposes, however, that the structure is stable.

Figure 1-6(a) shows a beam that has three reaction components. The structure is stable and statically determinate for any system of loads. If the location or line of action of one or more of the reactions is changed so that the lines of action intersect at a single point, the structure will be unstable since loads would have a moment about this point that could not be resisted by the reactions. The structure would rotate instantaneously about the intersection. If we try to compute the reactions, it will not be possible to obtain consistent results.

The same argument would apply if the roller supports were replaced by links. Of course, the movements would not be completely unrestrained in either case because only a small amount of rotation about the point of intersection is possible before the structure will deform. In any event, in the deformed position the reactions are a function of the deformations and are not statically determinate.

In general we can say that a structure is stable if for any incipient movement a resistance to the movement is developed. Such a resistance is mobilized if three nonconcurrent, but not parallel, resisting forces are developed. Thus the structure in Figure 1-6(b) is unstable; but, if the direction of one of the links is changed, the structure will be stable and statically determinate.

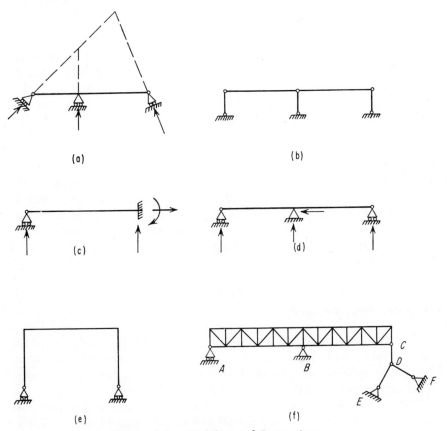

Figure 1-6.   Stability and Determinacy

We have seen that a structure is unstable if the reaction components intersect at a point. However, if the resultant of a system of loads also passes through this point, the reactions can be determined and they will keep the structure in equilibrium for this particular loading. Such a structure is still classed as unstable, but for the special condition it can be thought of as in a condition of unstable equilibrium. A slight shift of the loads would result in instability and movement.

The beams in (c) and (d) of Figure 1-6 are stable but statically indeterminate. In each case there are, as shown, four possible reaction components, but only three independent equations of statics are available. Consequently, the structures are statically indeterminate in the first degree—that is, in each case one reaction must be determined by other means before the remaining three can be computed by use of equations of equilibrium. Some structures are statically indeterminate in the tenth, twentieth, or greater degree. Statical indeterminacy and stability of various structural types are considered in Chapter 2. Statically determinate structures involving equations of condition are treated in Section 1.9.

The frame in Figure 1-6(e) is unstable because it is free to move sideways as a whole. There are only two reaction components possible, whereas a minimum of three is required for stability. If one end is restrained against sidewise movement, the structure is stable and statically determinate. If both ends are prevented from translating, the structure becomes statically indeterminate in the first degree. Furthermore, for each end that is fixed against rotation, an additional degree of indeterminacy results.

The structure in Figure 1-6(f) is stable and statically indeterminate in the first degree. This is, as previously explained in connection with Figure 1-5(a), readily determined by examining the supports at A, B, and C. The reactions at E and F are direct functions of that at C. If the structure were on rollers at B, we would apparently eliminate the indeterminacy, but with three parallel reactions the structure would become unstable (and, of course, the reactions could not be determined). The same thing would be true if the support at B consisted of a vertical linkage. A sloping linkage, however, would result in a stable and statically determinate structure.

1.6   Shear and Moment Diagrams

At all sections of a structure or structural member the resistance offered to imposed loads can be represented by a transverse component of force (shear force), a longitudinal component of force (axial force), a couple or moment (bending moment), or a combination of two or all three of these.

The *shear* at a section is defined as the sum, on either side of the section, of all external force components perpendicular to the longitudinal axis. For a structure in equilibrium the shear obtained by adding forces on one side of a section will be identical to that obtained by adding forces on the other side. Conventionally, shear at a section in a beam is considered positive when the sum of the forces acting to the left of the section tends to shear that portion upward and the forces to the right tend to shear that portion downward.

The *axial force* at a section is defined as the sum of all the external longitudinal components of force on one side (or the other) of the section. If the axial force at the section is a tension—that is, it tends to elongate the member—it is generally called positive. If the axial force is a compression— that is, it tends to shorten the member—it is generally called negative. Such negative axial force at a section is often referred to as *thrust*.

The *bending moment* at a section is equal to the sum of the moments of all forces, on either side of the section, about the centroidal bending axis of the section. Properly speaking, then, instead of saying "bending moment at a section" we should say "bending moment about a particular axis of the cross section." To obtain the contribution of a longitudinal force component to bending moment at a section, it must be multiplied by its distance from the centroidal bending axis of the section. For flexural loading only, this axis is the neutral axis. Bending moment will be designated positive when it results in concave upward bending (compression in the top fibers of a beam).

For the present the discussion is limited to members whose longitudinal centroidal axis (the longitudinal line through the centroids of the cross sections) is straight. In addition, the loads and reacting forces must lie in a plane through the shear center and parallel to or containing one of the principal axes of each section. The forces must pass through the shear center in order to prevent twist and must lie in a principal plane or parallel to it in order to prevent bending about the other principal axis. An axis of symmetry is always a principal axis (but the reverse is not true) and the shear center lies along it.

Figure 1-7(a) shows a beam with two loads W placed at the third-points of

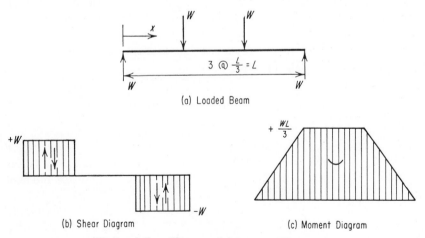

(a) Loaded Beam

(b) Shear Diagram

(c) Moment Diagram

Figure 1-7.   Shear and Moment Diagrams

the span L. The shear diagram in (b) was drawn commencing at the left end. It represents the shear at all sections along the beam, and, by definition, the shear is constant between successive vertical forces. The upward forces produce positive shear (or reduce negative shear), and the downward forces produce negative shear (or reduce positive shear). The sum of the forces in the middle third of the beam is zero, and therefore there is no shear along this portion. A characteristic feature of a shear diagram is that it "closes"—that is, it begins and ends on the same base line because the sum of all vertical forces must be zero. If the shear diagram were constructed commencing at the right end, it would be a mirror image about the horizontal base of the diagram in (b), with negative shears plotted above the base. The physical significance of positive and negative shear can be indicated by pairs of arrows, as shown. These represent the shear on opposite faces of a beam segment of differential length.

The bending moment, as shown in Figure 1-7(c), increases linearly between the end reaction and the first load because no other force is present. Its value anywhere in the outer third of the span is equal to $M = Wx$. At the one-third point, $x = L/3$ and $M = WL/3$. In the middle third of the beam the bending moment remains constant at $WL/3$ since any increase in moment due to the reaction is exactly balanced by a decrease due to the load. Thus

$$M = Wx - W\left(x - \frac{L}{3}\right) = \frac{WL}{3}$$

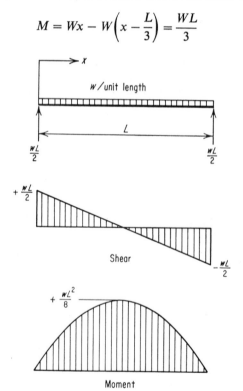

Figure 1-8.   *Shear and Moment Diagrams*

In the right-hand third of the beam

$$M = Wx - W\left(x - \frac{L}{3}\right) - W\left(x - \frac{2}{3}L\right) = W(L - x)$$

or, more simply, if x is now measured from the right-end support,

$$M = Wx$$

If we work from left to right, clockwise moment by a force will tend to produce positive bending moment. Therefore, if the result from a moment equation written with clockwise moment as positive yields a negative answer, the bending moment at the section under consideration is negative. The physical significance of the positive bending moment can be shown by a concave upward arc, as shown in Figure 1-7(c).

The beam in Figure 1-8 is uniformly loaded. At any section the shear is

$$V = \frac{wL}{2} - wx = w\left(\frac{L}{2} - x\right)$$

which is the equation of a straight line with slope equal to $-w$. To make $V = 0$,

$$\frac{L}{2} - x = 0$$

and

$$x = \frac{L}{2}$$

The bending moment at any section is

$$M = \frac{wL}{2}(x) - wx\left(\frac{x}{2}\right) = \frac{w}{2}(Lx - x^2)$$

which is the equation of a parabola. To make M a maximum,

$$\frac{dM}{dx} = \frac{w}{2}(L - 2x) = 0$$

$$L - 2x = 0$$

$$x = \frac{L}{2}$$

The maximum moment is then

$$M = \tfrac{1}{8}wL^2$$

For convenience, positive values of x in Figure 1-9 are measured toward the left, with origin at the right end. The shear at any section x is

$$V = P + wx$$

The bending moment at any section is

$$M = -Px - \frac{wx^2}{2}$$

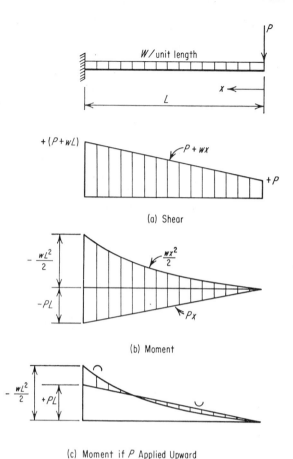

(a) Shear

(b) Moment

(c) Moment if P Applied Upward

Figure 1-9. Shear and Moment Diagrams

It is often convenient to plot the moment diagram separately for each of several loadings, as is done in Figure 1-9(b) for P and w. If the direction of P were upward, thus producing positive moment, its moment diagram would be superimposed on that for w in order to obtain the resultant moment diagram shown at the bottom of Figure 1-9.

In the general case of distributed loading, the intensity of load will vary along the beam. If the variation is such that it cannot be expressed as a function of x, or it is not convenient to do so, shears and bending moments can be determined quite accurately by dividing the beam length into a number of segments and substituting a concentrated load of approximately equal magnitude for the actual distributed load on each beam segment.

If the variation in distributed load can be represented as a function of x, then algebraic expressions can be derived for shear and bending moment. As an example, consider Figure 1-10. The shear at any section a distance x_1 from the free end will be

$$V = \int_0^{x_1} w \, dx = \int_0^{x_1} f(x) \, dx$$

14

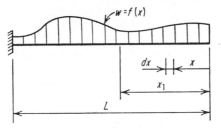

Figure 1-10. Beam with Nonuniformly Distributed Loading

The bending moment at $x = x_1$ will be

$$M = -\int_0^{x_1} (x_1 - x)w\,dx = -\int_0^{x_1} (x_1 - x)f(x)\,dx$$

Figure 1-11(a) shows the same beam as that in Figure 1-4. The reactions are the values previously computed in connection with the latter figure, and they are now shown in their true directions. The shear, axial force, and bending moment diagrams are shown in (b), (c), and (d).

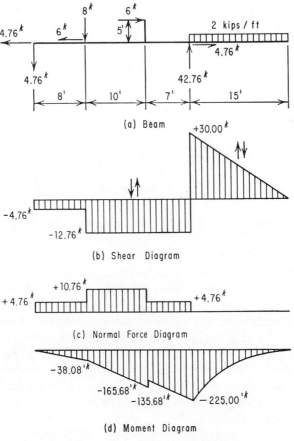

(a) Beam

(b) Shear Diagram

(c) Normal Force Diagram

(d) Moment Diagram

Figure 1-11. Shear and Bending Moment

15

1.7   Relationship between Load, Shear, and Bending Moment

Figure 1-12 shows a loaded segment of differential length removed from a flexural member. The shear and moment each side of the segment are shown in their positive sense. Two equations of equilibrium, one for vertical forces and

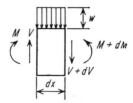

Figure 1-12.   Differential Length of Loaded Beam

one for moments about the bending axis in the right face of the segment, can be written as follows:

$$V - w \, dx - (V - dV) = 0 \tag{1.3}$$

$$M + V \, dx - w \, dx \, \frac{dx}{2} - (M + dM) = 0 \tag{1.4}$$

From Equation (1.3),

$$\frac{dV}{dx} = w \tag{1.5}$$

and from Equation (1.4), neglecting differential quantities of second order,

$$\frac{dM}{dx} = V \tag{1.6}$$

or, between x_1 and x_2 the change in moment is

$$M_2 - M_1 = \int_{x_1}^{x_2} V \, dx \tag{1.7}$$

Equation (1.6) indicates that when the shear is positive, the rate of change of bending moment is positive and the bending moment is increasing. It would also seem to indicate that the bending moment is a maximum or a minimum when the shear is equal to zero. It is possible, however, for a maximum to occur at the end of a curve or at a point of discontinuity along a curve. An example of this is a cantilever beam, for which maximum moment occurs at a section for which shear is not zero. As a matter of fact, if all loads on the cantilever are applied downward, the maximum moment occurs where the shear is also a maximum.

Equation (1.7) shows that the change in moment between any sections 1 and 2 is equal to the area of the shear diagram between section 1 and section 2.

Figure 1-13 shows an inclined beam, such as might occur in a stairway. The vertical reactions are found exactly as before. In order to draw diagrams of axial force, shear, and bending moment, it is necessary to resolve loads and reactions into components along the longitudinal axis of the beam and components perpendicular to this axis. This must be done because only the former components contribute to axial force, and only the latter components contri-

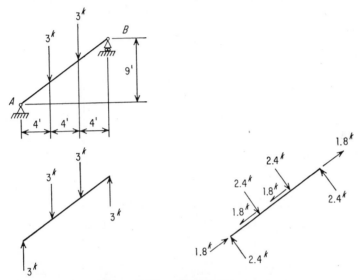

Figure 1-13.   Sloping Beam

bute to shear and bending moment. The student should draw the diagrams. In addition, he should rework the problem with the rollers at B in a vertical line, so that only horizontal reaction can develop at B.

A frame is shown in Figure 1-14(a). The corners B and C are rigid—that is, bending moment can be resisted there. If this were not so at even one corner, the structure would be unstable. If the structure shown were restrained horizontally at D as well as at A, it would be a statically indeterminate frame generally referred to as a rigid frame.

The reactions are determined as for a beam, as follows:

$$\sum M_A = 20 \times 10 + 2 \times 30 \times 15 - 30R_{Dy} = 0$$

$$R_{Dy} = \frac{200 + 900}{30} = 36.67^k$$

$$\sum M_D = R_{Ay} \times 30 + R_{Ax} \times 0 + 20 \times 10 - 2 \times 30 \times 15 = 0$$

$$R_{Ay} = \frac{900 - 200}{30} = 23.33^k$$

$$\sum F_x = 20 - R_{Ax}$$

$$R_{Ax} = 20.00^k$$

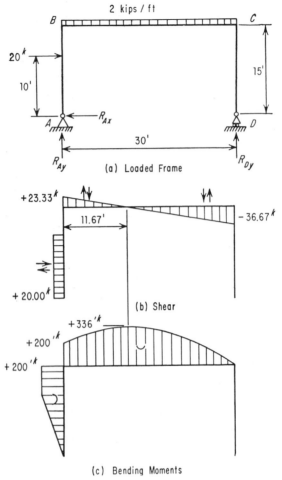

2 kips / ft

B C

20^k

10'

15'

A R_{Ax} D

30'

R_{Ay}

(a) Loaded Frame

$+23.33^k$

11.67'

-36.67^k

$+20.00^k$

(b) Shear

$+336'^k$

$+200'^k$

$+200'^k$

(c) Bending Moments

Figure 1-14. Shears and Moments in Frame

The shear diagram is shown in (b) and the bending moment diagram in (c). Bending moments have been considered positive when they result in tension along an inner face of the structure.

There is no moment at corner C because the line of action of the reaction at D passes through C. The student should do the same problem, but with the leg CD at an angle to the vertical. What about corner C then? The student should also draw the bending moment diagram for the frame of Figure 1-14 by superposition, as in Figure 1-9, of the separate effects of the two loadings, remembering first to determine the two sets of reactions.

1.8 Principle of Superposition

In Figure 1-9 the bending moment diagram corresponding to the uniformly distributed load and the bending moment diagram corresponding to the concentrated load were obtained separately and then superimposed to obtain the

18

resulting bending moment diagram. The shear diagram could have been obtained in the same manner. As a matter of fact, for any of the loaded beams or frames considered so far, final reactions, shears, or moments can be determined by combining values for individual loads. This is permissible because all the computations heretofore considered, and indeed the vast majority of structural computations, involve linear effects and noncritical changes in geometry.

Superposition is not permissible in the following cases:

1. when the material is nonelastic,
2. when the material is stressed beyond its elastic limit,
3. when the geometry of the deflected structure induces changes in forces or moments from those computed for the original geometry.

The first two cases involve nonlinearity of stress and strain and are obvious. With respect to the third case, the changes in geometry due to loading in the problems considered so far had no effect on reactions, shears, and bending moments. This was so because the resulting deflections are so small compared to the over-all dimensions of the structure as to have virtually no effect on them. That is, positions of the loads and reactions were, for all practical purposes, unchanged. For such structures, resulting forces, moments, and deflections are directly proportional to the intensity of any particular load.

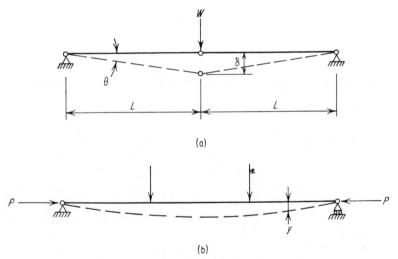

(a)

(b)

Figure 1-15. Nonlinear Structures

Consider Figure 1-15(a), however. When load W is increased, the two segments elongate and the center hinge moves downward a distance δ as indicated by the broken lines. The tensile force in each of the two segments is

$$F = \frac{1}{2}\frac{W}{\sin \theta} \qquad\qquad \text{(a)}$$

The angle θ is an extremely small angle and $\sin \theta$ can be replaced by $\tan \theta$, which is equal to δ/L. Thus

$$F = \frac{1}{2}\frac{WL}{\delta} \tag{b}$$

The unit elongation of each segment is, by Hooke's law,

$$\varepsilon = \frac{F}{AE} \tag{c}$$

or, from Figure 1-15,

$$\varepsilon = \frac{\sqrt{L^2 + \delta^2} - L}{L} \tag{d}$$

Expanding the quantity under the square root sign by the binomial theorem, we obtain (using two terms of the expansion)

$$\varepsilon = \frac{1}{2}\frac{\delta^2}{L^2} \tag{e}$$

Equating (c) and (e), we obtain

$$\delta^2 = 2\frac{L^2 F}{AE} \tag{f}$$

and substituting from (b) for F,

$$\delta = L\left(\frac{W}{AE}\right)^{\frac{1}{3}} \tag{g}$$

From (b) and (g) it is seen that neither stress nor deflection is directly proportional to the load.

A more common situation in which superposition is not valid, because of the effect of the geometry of the deflected structure, occurs when a slender member is subjected to both transverse and axial loads. Such a member is shown in Figure 1-15(b). The maximum stress at any cross section is

$$\sigma = \frac{P}{A} + \frac{Mc}{I} \tag{1.8}$$

in which

P = axial force
A = area of cross section
M = bending moment
c = distance to extreme compression fiber from centroidal bending axis
I = moment of inertia of cross section

The axial force P contributes an amount Py to the bending moment M at each section along the member, and this induces additional deflection, which in turn induces additional moment, and so forth, until an equilibrium deflected position is reached. Stresses, moments, and deflections due to axial loads are not linear, and the effect of an axial load $P_1 + P_2$ is not equal to the sum of the effects of P_1 and P_2 acting separately. Stress intensification due to axial loads is treated in Chapter 12.

1.9   Equations of Condition

The beam in Figure 1.6(d) is statically indeterminate in the first degree. There are four possible reaction components, and only three equations of statical equilibrium can be written. If a hinge is introduced in one of the spans of such a beam, as shown in Figure 1-16, the structure becomes statically determinate. This follows because another equation of statics, expressing the fact that the bending moment at the hinge is zero, can now be written. As before, we can compute reactions directly through proper selection of moment centers and thus avoid solution of simultaneous equations. First take moments about C of all forces to the right of C, assuming R_{Dy} acting upwards.

$$\sum M_c = 2 \times 15 \times 7.5 - R_{Dy} \times 15 = 0$$

$$R_{Dy} = 15^k$$

Now we can take moments about A and B, in either order, of all forces and determine the remaining reactions as follows, assuming they act upwards:

$$\sum M_A = -R_{By} \times 20 + 2 \times 20 \times 30 - 15 \times 40 = 0$$

$$-20 R_{By} = 600 - 1200$$

$$R_{By} = 30^k$$

$$\sum M_B = R_{Ay} \times 20 + 2 \times 20 \times 10 - 15 \times 20 = 0$$

$$20 R_{Ay} = -400 + 300$$

$$R_{Ay} = -5^k$$

The shear and bending moment diagrams can now be obtained as before, and they are shown in Figure 1-16.

If desired, the structure can be broken at the hinge for purposes of analysis, as shown in Figure 1-16(e), and the reactions of each portion determined separately. The "reaction" at C of the portion CD is the shear transmitted by the hinge, and it is treated as a load on the portion of the structure to the left of C. With the reactions known, the shear and moment diagrams can be drawn as before. Alternatively, the shear and moment diagrams can be drawn for each portion separately and then combined.

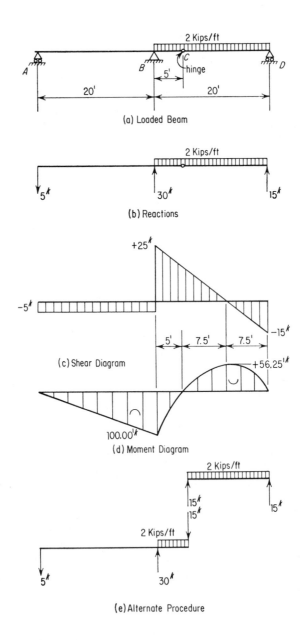

2 Kips/ft

C
hinge

A   B   5'   D

20'   20'

(a) Loaded Beam

2 Kips/ft

5^k 30^k 15^k

(b) Reactions

+25^k

−5^k

−15^k

5'   7.5'   7.5'

(c) Shear Diagram

+56.25$'^k$

100.00$'^k$

(d) Moment Diagram

2 Kips/ft

15^k
15^k 15^k

2 Kips/ft

5^k 30^k

(e) Alternate Procedure

Figure 1-16.   Continuous Beam with Hinge

Frames and arches which are statically determinate because of hinges in their span can be analyzed in the same manner as above. They are treated in Chapter 2. In Chapter 5 it is shown that moment diagrams for statically determinate continuous beams can be obtained more directly.

22

1.10　The String Polygon

Suppose that it is desired to determine the resultant (or antiresultant) of several coplanar but nonconcurrent forces. This can be done by resolving the forces into x-components and y-components. The magnitude and direction (slope) of the resultant can then be found from the sums of these components. To determine the line of action of the resultant, we make use of a third condition of equilibrium—that is, $\sum M = 0$. Thus the moment of the resultant, whose magnitude and direction are known, about any point in the xy-plane must be equal to the total moment of the forces (or their components) about the same point.

The same thing can be done graphically, combining any two forces vectorially to determine their resultant, then combining this resultant with any other force to obtain a new resultant which is then combined with still another force, and so forth, until the final resultant is determined. In Figure 1-17(b)

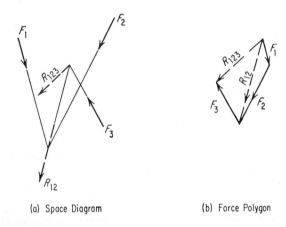

(a) Space Diagram　　　　　　　　　(b) Force Polygon

Figure 1-17.　Resultant of Coplanar Force System

the force polygon for the system of forces F_1, F_2, and F_3 shown in (a) has been drawn. This was done by combining the forces to scale and in chain fashion, tail to head of arrow. The forces can be combined in any order.

The resultant of F_1 and F_2 is R_{12}, and R_{123} is the resultant of R_{12} and F_3. The magnitude and direction of R_{123} is as shown in (b), but its point of application must be determined in (a). We draw R_{12} (not necessarily to scale) through the intersection of F_1 and F_2, and parallel to its direction in (b). We then draw R_{123} through the intersection of R_{12} and F_3, and parallel to its direction in (b). Thus the line of application of the resultant is obtained in the space diagram of the forces, and its magnitude and direction are obtained in the force polygon.

Theoretically, a construction such as that in Figure 1-17 can be made for any number of forces, providing they are not all parallel. Practically, however, it can be impossible to do so because the lines of action of the forces may not all intersect within the limits of the drawing.

A more general method, which works for any system of forces, whether parallel or not, is illustrated in Figure 1-18. It is desired to obtain the resultant

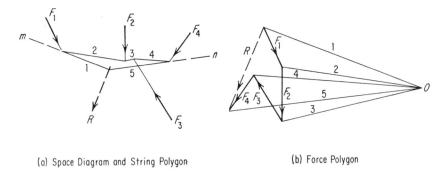

(a) Space Diagram and String Polygon   (b) Force Polygon

Figure 1-18.   Resultant by Force and String Polygons

or antiresultant (reaction) of forces F_1, F_2, F_3, and F_4 shown in (a). A force polygon is drawn, as before, in (b) to obtain the resultant force R, which is represented by the line necessary to close the polygon. Each force of the polygon can be resolved into any two components, which with the given force will form a triangle of forces. For example, lines 1 and 2 represent components of F_1 since together they form a triangle with apex at point O. Similarly, lines 2 and 3 represent components of F_2, lines 3 and 4 represent components of F_3, lines 4 and 5 represent components of F_4, and lines 5 and 1 represent components of the resultant R. Notice that by having a common point of intersection, O, each of lines 1 through 5 represents a common component for the adjacent pair of forces which intersect it in the force polygon. These lines (or components) are generally called rays, and their common point of intersection is generally called a pole.

The force components represented by the rays in (b) must intersect the lines of action of the forces in (a) of which they are components. Thus line 2 in (a) is drawn parallel to ray 2 in (b), and it intersects the lines of action of forces F_1 and F_2, for both of which it is a component. In a similar manner, we draw lines 3 and 4. Line 1 is then drawn so as to make a common intersection with line 2 and the line of action of F_1, because 1 and 2 are components of F_1. Line 5 is then drawn so as to make a common intersection with line 4 and the line of action of F_4. Now, since lines 1 and 5 are components of the resultant force R, their intersection must be a point on the line of action of R, whose direction is parallel to that in the force polygon.

The construction in Figure 1-18(a) is called a string (or funicular) polygon for the following reason. If a weightless string, or cable, were held at some

point m along line 1 and at some point n along line 5, and if it were then subjected to forces F_1, F_2, F_3, and F_4, it would take the shape indicated by the
dashed lines and lines 2, 3, and 4. The string polygon is also referred to as an
equilibrium polygon because the bent string and the forces are in equilibrium.

The student should determine the resultant for the forces in Figure 1-18 by
constructing the string polygon with the forces taken in different order when
drawing the force polygon. Although the shape of the string polygon will be
different, he should obtain the same result for R. It is emphasized, also, that
the pole O can be chosen anywhere, on either side of the forces or, indeed,
between them. The important considerations are accuracy and ease of
graphical construction.

In Figure 1-18 we determined a single force which was the resultant of a
system of forces. If the direction of this resultant is reversed, we have the antiresultant, or force necessary to keep the given forces in equilibrium. If the
system of forces were applied to a simply supported structure, we could resolve
the antiresultant into components that would represent the reactions at the
supports of the structure. This is done in Figure 1-19 for a beam.

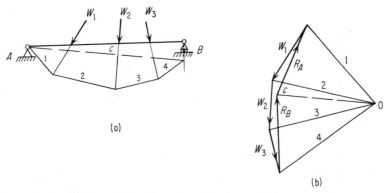

Figure 1-19.   *Reactions by String Polygon*

The string polygon in (a) is constructed as before, but we must begin it at
the pin at A because it is the only known point on the line of action of R_A, the
reaction at A. At the other end we know that the line of action of R_B is
vertical, and consequently line 4 can intersect R_B anywhere along this vertical
line. To obtain R_A and R_B, instead of a single reacting force, a line c is drawn
to close the string polygon. This closing line, which intersects the line of action
of R_A as well as that of R_B, represents a component of each reaction. If a line
parallel to it is drawn through O in Figure 1-19(b), we can then lay out the
magnitude and direction of each reaction.

The reactions for any statically determinate structure, whether beam,
frame, or truss, can be determined by constructing a string polygon, beginning
through the support at which the reaction is not vertical. If the loads are all
vertical, the construction can begin anywhere along a vertical line through

either support. If the structure is subjected to distributed load, a very close approximation to the string polygon, and thus to the reactions, can be obtained by replacing the distributed load with a series of concentrated loads.

Before considering further use of the string polygon, it is desirable to consider briefly the string (cable) as a load-carrying structure. This is done in the following section.

1.11 The Cable

As stated in the preceding section, a weightless string suspended between two points and subjected to loads will take the shape of a string polygon for the given forces. Such a flexible cable, with vertical concentrated loads, is shown in Figure 1-20. If the weight of the cable is significant, its effect can be

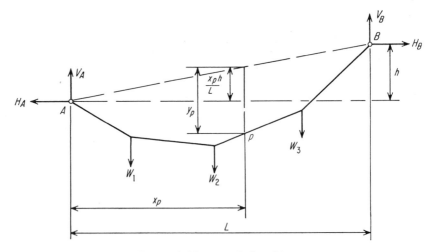

Figure 1-20. Loaded Cable

closely approximated by treating the distributed weight as a series of concentrated loads.

From $\sum F_x = 0$, we obtain

$$H_A = H_B = H \qquad (1.9)$$

and it can be seen that the horizontal component of tension in the cable is a constant value, H. However, to determine the magnitude of H and of the vertical components of reaction, only two other equations of equilibrium seem to be available at first glance.

In Section 1.9 it was seen that if a hinge is present the bending moment at the hinge must be zero and an additional equation of equilibrium becomes available. Such an equation of condition can be written for a flexible cable since about any point along the cable the moment of all forces on one side or the other must equal zero. From moments about B,

$$Hh + V_A L - \sum M_B = 0 \qquad (1.10)$$

in which $\sum M_B$ represents the sum of the moments of all loads W about B. From moments about a point p on the cable of all forces acting to the left of p,

$$-H\left(y_p - \frac{x_p}{L}h\right) + V_A x_p - \sum M_p = 0 \qquad (1.11)$$

in which $\sum M_p$ represents the sum of the moments about p of all loads to the left of p.

If we now solve Equation (1.10) for V_A and substitute the resulting expression in Equation (1.11), we obtain

$$Hy_p = (\sum M_B)\frac{x_p}{L} - \sum M_p \qquad (1.12)$$

The right-hand side of Equation (1.12) is equal to the simple-beam bending moment at p—that is, it is the moment obtained neglecting H. We can conclude that at any point along a flexible cable supporting vertical loads, the horizontal component of cable tension times the vertical distance to the point from the chord joining the two cable ends is equal to the simple-beam bending moment. Thus, to obtain H divide the simple-beam bending-moment at any point along the span by the corresponding distance y. With the value of H known, the values of V_A and V_B can be readily obtained.

Suppose that one or more of the loads W in Figure 1-20 is not vertical. Equation (1.9) now becomes

$$H_A + H_B + \text{horizontal components of loads} = 0 \qquad (1.9a)$$

and Equations (1.10) and (1.11) become

$$H_A h + V_A L - \sum M_B = 0 \qquad (1.10a)$$

$$-H_A\left(y_p - \frac{x_p}{L}h\right) + V_A x_p - \sum M_p = 0 \qquad (1.11a)$$

A simultaneous solution of Equations (1.10a) and (1.11a) yields

$$H_A y_p = (\sum M_B)\frac{x_p}{L} - \sum M_p \qquad (1.12a)$$

The difference between this equation and Equation (1.12) is that, as the loads are not all vertical, the right-hand side no longer represents the simple-beam bending moment. With H_A obtained from Equation (1.12a), the values of H_B and V_A can be obtained from Equations (1.9a) and (1.10a), respectively.

The cable is considered further in Section 1.13, in connection with passing a string polygon through specified points.

1.12   The String Polygon as a Moment Diagram

From the preceding discussion we can conclude that a string supporting vertical loads, and thus the string polygon for those loads, represents the simple-beam bending moment diagram to a scale determined by the magnitude of the vertical ordinates between string and closing line. The graphical determination of bending moments is illustrated in what follows.

Figure 1-21 shows a beam with three concentrated vertical loads. The forces

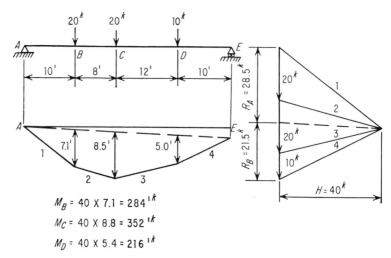

$$M_B = 40 \times 7.1 = 284^{'k}$$
$$M_C = 40 \times 8.8 = 352^{'k}$$
$$M_D = 40 \times 5.4 = 216^{'k}$$

Figure 1-21.   Bending Moments by String Polygon

are laid out to scale in the force polygon, and the string polygon constructed as before. To obtain the bending moment at any section of the beam, the ordinate from "string" to closing line is multiplied by the horizontal component, H, of the rays in the force diagram. The bending moments at the load points have been obtained in Figure 1-21. The values are very nearly equal to the true values. Obviously, the accuracy of any values is directly dependent on the care with which the construction is made.

It is convenient to pick a pole such that H is a simple whole number. Often it is taken as 10 or 100 or 1000.

If any loads are not vertical, they can be resolved into vertical and horizontal components. The string polygon is then drawn for the vertical components, since the horizontal components do not affect the bending moment. Of course, the reactions obtained will be those for vertical loading only.

The string polygon in Figure 1-22, for the beam with cantilevered ends, is begun at A', directly below the fixed support at A. Note that string 1 and 2 now represent components of F_1 and, consequently, intersect along its line of action. The closing line c intersects some of the strings, and this gives the resulting positive and negative moments shown. The value of the bending moment at a particular section can be found, as before, by multiplying the corresponding ordinate in the string polygon construction by the value of

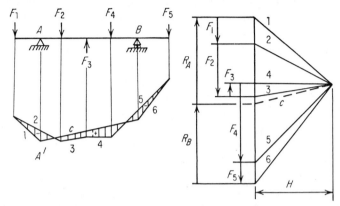

Figure 1-22.   Beam with Overhang

H from the force polygon. As a result of the relatively small ordinates generally obtained in the string-polygon construction for such beams, great accuracy cannot be expected in determining bending moments by this method.

1.13   String Polygon Constructed through Specified Points: Cables and Arches

It may be desired to pass a string polygon through two particular points. A physical example of such a polygon is furnished by a loaded cable supported at two points, *A* and *B*. Any length of cable between *A* and *B* will support the loads. Therefore, an infinite number of equilibrium polygons can be constructed so as to pass through two points.

Figure 1-23 shows several loads. It is desired to construct an equilibrium polygon that will pass through *A* and *B*. The force polygon is laid out and a

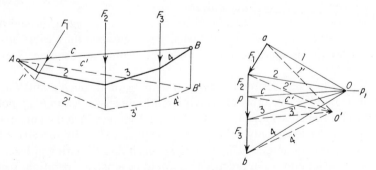

Figure 1-23.   String Polygon (or Cable) Through Two Points

trial pole, O', selected. The string polygon is then constructed, starting at A, but it is found that it does not pass through B, but rather through point B'. This procedure of selecting a pole and constructing the corresponding string polygon could be repeated until a string polygon passed through B. In general this would be tedious and impractical. Instead, proceed as explained in the following paragraph.

Notice that all closing lines must pass through point p. This follows because if the forces were applied to a beam supported at A and B, with rollers at B, the reaction at B would be represented by bp in the force polygon, and the reaction at A by a vector pa, regardless of the location of the pole O'. Consequently, if a line pp_1 is now drawn parallel to the chord AB, any pole O selected on that line will result in a string polygon passing through A and B.

If the string polygon passing through A and B of Figure 1-23 is considered to represent an actual cable with loads F_1, F_2, and F_3 applied at the intersections of segments 1, 2, 3, and 4, the resulting force in any segment can be determined from the length of the corresponding ray in the force polygon. For example, ray 1 represents, to scale, the tension in segment 1 of the cable. The horizontal projection of this ray represents H_A, and the vertical projection represents V_A. Also, the length of the cable and its sag at any point can be scaled from the string polygon. With the sag known at any point, values of H_A, V_A, and so forth, can, of course, be determined directly from Equations (1.9a), (1.10a), and (1.12a).

It is emphasized that any number of string polygons can be passed through two points. Correspondingly, any number of cables can be used to support the imposed loads. The more that pole O is moved to the left along pp_1, the smaller the cable stresses. The cable, however, is longer, and the sag is greater.

If the pole O is located to the left of p, along pp_1 extended, then the resulting string polygon will also pass through points A and B, but will lie above chord AB. An arch with the shape of this string polygon, and with loads F_1, F_2, and F_3 applied at the intersections of the straight-line segments of the arch, will carry these loads by direct thrust in the segments. There will be no bending moment developed, and the thrust in any segment can be determined from the corresponding ray of the force polygon.

More generally, it may be desired to pass a string polygon through three points, as, for example, when a particular sag is specified for a cable or when a particular rise is specified for an arch undergoing no bending. See also, Section 2.2.

In Figure 1-24 it is desired to pass a string polygon through point N as well as points A and B. We proceed exactly as in Figure 1-23, assuming a pole O' and then locating line pp_1, parallel to chord AB, along which the pole must lie in order for the string polygon to pass through A and B. By successive trials we could locate an unique pole O along pp_1 such that the string polygon also passes through point N. In practice this would be a messy operation. Instead, we can proceed in a direct manner, as explained in the following paragraph.

Consider points A and N. The line c_L' is the closing line of the string

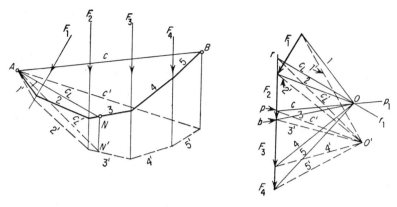

Figure 1-24. String Polygon (or Cable) Through Three Points

polygon $1'$, $2'$, $3'$. If a line is drawn parallel to c'_L from O' in the force polygon, point r on this line can be located, and br will represent the simple-beam vertical reaction at N due to loads between A and N. It follows that a line rr_1, drawn parallel to chord AN (closing line c_L), represents the locus of all poles that will pass a string polygon through A and N. Therefore, the intersection of this line with line pp_1 gives the pole O, which will result in a string polygon through all three specified points.

For an actual cable having the shape of the string polygon, the same results can be obtained analytically. First determine H_A and V_A from Equations (1.12a) and (1.10a). The forces in succeeding segments and the positions of the segments in space can then be found. It should be pointed out that in a cable the segments will lengthen because of tensile force, and, as a result, the position of the cable will shift somewhat. Furthermore, a change in load, as occurs constantly in structures supporting moving loads, can result in large vertical and horizontal displacements of the cable. Such displacements cannot be considered here. The interested reader is referred to a numerical procedure[1] for determining such movements.

1.14 Principle of Virtual Displacements

Suppose that a body or structure, as, for example, the beam in Figure 1-25, is given a small displacement *independent of any forces acting on it*. The total

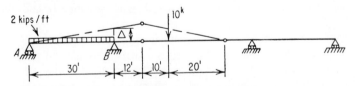

Figure 1-25. Application of Virtual Displacement

[1] James Michalos and Charles Birnstiel, "Movements of a Cable Due to Changes in Loading," *Transactions*, ASCE, **127** (1962), Part II, pp. 267–303.

work done by all forces acting through this virtual displacement is equal to zero. Thus if a small movement Δ is imposed at the first interior support, then, since this movement is made as if no loads are present, the resulting shape is as shown by the dashed line. Observe that the movement must be very small so that there is no change in position of loads or supports along the structure. As a result of this virtual movement, virtual work is done by the loads and by the reaction at B. This total work is then set equal to zero, as follows:

$$-2(30)\frac{\Delta}{2} + R_B\Delta - 10\left(\frac{20}{30}\right)\left(\frac{42}{30}\right)\Delta = 0$$

Negative signs are used in the expression involving the loads because they act opposite to the movement. Notice that Δ cancels out from all terms. As a result, the imposed virtual displacement can be taken as any convenient number, generally 1.

The equation of virtual work can be solved for R_B to obtain

$$R_B = 39.33 \text{ kips}$$

Thus the principle of virtual displacements furnishes an alternate tool for computing reactions. In this book, this principle is applied primarily in connection with influence lines (Chapter 3). It will there be seen that in Figure 1-25 we have actually drawn an influence line for reaction at B.

Problems

1.1. Compute the reactions and draw the complete shear and moment diagrams. (*Ans.:* Max. $M = 53.5$ ft-kips.)

1.2. Determine the reactions and draw the shear and moment diagrams. What is the axial force in each member?

1.3. Compute the reactions and draw the shear and moment diagrams. (*Ans.:* Max. $V = 2{,}125$ lb; Max. $M = 8{,}800$ ft-lb.)

1.4. Compute the reactions and draw the shear and moment diagrams. (*Ans.:* M at interior support $= -400$ ft-kips.)

1.5. Rework Problem 1.4, but with the cable passing over an identical pulley 10 ft from the right-hand support and the end of the cable fastened to the beam.

1.6. Obtain the reactions and the moment diagram graphically and check the values analytically.

1.7. Obtain reactions and moment diagram graphically.

1.8. In Figure 1-20, assume $L = 100$ ft, $h = 20$ ft, and $y_p = 30$ ft. Then, with $W_1 = W_2 = W_3 = 10$ kips, spaced at 25-ft intervals, pass the string polygon through points A, p, and B and determine the cable forces. Check results analytically.

1.9. Construct the string polygon through points A, B, and C and determine the reactions and forces in the corresponding arch. (*Ans.:* $H_A = 18^k$.)

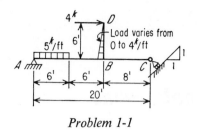

Problem 1-1

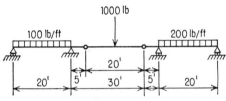

Problem 1-2

Problem 1-3

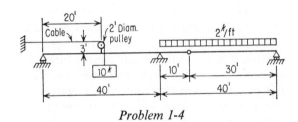

Problem 1-4

Problem 1-6

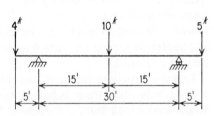

Problem 1-7

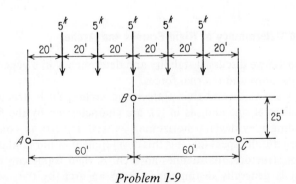

Problem 1-9

Chapter **2**

Statically Determinate Plane Structures

Statically determinate structures are treated in this and the two following chapters. These are structures in which forces, moments, and shears can be determined by application of the conditions of equilibrium alone. In this chapter we concentrate on the analysis of statically determinate plane structures, including frames, arches, and trusses.

While it is true that virtually all structures are three-dimensional, the stress analysis for a vast majority can be performed as if they were plane structures. For example, some structures (many bridges, for instance) are composed of two or more parallel trusses. The stresses in the trusses can be determined by treating the trusses separately as plane structures. Because the trusses are interconnected by load distribution systems, or lateral bracing, or both, the stresses obtained by analyzing the trusses separately as plane structures may not be strictly correct for certain loading, but this effect is generally small and may be neglected.

In some structures the main load-carrying trusses or frames are oriented in such a way that their behavior cannot be considered two-dimensional. Frameworks with three-dimensional behavior are considered in Chapter 4, and in Sections 7.16, 9.8, and 9.9.

2.1 Stability and Determinacy of Rigid Frames and Arches

In Section 1.5 we discussed stability and determinacy in a general way with respect to reactions and internal forces.

Figure 2-1 shows several rigid frames and arches. Such structures, except when on rollers at one end, as in (c), are characterized by the fact that for vertical loading they develop horizontal, as well as vertical, components of reaction. Structurally speaking, it is this development of horizontal forces, and not shape of structure, that defines an arch. A rigid frame can be called an arch, but it is generally distinguished from an arch by the fact that it is composed of vertical legs and straight, or generally straight, "horizontals."

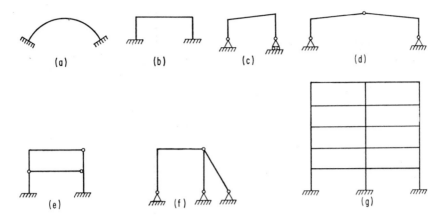

Figure 2-1. Arches and Rigid Frames

It is quite simple to decide whether an arch is stable and statically determinate. For example, the arch in Figure 2-1(a) is fixed against translation and rotation at both supports. Therefore, there are a total of three reaction components (moment, and horizontal and vertical components of force) that can be developed at each support, for a total of six. This is three more than can be obtained by a consideration of equilibrium alone, and the structure is statically indeterminate in the third degree.

If a frictionless hinge is introduced at a support or at any point along the arch, we obtain an equation of condition (moment must be zero at the hinge) to add to the three available equations of equilibrium. The structure is now statically indeterminate in the second degree. If a second hinge is added, the structure becomes indeterminate in the first degree. Finally, with three hinges the structure is statically determinate. If, however, a fourth hinge is added, a mechanism is formed, and no resistance to movement will be developed. The arch is unstable.

We can reason exactly the same way for the frame in Figure 2-1(b), but there is an important difference. If we place hinges at the junctures of vertical and horizontal members, the horizontal member becomes a simply supported beam. For vertical loading, no horizontal component of reaction is developed, and we no longer have a so-called rigid frame. Furthermore, if a third hinge is placed anywhere along the horizontal member, it can no longer function as a flexural member but rather as in Figure 1-15(a). As a frame, the structure is unstable.

From the preceding discussion it is seen that at least one joint of a frame such as that in Figure 2-1(b) must be rigid. It is the presence of one or more of these moment-resisting joints which makes a frame a "rigid frame." When frames such as those in Figure 2-1 are shown in this book, all joints will be considered rigid unless a pin joint is indicated by a small circle.

The total number of independent unknowns in a rigid frame is equal to the sum of the unknown reaction components plus the sum of the independent unknown force components in the members. In a rigid frame each member may

35

develop resisting moment and axial and transverse components of force. Thus, if we call the number of members b and the number of unknown reaction components r, the total number of independent unknowns in a rigid frame is equal to $3b + r$.

Each rigid joint in a frame is subjected to forces and moments, and three equations of equilibrium are available. For j rigid joints there are, therefore, $3j$ equations of static equilibrium available. If s represents the number of special equations of condition, the total number of equations available for determining the unknowns is $3j + s$. Consequently, a rigid frame is statically determinate when

$$3j + s = 3b + r \qquad (2.1)$$

When the value of the left-hand side of Equation (2.1) is less than the value of the right side, the structure is statically indeterminate. When greater, the structure is unstable. It is emphasized, however, that Equation (2.1) is a necessary but not sufficient criterion for establishing stability. If $3j + s$ is greater than $3b + r$, the frame definitely is unstable, but if $3j + s$ is equal to or less than $3b + r$, this does not prove definitely that the structure is stable. Hinges properly placed will result in a stable structure, whereas the same number of hinges improperly placed can result in an unstable structure.

For Figure 2.1(c), j is equal to 4, s is equal to zero, b is equal to 3, and r is equal to 3 (2 at the left support and 1 at the right support). Equation (2.1) becomes $12 + 0 = 9 + 3$, and the structure is statically determinate. For (d), with $j = 5$, $s = 1$, $b = 4$, and $r = 4$, we get $15 + 1 = 12 + 4$, and the structure is determinate.

For Figure 2-1(e) the quantities j, b, and r are counted as before, but some additional explanation is necessary before determining the value of s. The hinge on the left-hand side introduces two special conditions because it involves three members rather than two. In general a hinge introduces a number of conditions equal to one less than the number of members framing into it. The hinge on the right side affects the horizontal member only and thus introduces one special condition. The total value of s is $1 + 2 + 1 = 4$, and Equation (2.1) becomes $18 + 4 = 18 + 6$. The frame is statically indeterminate in the second degree.

For (f) we have $15 + 2 = 12 + 6$, and the structure is statically indeterminate in the first degree. The frame in (g) is statically indeterminate in the thirtieth degree.

2.2   Arches, Rigid Frames, and the Pressure Line

Figure 2-2(a) shows a three-hinged, and therefore statically determinate, arch. The reactions, shears, and moments can be calculated in a manner similar to that used for the beam of Figure 1-16. Although there are four reaction components in Figure 2-2(b), the presence of a hinge at C yields the

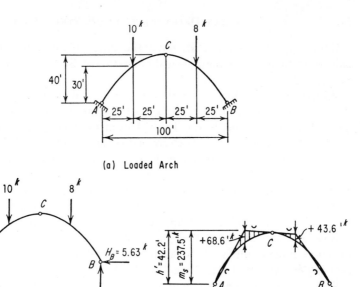

(a) Loaded Arch

(b) Forces Acting on Arch   (c) Pressure Line and Moments

Figure 2-2.   Three–Hinged Arch and the Pressure Line

additional equation necessary to obtain a solution. First, sum moments about
B and solve for V_A, and sum moments about A and solve for V_B. Now sum
moments about C of forces on *either* side of this point and solve for H_A
(or H_B). Finally, sum forces in the horizontal direction to obtain the other
horizontal component of reaction.

$$\sum M_B = V_A \times 100 - 10 \times 75 - 8 \times 25 = 0$$

$$V_A = 9.5 \text{ kips}$$

$$\sum M_A = 10 \times 25 + 8 \times 75 - V_B \times 100 = 0$$

$$V_B = 8.5 \text{ kips}$$

$$\sum_{A}^{C} M_C = -H_A \times 40 + V_A \times 50 - 10 \times 25 = 0$$

$$= -40H_A + 9.5 \times 50 - 250 = 0$$

$$H_A = 5.63 \text{ kips}$$

$$\sum F_{x'} = H_A - H_B = 0$$

$$= 5.63 - H_B = 0$$

$$H_B = 5.63 \text{ kips}$$

Alternatively, the value of H_B can be obtained from $\sum_{B}^{C} M_C = 0$. When there is
no horizontal loading, H_A will always equal H_B, and the subscripts can be
deleted.

If the supports at A and B are not at the same elevation, the solution of two pairs of simultaneous equations will be necessary. Such a case is discussed in Section 2.3.

With the reactions known, axial thrust, shear, and moment at any section of the arch can be determined. The moment diagram is shown, with the axis of the arch as a base line, in (c). The values at the load points were obtained through use of the previously determined values of H and V. For the present, pay no attention to the quantities h' and m_s. The segments of the moment diagram passing through the end hinges lie along the lines of action of the resultant end reactions. The intermediate segment of the moment diagram must pass through the third hinge. Notice that the segmental line, which together with the arch axis delineates the moment diagram, represents successive resultants of forces. Thus the intermediate segment represents the line of action of the resultant of the reaction at A and the 10-kip load or the resultant of the reaction at B and the 8-kip load.

Such a segmental line is commonly called a pressure line. The reader will recognize that the pressure line in Figure 2-2(c) is a string polygon drawn upside down. It could be obtained graphically, for any loading condition, exactly as in Figure 1-24 but with the trial pole located to the left of the forces in the force polygon.

The quantity m_s in Figure 2-2(c) represents the moment that would occur at a section if one end of the structure were free to move horizontally ($H = 0$)—that is, m_s represents a simple-beam moment. The quantity h' represents a height to the pressure line. This value is known at the intermediate hinge and can be determined readily at any other point by ratio from the simple-beam moments. If the pressure line has been constructed graphically (string polygon), h' can be scaled directly.

Since the moment anywhere along a "string" (line of action of resultant force) must be zero

$$Hh' = m_s$$

and

$$H = \frac{m_s}{h'} \qquad (2.2)$$

We can use any point along the pressure line, and, if we divide the simple-beam moment at that point by the height to the pressure line at the same point, we will obtain the horizontal thrust for vertical loading.

On the basis of the previous discussion, the student should convince himself that the vertical ordinates between the pressure line and the arch axis represent the bending moment along the axis, and the value of this moment at any location is

$$M = H\eta \qquad (2.3)$$

in which η is the height of the ordinate at the location under consideration.

2.3   Applications of the Pressure Line

Referring once more to Figure 2-2, the simple-beam moment at C is

$$m_s = V_A \times 50 - 10 \times 25 = 9.5 \times 50 - 10 \times 25 = 225 \text{ ft-kips}$$

The corresponding value of h' is 40 ft. Then from Equation (2.2)

$$H = \tfrac{225}{40} = 5.63 \text{ kips}$$

This is the identical value previously obtained from the equations of equilibrium. The value of m_s at the 10-kip load is $9.5 \times 25 = 237.5$ ft-kips, and the corresponding value of h' can be found by ratio from that at C as follows:

$$h' = \tfrac{237.5}{225} \times 40 = 42.2 \text{ ft}$$

The value of H is $237.5/42.2 = 5.63$ kips, as before.

The vertical ordinate between the pressure line and the arch at the same load point is

$$\eta = h' - 30 = 42.2 - 30 = 12.2 \text{ ft}$$

The bending moment is then, from Equation (2.2),

$$M = 5.63 \times 12.2 = 68.6 \text{ ft-kips}$$

The bending moment at any other location can be obtained in the same manner.

Observe that if only a single load is placed on the three-hinged arch or rigid frame, the correct pressure line can be drawn immediately because it consists of only two segments, one of which must pass through the intermediate hinge as well as an end hinge. For the arch of Figure 2-2(a), separate pressure lines are shown in Figure 2-3 for each of the two loads.

Values of reaction components and bending moments in (a) and (b) of Figure 2-3 can be combined to obtain the same values as those previously determined for the actual load condition of Figure 2-2. For example, from Equation (2.3) the moment at the 10-kip load point in Figure 2-3(a) is

$$3.13(60 - 30) = 93.9 \text{ ft-kips}$$

and in Figure 2-3(b) it is

$$2.50(20 - 30) = -25.0 \text{ ft-kips}$$

The total moment is $93.9 - 25.0 = 68.9$ ft-kips. The slight difference from the value in Figure 2-2(c) is due to round-off error.

It is important to recognize that the pressure lines in Figure 2-3 cannot be combined directly to obtain that in Figure 2-2 because the values of H in (a) and (b) of Figure 2-3 are not identical. We must determine bending

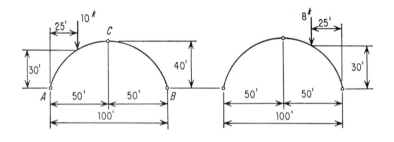

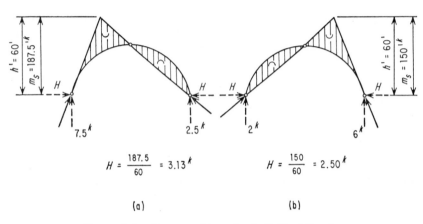

$$H = \frac{187.5}{60} = 3.13^{k} \qquad\qquad H = \frac{150}{60} = 2.50^{k}$$

(a)   (b)

Figure 2-3.   Pressure Lines for Individual Loads

moments separately and then combine them to obtain the correct pressure line and moments for the arch of Figure 2-2.

If an arch or rigid frame is subjected to a load uniformly distributed along its horizontal projection, the pressure line is a parabola and m_s at midspan is $(\frac{1}{8})wL^2$, in which w is the intensity of load per unit length. From Equation (2.2),

$$H = \frac{(\frac{1}{8})wL^2}{h'}$$

An unsymmetrical arch is shown in Figure 2-4(a). The geometry and loading are identical to those of the arch of Figure 2-2(a) except that end B is now farther to the right and below the elevation of end A.

$$\sum M_B = V_A \times 105 + H_A \times 8.4 - 10 \times 80 - 8 \times 30 = 0$$

$$V_A = 9.905 - 0.080H_A$$

$$\sum M_C = V_A \times 50 - H_A \times 40 - 10 \times 25 = 0$$

$$H_A = 1.25V_A - 6.25$$

Substituting this expression for H_A into the expression for V_A, we get

$$V_A = 9.905 - 0.080(1.25V_A - 6.25); \qquad \therefore V_A = 9.46 \text{ kips}$$

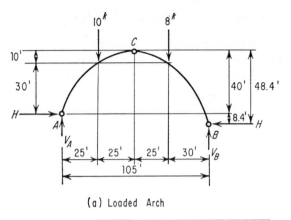

(a) Loaded Arch

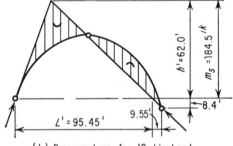

(b) Pressure Line for 10-kip Load

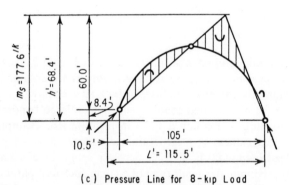

(c) Pressure Line for 8-kip Load

Figure 2-4.   Unsymmetrical Arch

Substituting back, we obtain

$$H_A = 5.57 \text{ kips}$$

Similarly, using $\sum M_A = 0$, and $\sum\limits_{B}^{C} M_C = 0$,

$$V_B = 8.54 \text{ kips}; \qquad H_B = 5.57 \text{ kips}$$

The solution can be checked by summing vertical forces and horizontal forces, respectively.

41

In Figure 2-4(b) the pressure line for the 10-kip load is shown. The symbol h' represents the vertical height to any point on the pressure line measured from any horizontal line joining the two segments of the pressure line. The symbol m_s represents the simple-beam moment corresponding to the same point and computed for a span L' corresponding to the length of the horizontal line between segments of the pressure line. The value of h' in Figure 2-4(b) was determined from the known slope of the right-hand segment of the pressure line. The value shown for m_s is the simple-beam moment under the 10-kip load for a span L' of 95.45 ft. Then

$$V_A = \frac{10(80 - 9.55)}{95.45} = 7.38 \text{ kips}$$

$$V_B = 10.00 - 7.38 = 2.62 \text{ kips}$$

$$m_s = 7.38 \times 25 = 184.5 \text{ ft-kips}$$

and, from Equation (2.1),

$$H = \frac{184.5}{62.0} = 2.98 \text{ kips}$$

In a similar manner, for Figure 2-4(c) we get

$$V_B = \frac{8(75 + 10.5)}{115.5} = 5.92 \text{ kips}$$

$$V_A = 8.00 - 5.92 = 2.08 \text{ kips}$$

$$m_s = 5.92 \times 30 = 177.6 \text{ ft-kips}$$

$$H = \frac{177.6}{68.4} = 2.60 \text{ kips}$$

If the values for reaction components in (b) and (c) of Figure 2-4 are superimposed, the values previously computed directly for (a) are obtained.

As has been seen in this article and in Section 1.13, an arch having the shape of the pressure line for a particular loading will not undergo bending when subjected to that loading. If loading is fixed in position (for example, dead load with no live load), there is a structural advantage in so shaping the structure. Since dead load is fairly uniform across a span, the efficient shape when such loading predominates tends toward a curve such as a parabola or a segment of a circle. This predominance of dead load in ancient structures led to the popularity of the masonry arch, which had virtually no resistance to bending but could develop large resistance to axial thrust. For such preponderance of fairly uniform dead load, a rigid frame such as that in Figure 2-1(b) would be subjected to large bending moments.

As the live load becomes more important relative to the dead load, the advantages of the arch over the rigid frame tend to vanish. An arch can be shaped to eliminate bending moments due to dead load, but large bending moments can occur due to live load. Furthermore, modern metals and the development of reinforced and prestressed concrete make possible a large moment-resisting capacity. This and certain functional advantages, such as constant headroom and bigger enclosed area for the same rise, have made the rigid frame popular.

2.4   Introduction to Simple and Compound Trusses

A truss consists of straight bars connected at their ends and arranged in such a way as to form a rigid framework capable of supporting loads. In this chapter we deal only with statically determinate trusses whose bars all lie in one plane.

Figure 2-5 shows two elementary geometric configurations with pinned-end

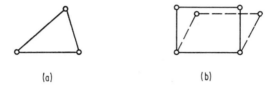

(a)   (b)

Figure 2-5.   Stable and Unstable Shapes

connections. A little thought should convince the student that the triangular configuration of bars is the only inherently stable one. Its shape cannot be changed except by changing the length of one or more of the bars. If any other configuration is used, stability can be obtained only by making one or more joints rigid.

Trusses are analyzed as if all bars were connected by frictionless pins. Consequently, a load applied to a joint is resisted by axial stress in the bars. In practice the connections between bars of trusses are quite rigid. However, the dimensions are such that the axial stresses computed in the bars by assuming frictionless pins are essentially correct. These are the so-called primary stresses.

In Section 12.8 we consider bending stresses induced by the rigid joints. These so-called secondary stresses generally have little effect on the magnitude of the primary stresses. They may be important, however, in conjunction with the primary stresses in trusses with relatively short and deep members.

For ideal truss action (axial stresses only), it is necessary that all loads be applied at joints. The dead load of the bars is also assumed applied at the joints, usually neglecting the relatively small bending stresses due to the actual distribution of the dead load. Sometimes it is necessary to apply load between joints of the truss. The bending stress must then be taken into account in design.

If we begin with a triangular arrangement of bars, we can construct a rigid plane truss by successive addition of two new bars and a pin. Several such

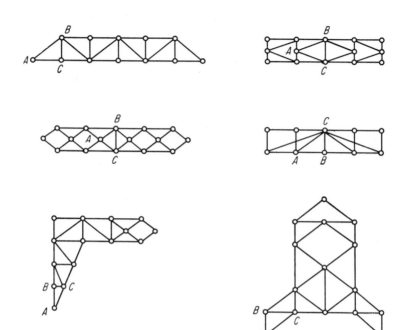

Figure 2-6.   Simple Trusses

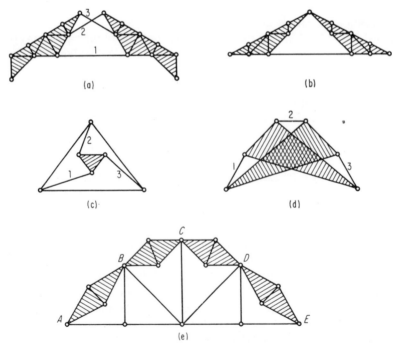

Figure 2-7.   Compound Trusses

trusses are shown in Figure 2-6. In each case the truss has been constructed beginning with triangle *ABC*. A truss constructed in this elementary manner is termed a *simple truss*, but such trusses are not necessarily "simple."

If a simple truss is now supported so that three nonconcurrent, nonparallel reaction components are developed (see Section 1.5), the structure will be stable and the reactions will be statically determinate. The question of stability and determinacy will be discussed further in Section 2.5.

A *compound truss* is formed by interconnecting two or more simple trusses so that each of these trusses is completely restrained as a unit. This requirement is satisfied when three nonconcurrent, nonparallel linking forces can be developed.

Figure 2-7 shows several examples of compound trusses. The simple trusses that are joined are shown crosshatched. In (a), (c), and (d) the simple trusses are interconnected by three linkages labeled 1, 2, and 3. In (b) the simple trusses are interconnected by a common hinge and one bar. The restraint furnished by the common hinge is equivalent to that of two links.

The simple trusses in (e) are connected in another way. The structure is stable because one can consider that each simple truss has replaced a straight chord member, such as *AB*, of an originally simple truss *ABCDE*.

2.5   Stability and Determinacy of Trusses

We have seen that a rigid truss can be constructed by beginning with three bars pinned together at their ends and then using two other bars to form each additional joint. The total number of bars required is the original three plus two additional bars for each joint beyond the original three. This relationship between the number of bars, b, and the number of joints, j, can be stated as follows:

$$b = 3 + 2(j - 3)$$

$$b = 2j - 3 \tag{2.4}$$

Equation (2.4) gives the minimum number of bars necessary to form a stable truss, whether simple or compound. Fewer bars will result in an unstable truss unless additional external supports are provided. More bars are unnecessary and will result in statical indeterminacy. If a truss satisfies Equation (2.4) and is supported in such a way that three nonconcurrent and nonparallel reaction components can be developed, it is stable and statically determinate. As will be illustrated later, however, Equation (2.4) is a necessary but not sufficient condition for stability. The bars and reaction elements must be of sufficient number and properly arranged in order to insure stability. If they are not, the structure is said to be geometrically unstable.

A more general look at stability and determinacy is desirable. For a truss, two independent equations of equilibrium ($\sum F_x = 0$; $\sum F_y = 0$) can be written at each joint. This will result in a total of $2j$ independent equations available for the complete stress analysis, involving as unknowns the b bar forces and the r reaction components. The truss is statically determinate if

$$2j = b + r$$

or

$$b = 2j - r \tag{2.5}$$

This is a more general statement than Equation (2.4). Observe that for the minimum possible number of reaction components (three) required for stability the equations are identical.

As stated in connection with Equation (2.4), Equation (2.5) is a necessary but not sufficient condition for stability. When b is greater than $2j - r$, the truss is statically indeterminate. When b is less than $2j - r$, the truss is unstable. If there is doubt as to the stability of a structure, it can be resolved by attempting a stress analysis. If the structure is unstable, the results will be inconsistent or indeterminate. (See Section 2.10).

Figure 2-8 shows several trusses which will be used to illustrate stability and determinacy. In (a), application of Equation (2.5) indicates that the truss is determinate, but inspection shows that the structure will collapse if loaded because a mechanism will be formed under load. The third panel from the left cannot resist shear. If a diagonal bar is added in this panel, the structure becomes statically indeterminate in the first degree. As the reactions are statically determinate, the structure would be said to be indeterminate internally.

The truss in (b) is stable and statically determinate. The extra reaction component is required for stability. The additional equation necessary to compute the reactions is obtained from the fact that the moment at the hinge must be zero. If the gap in the top chord is filled through the insertion of a bar that is not free to move longitudinally at one end, the structure will become statically indeterminate in the first degree. When indeterminateness results from the presence of more than three possible reaction components, the structure is said to be statically indeterminate externally.

The structure in Figure 2-8(c) is statically determinate. The interior support takes the place of the long diagonal that would otherwise be required. In (d) the structure is statically indeterminate in the first degree. If the interior pin is removed, then $b = 9$, $j = 6$, and $2j - r = 9$. The structure is now statically determinate.

The truss in Figure 2-8(e) is stable and statically determinate. If bars bd and bf are removed (ac becoming one bar) and bars ae and ce added, we have $b = 34$, $j = 18$, and $2j - r = 33$. The structure is now statically indeterminate in the first degree. In (f) the structure is statically indeterminate in the third degree. The structure is statically indeterminate both externally (twice) and internally (once). The internal indeterminacy results from the force in the horizontal tie between the two interior supports. This tie makes possible the arch action. Without the tie the structure becomes a three-span continuous truss rather than a continuous arch truss.

The truss in Figure 2-8(g) is a continuous structure but is actually statically determinate because of its configuration over the supports. Sloping the lower chord at the interior supports makes possible the elimination of the vertical bars. Such a truss is called a Wichert truss, after its inventor. It is stable, providing the slope of the bars framing into the supports is not the same as the slope of the diagonals in the adjacent panels.

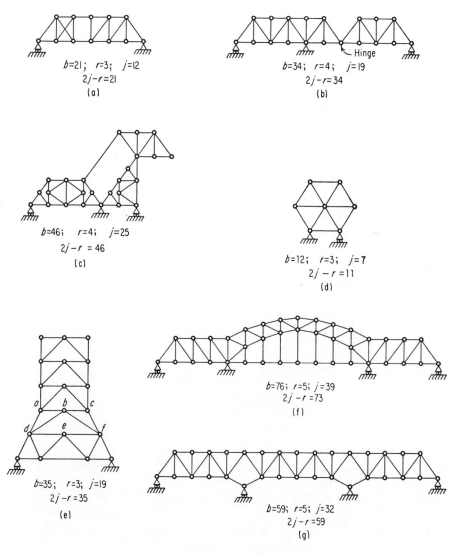

Figure 2-8.   Stability and Determinacy

2.6   Simple Trusses

The fundamental method of stress analysis for trusses consists of satisfying the conditions of equilibrium for successively isolated portions of the structure. If the portion of the truss isolated as a free body consists of bars all of which intersect at one point, two equations of equilibrium ($\sum F_x = 0; \sum F_y = 0$) are available. Using this so-called method of joints, we can determine no more than two of the unknown bar forces at a joint.

If the isolated portion of the truss consists of bars all of which do not intersect at a common point, three equations ($\sum F_x = 0; \sum F_y = 0; \sum M = 0$) are available, and no more than three bar forces can be determined. This is the so-called method of sections. It is emphasized that a free-body diagram must be "free." A joint must be completely isolated, and a section must pass (straight or jagged) completely through the structure.

Figure 2-9(a) shows a Pratt bridge truss with curved upper chord. The bars (or members, as they are referred to in truss design and construction) other than those of the chords are spoken of as verticals and diagonals. The end diagonals are also part of the upper chord and are called end posts. If the interior diagonals sloped outward from top to bottom, a Howe truss would result. If the diagonals were arranged to form a continuous V-pattern, we would have a Warren truss.

The reactions in Figure 2-9(a) were computed by taking moments about L_0 and L_6 successively. As all loading is vertical, the horizontal component of reaction at L_0 is zero. We now proceed to compute bar forces by successively isolating the joints.

Joint L_0 is isolated in (b). If we assume the unknown forces are tensions,

$$\sum F_y = 40 + \tfrac{30}{42.4}L_0 U_1 = 0$$

$$\sum F_x = L_0 L_1 + \tfrac{30}{42.4}L_0 U_1 = 0$$

From the first equation,

$$L_0 U_1 = -56.5 \text{ kips}$$

Substituting this value in the second equation,

$$L_0 L_1 = +40.0 \text{ kips}$$

The minus sign for $L_0 U_1$ indicates the force acts opposite to the direction assumed and is therefore a compression. The plus sign for $L_0 L_1$ indicates the force acts in the direction assumed and is therefore a tension.

If an unknown bar force is assumed to be a tension, a positive answer will mean tension actually exists, whereas a negative answer will mean the member is in compression. Thus results will be consistent with the universal use of + to denote tension and − to denote compression.

Of course, in a great many cases the student can tell in advance whether a

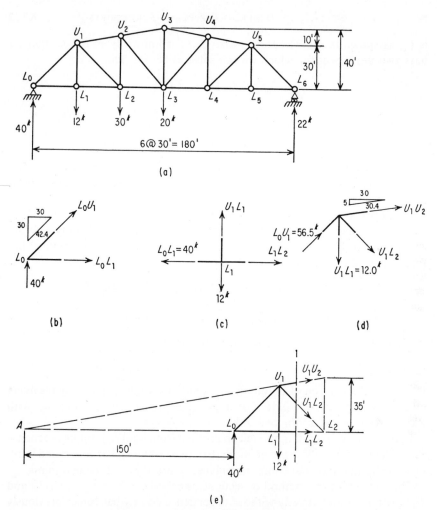

Figure 2-9. *Analysis of a Simple Truss*

member will be in tension or in compression. For example, it can be seen that the force $L_0 U_1$ must be a compression. Then

$$\Sigma F_y = 40 - \frac{30}{42.4} L_0 U_1 = 0$$

and

$$L_0 U_1 = +56.5 \text{ kips}$$

The plus sign indicates the force is as assumed (a compression, and not a tension). Signs now are not automatically in conformity with the sign convention followed herein ($+$ for tension, $-$ for compression). In the illustrations in this book, unknown bar forces will be assumed as tensions, and signs will be automatic.

Continuing the analysis of the truss in Figure 2-9, the next joint considered

49

is L_1, as shown in (c). The force in bar L_0L_1 is known from (b), so that we have two unknowns for which we can solve as before. Thus

$$\sum F_y = U_1L_1 - 12 = 0$$
$$\sum F_x = -40 + L_1L_2 = 0$$

and

$$U_1L_1 = +12.0 \text{ kips}; \qquad L_1L_2 = +40.0 \text{ kips}$$

Observe that once the magnitude and sense (tension or compression) of a force are determined, it is shown in its true sense in all succeeding free-body diagrams.

We now proceed to joint U_1 because we know the forces L_0U_1 and U_1L_1, leaving two unknowns which we can obtain as before. The free-body diagram of the joint is shown in (d). The true sense of the previously determined bar forces is shown: compression for L_0U_1 and tension for U_1L_1. Then

$$\sum F_y = (\tfrac{30}{42.4})\,56.5 - 12.0 - \tfrac{30}{42.4}\,U_1L_2 + \tfrac{5}{30.4}\,U_1U_2 = 0$$
$$\sum F_x = (\tfrac{30}{42.4})56.5 + \tfrac{30}{42.4}\,U_1L_2 + \tfrac{30}{30.4}\,U_1U_2 = 0$$

A solution of these simultaneous equations yields

$$U_1U_2 = -59.1 \text{ kips}; \qquad U_1L_2 = 25.9 \text{ kips}$$

If desired, the solution of simultaneous equations can be avoided by resolving all forces along each of a pair of orthogonal axes, one of which coincides with the direction of one of the two unknown bar forces.

In the same manner, it is possible to proceed from joint to joint in a sequence that will insure that there are no more than two unknown bar forces at a joint. Obviously, an error at any joint introduces errors at all subsequent joints.

Through use of the method of sections, the forces in bars L_1L_2, U_1U_2, and U_1L_2 can be found directly without dependence on any bar forces previously determined. Either of the two portions in which the truss is divided by the section can be treated as a free-body diagram. The portion to the left of Section 1-1 is shown in (e). There are three unknown bar forces, but three equations of equilibrium are available when the forces are nonconcurrent and nonparallel. Furthermore, it is generally possible to avoid the solution of simultaneous equations.

Force U_1U_2 is found by taking moments about the intersection at L_2 of the lines of action of the other two forces. Rather than compute the moment arm for force U_1U_2, it is generally easier to resolve such a force into horizontal and vertical components. It is convenient to make this resolution at a point vertically above the moment center, because the vertical component then drops out of the moment equation. Taking moments about L_2,

$$\sum M = 40(60) - 12(30) + \tfrac{30}{30.4}\,U_1U_2(35) = 0$$
$$U_1U_2 = -59.1 \text{ kips}$$

To find force L_1L_2, take moments about U_1, the intersection of forces U_1U_2 and U_1L_2.

$$\sum M = 40(30) - L_1L_2(30) = 0$$

$$L_1L_2 = +40 \text{ kips}$$

The reader will have noticed that the horizontal component of force in a chord member is simply the moment about the opposite panel point divided by the arm of the force.

The force in U_1L_2 can be computed through use of $\sum F_y = 0$, but we would have to make use of the previously computed value of U_1U_2. Instead, we can find force U_1L_2 directly by taking moments about the intersection of U_1U_2 and L_1L_2 at A. It is convenient to resolve U_1L_2 into components at L_2 so that the horizontal component will not enter the equation.

$$\sum M_A = -40(150) + 12(180) + \tfrac{30}{42.4} U_1L_2(210) = 0$$

$$U_1L_2 = +25.9 \text{ kips}$$

If bar U_1U_2 were horizontal, the force in U_1L_2 could be determined independently from $\sum F_y = 0$.

Except for U_3L_3, the forces in all bars of the truss in Figure 2-9 can be found directly, without dependence on a previously determined force. The force in U_3L_3 is computed as the sum of the vertical components of the bar forces in U_2U_3 and U_3U_4.

The reactions shown at U_0 and L_0 of the cantilevered truss of Figure 2-10 were computed in the usual manner by taking moments about the support points. Stresses can be found systematically for all members by isolating the joints in the following order: U_4, L_4, M_4, U_3, L_3, M_3, and so forth. As previously mentioned, a mistake at one joint will be carried through all remaining joints. If only one or two bar forces are required or if it is desired to check the results obtained by the method of joints, this can be done conveniently by using the method of sections.

Assume it is required to determine the forces in bars U_1U_2 and U_1M_2. Section 1-1 cuts four bars, but the lines of action of the forces in three of them intersect at a common point, L_2. As a result, the force in U_1U_2 can be obtained directly by using the free-body diagram in (b) and taking moments about L_2, as follows:

$$\sum M = 40(40) + 20(30) - U_1U_2(30) = 0$$

$$U_1U_2 = +73.3 \text{ kips}$$

From section 2-2 we obtain the free-body diagram shown in (c). This section cuts four bars, of which the lines of action of only two intersect at a common point. The value of U_1M_2 can be determined, however, by making use of the previously determined value of U_1U_2. Taking moments about L_1,

$$\sum M = 40(60) + 20(30) - 73.3(30) - \tfrac{20}{25} U_1M_2(30) = 0$$

$$U_1M_2 = +33.3 \text{ kips}$$

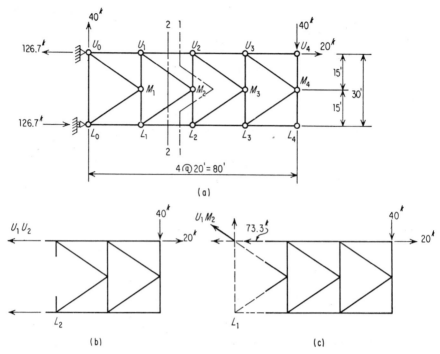

Figure 2-10. Cantilever Truss

It is possible to obtain $U_1 M_2$ directly without using any previously computed force by observing that the x-component of force in $U_1 M_2$ must be equal and opposite to that in $L_1 M_2$. From this known relationship, the individual y-components can be determined, noting that their sum must equal the panel shear. In the case under consideration, the slopes of $U_1 M_2$ and $L_1 M_2$ are numerically equal, and the panel shear of 40 kips is shared equally. Thus, isolating the portion of the truss to the right of Section 2-2,

$$\sum F_y = -\tfrac{40}{2} + \tfrac{15}{25} U_1 M_2 = 0$$
$$U_1 M_2 = +33.3 \text{ kips}$$

as before. The force in bar $L_1 M_2$ is -33.3 kips.

The bridge truss shown in Figure 2-11 is a subdivided deck-type structure. It is called a subdivided truss because members such as $U_1 M_1$ and $U_2 M_1$ have been superimposed on the basic truss. It is called a deck truss because the truss is below the roadway level. If the truss were turned upside down, it would be a through truss.

The force in $U_3 U_4$ can be found directly by considering the portion of the structure to the left of section 1-1. The free-body diagram is shown in Figure 2-11(b). Taking moments about L_2,

$$\sum M = 65(60) + 80(30) + U_3 U_4(40) = 0$$
$$U_3 U_4 = -157.5 \text{ kips}$$

52

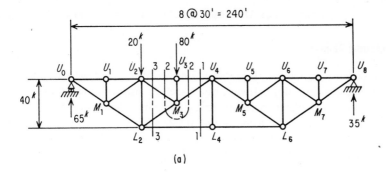

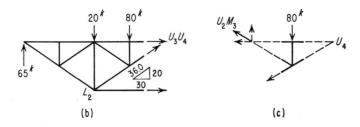

(b)

(c)

Figure 2-11.   Subdivided Truss

Using the same free-body diagram,

$$\sum F_y = 65 - 20 - 80 + \tfrac{20}{36.0} M_3 U_4 = 0$$

$$M_3 U_4 = +63.0 \text{ kips}$$

The force in member $U_2 M_3$ can be found directly by isolating the portion of the truss cut by section 2-2. This is done in Figure 2-11(c), and moments are then taken about U_4.

$$\sum M = \tfrac{20}{36} U_2 M_3(60) - 80(30) = 0$$

$$U_2 M_3 = +72.0 \text{ kips}$$

The force in bar $L_2 M_3$ can be found by writing $\sum F_y = 0$ for the portion to the left or right of section 3-3, using the vertical component of the previously determined force in $U_2 M_3$.

For the loads shown in Figure 2-11(a), the force in bar $U_3 M_3$ is, by inspection of joint U_3, -80 kips. The force in similar bar $U_5 M_5$ is zero because no load is applied at U_5. If joint M_5 is isolated and forces summed perpendicular to $U_4 L_6$, it is seen that the force in $M_5 U_6$ must also be zero. Notice that removal of bars such as $U_5 M_5$ and $M_5 U_6$ leaves a basic, stable truss. Such bars are necessary only when loads are to be applied between panel points of the basic truss.

2.7 Compound Trusses

In a compound truss it is generally impossible to complete an analysis by the method of joints alone. Invariably, a section must be cut so that it includes one or more of the bars interconnecting the component simple trusses.

Once the reactions of the compound truss in Figure 2-12(a) are computed, a section is passed cutting the bars which link truss ABC to truss DEF. The inner portion is isolated and shown in (b). The force in bar CE is determined by taking moments about the intersection of the lines of action of forces DA and FB. This intersection was found, from a simultaneous solution of the

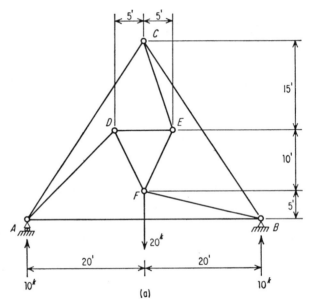

(a)

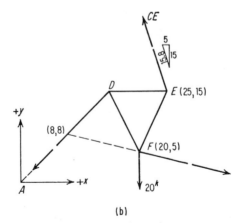

(b)

Figure 2-12. Compound Truss

equations for line AD and line FB, to be at $x = 8$, $y = 8$. It is convenient to resolve CE into components at the known location of E. This means both vertical and horizontal components of CE will appear in the moment equation.

$$\sum M_{(8,8)} = 20(20 - 8) - (\tfrac{15}{15.8}\, CE)(25 - 8) - (\tfrac{5}{15.8}\, CE)(15 - 8) = 0$$

$$CE = 13.1 \text{ kips}$$

The forces in DA and FB can be determined directly in a similar manner, and the results for the three connecting links can then be checked by $\sum F_x = 0$ and $\sum F_y = 0$. The stresses in each of the simple trusses can finally be determined by isolating each joint.

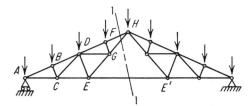

Figure 2-13. Compound Truss

The compound truss in Figure 2-13 is composed of two simple trusses connected by a hinge at H and by a link EE'. The method of joints can be applied successively at A, B, and C. At D or E, however, there will be three unknown concurrent bars forces, but only two independent equations can be written. Section 1-1 is used to isolate a portion of the structure, and the force in EE' is found by taking moments about H. With force EE' known, the method of joints can now be applied to E, D, F, and so forth to complete the analysis.

This procedure of taking a section that cuts the bar or bars linking the simple trusses of the compound truss is generally necessary. In the case of the so-called Fink truss of Figure 2-13 it is, however, possible to obtain all stresses by the method of joints because DFH and EGH are straight lines. As a result, we can skip from joint E to joint F, and obtain the force in FG. Then obtain force DG by isolating joint G and summing forces in the direction perpendicular to EH. The analysis can now be completed.

The compound truss in Figure 2-14(a) consists of two simple trusses, BCF

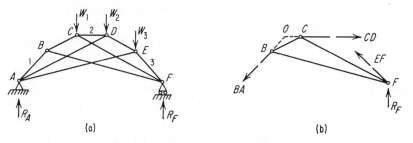

Figure 2-14. Compound Truss

and ADE, connected together by links 1, 2, and 3. The reactions are determined as usual, and the connecting links are then cut, isolating the portion of the structure shown in (b). Force in EF is found by taking moments about O. Forces BA and CD can then be determined from $\sum F_x = 0$ and $\sum F_y = 0$.

A compound truss of the type shown in Figure 2-15(a) can be considered as

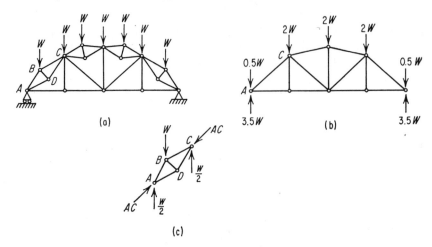

Figure 2-15.   Compound Truss

equivalent to the simple truss in (b) but with the top chord members replaced by simple trusses such as those in (c). First we analyze the structure in (b), with the intermediate loads in (a) transferred to the main panel points. This gives us the correct forces in all lower chord and web members. The upper chord forces, such as AC, are applied to free-body diagrams such as that in (c). The bar forces for these simple trusses can now be found, thus completing the analysis.

2.8   Graphical Analysis of Trusses

The method of joints can be applied graphically exactly as it was algebraically. Thus, after determining the reactions either algebraically or graphically, the bar forces can be obtained by drawing one force polygon for each joint at which there are no more than two unknowns.

The loaded truss in Figure 2-16(a) is redrawn in (b), showing reactions and a letter-number system for conveniently identifying bar forces, loads, and reactions in a force polygon. By means of this method of force designation, known as Bow's notation, a load or reaction is designated by the letters of the alphabet on each side of it. For example, the horizontal component of reaction at A is designated $f - a$, the load at C is $b - c$, and the reaction at E is $c - d$. All bar forces are designated by the numbers or letters on each side of the

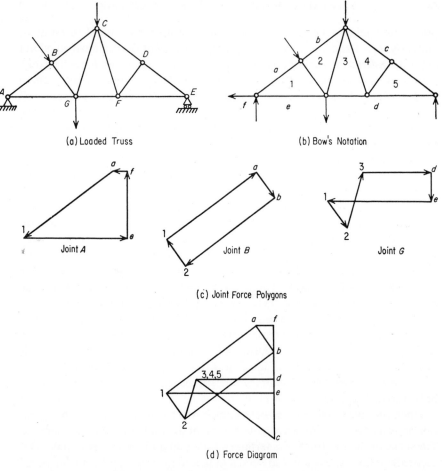

Figure 2-16. *Graphical Analysis of Truss*

corresponding bar. Thus the force in bar *BG* is designated $1 - 2$, and the force in bar *GF* is $3 - d$.

If the truss diagram in (b) is drawn to scale, force polygons can be constructed for each joint, commencing at *A*, by drawing lines of force parallel to the bars. Such joint force polygons are shown in (c). For joint *A*, the reactions $e - f$ and $f - a$ are first laid out to scale. Proceeding clockwise around the joint, the line of action of force $a - 1$ is drawn parallel to the corresponding bar. The line of action of $e - 1$ is then drawn, and its intersection with the line of action of $a - 1$ locates point 1. Inspection of the force polygon shows that force $a - 1$ pushes into joint *A* and is therefore a compression, whereas force $1 - e$ pulls out of the joint and is therefore a tension.

The force polygons at joints *B* and *G* were drawn in the same manner, proceeding clockwise around each joint. Observe that force $1 - a$ at joint *B* is drawn opposite to the direction of the same force ($a - 1$) at joint *A*. Thus it

57

pushes into joint B and is a compression, just as it was found to be at A. Similarly, $e - 1$ and $1 - 2$ of the force polygon at joint G are shown equal but opposite in direction to the corresponding forces at joints A and B, respectively.

Instead of drawing a separate force polygon at each joint of the truss, a single force, or Maxwell, diagram can be drawn. Such a diagram combines all joint diagrams and eliminates the repetition of force vectors at successive joints. In the preceding work it was not necessary to proceed clockwise (or counterclockwise) about all joints, but in drawing a force diagram this must be done so as to obtain the correct sense of the bar forces.

The force diagram for the truss in Figure 2-16(a) is shown in (d) of the same figure. First a force polygon, $a - b - c - d - e - f - a$, is drawn for all external forces, going clockwise around the structure. Now proceed as before, and draw polygon $f - a - 1 - e - f$ for joint A. Next draw polygon $a - b - 2 - 1 - a$ for joint B, noting that lines $a - b$ and $2 - 1$ have been drawn previously. Then draw the force polygon for joint G. Notice that lines $d - e$, $e - 1$, and $1 - 2$ are already in place. At joint C we have $3 - 2 - b - c - 4 - 3$, with $3 - 2$, $2 - b$, and $b - c$ already located. Line $c - 4$ passes through 3, and therefore point 4 lies on point 3 (zero force in bar $3 - 4$). From a consideration of joint D, it is found that point 5 must fall on point 4. Inspection of the truss verifies that, since there is no load applied at C, bar $4 - 5$ is unstressed. Consideration of joint F verifies that bar $3 - 4$ is unstressed. Still another way of looking at this is to note that if bars $3 - 4$ and $4 - 5$ were removed, the structure would still be stable. These bars are needed only if load is applied at D or F.

When the force diagram has been completed, the magnitude of a bar force can be determined by measuring its corresponding line in the force diagram. The sense of the bar force is determined by reading the numbers or letters on each side of the bar clockwise around a joint and then using the same sequence to obtain the direction of the corresponding vector in the force diagram. For example, at joint B in the truss we read $1 - a$, and on the force diagram the direction of the vector is from 1 to a, which indicates a push into the joint, or compression. For bar $b - 2$ at joint B, we find the direction of the corresponding vector in the force diagram to be from b to 2, indicating compression. Similarly, for bar $2 - 1$ we also obtain compression. If we consider joint G, the latter bar is designated $1 - 2$. From 1 to 2 in the force diagram indicates a push into the joint, or compression, which is the same result obtained going from 2 to 1 at joint B.

The truss in Figure 2-17 is a subdivided version of that in Figure 2-16. It is a compound truss, known as the Fink roof truss. For the present ignore the numbers $4'$ and $6'$ as well as the dashed line lying between them.

The force diagram for the external forces and for the first three joints at the left end of the truss is constructed exactly as before. The next joint on either the top chord or the bottom chord has three unknown bar forces, and it appears that the stress analysis cannot proceed.

If it is assumed that bars $4 - 5$ and $5 - 6$ are replaced by the a member $4' - 6'$, shown dashed, the forces in members $e - 6, 6 - 7$, and $7 - k$ will not be affected. This can readily be seen by noting that if those bars are cut by a section through the truss, the bar forces are independent of the arrangement of the other bars.

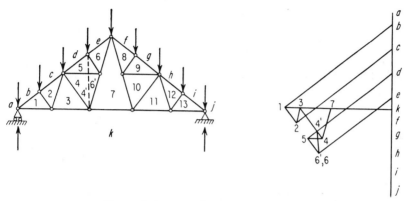

Figure 2-17. Analysis of Fink Truss

Using the substitute member $4' - 6'$, points $4'$ and $6'$ can be located on the force diagram. Then, since force $e - 6$ in the actual structure must be equal to $e - 6'$, points 6 and $6'$ are identical and point 5 can now be located. Also, since the lines of action of $3 - 4$ and $3 - 4'$ must be identical, and since point 5 is known, point 4 can be located.

For a symmetrical structure with symmetrical loading, it is only necessary to construct the force diagram for one half the structure. The diagram for the other half of the members will be a mirror image about line $1 - k$ of that shown in Figure 2-17. Attention is called to the fact that a special construction, such as that used in Figure 2-17, never needs to be repeated. For a Fink truss observe that points 1, 2, 5, and 6 must lie on a straight line, and vector $3 - 4$ must be parallel to that line.

2.9   Complex Trusses

Some trusses satisfy Equation (2.5) but cannot be classified as either simple or compound. Such structures are called *complex trusses*, and several examples are shown in Figure 2-18.

It is not possible to make a complete stress analysis of a complex truss by using only the method of joints and method of sections. For example, in Figure 2-18(a) all joints have three or more members, and no section can be taken which would make possible the direct determination of bar force. Note that if a pin is introduced at the intersection of the long interior bars, the truss becomes statically indeterminate in the first degree.

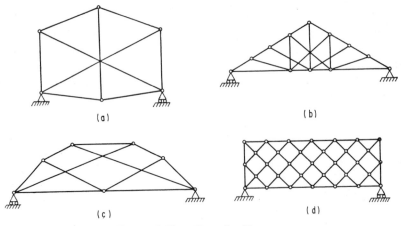

Figure 2-18. Complex Trusses

In (b) the method of joints can be applied at the support and the two adjacent joints at each end. Farther in the interior neither the method of joints nor the method of sections is applicable. The arguments used for (a) also apply to (c) and (d). No further progress in the analysis can be made either by isolating joints or sections.

Of course, two equations ($\sum F_y = 0$; and $\sum F_x = 0$) can be written at each joint, and this will result in $2j$ simultaneous equations for determining the bar forces and the reactions. For the statically determinate structures under consideration, the reactions can be determined directly, and $2j - 3$ equations can be solved for the bar forces. The other three equations can be used to check results. Analysis by the solution of such simultaneous equations is possible for any complex truss. However, except for structures with few joints, a large number of equations must be solved, and this is generally feasible only by means of an electronic digital computer. The solution of sets of linear algebraic equations is discussed in Section 9.4.

When a digital computer is not available, the solution of even a relatively small number of equations becomes tedious and difficult. An analysis of a complex truss can generally be made much more readily through use of substitute members, a method attributed to Henneberg. This method is explained in connection with Figure 2-19.

The complex truss of Figure 2-19(a) can be transformed into the simple truss

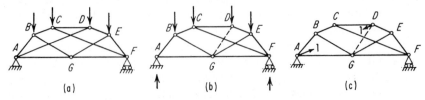

Figure 2-19. Method of Substitute Member

of (b) by removing member AD and substituting member DG for it. Of course this substitution must be such that the structure remains stable. This can be checked by noting that A, B, G, E, and F are apexes of triangles, and C and D can each be located from two of these fixed points.

All bar forces, F', for the simple truss in (b) can be determined by the method of joints. Next apply equal and opposite unit tensile forces at A and D, with line of action along AD, and compute the resulting bar forces, u. The force in a bar for the actual truss in (a) will be

$$F = F' + Xu \tag{2.6}$$

in which X represents the true force in bar AD. The correct value of X is that which makes the force in the substitute bar zero. If the substitute bar is identified by the subscript s, Equation (2.6) for that bar becomes

$$0 = F'_s + Xu_s$$

from which

$$X = -\frac{F'_s}{u_s} \tag{2.7}$$

With the value of X determined, the true force in any bar in (a) can be obtained by means of Equation (2.6).

If it is necessary to replace two bars of a complex truss in order to obtain a simple truss, then we will have two unknown forces, X_1 and X_2. Similarly, we will have u_1 and u_2, corresponding to unit force applied respectively along the line of action of each replaced bar. The force in a bar of the actual truss will then be

$$F = F' + X_1 u_1 + X_2 u_2 \tag{2.8}$$

The correct forces, X_1 and X_2, in the replaced bars are those which make the forces in the two substitute bars zero. If we identify the substitute bars by the subscripts $s1$ and $s2$, we have from Equation (2.8),

$$0 = F'_{s1} + X_1(u_1)_{s1} + X_2(u_2)_{s1}$$

$$0 = F'_{s2} + X_1(u_1)_{s2} + X_2(u_2)_{s2}$$

from which

$$X_1 = \frac{(u_2)_{s1}F'_{s2} - (u_2)_{s2}F'_{s1}}{(u_1)_{s1}(u_2)_{s2} - (u_1)_{s2}(u_2)_{s1}}$$

$$X_2 = \frac{(u_1)_{s2}F'_{s1} - (u_1)_{s1}F'_{s2}}{(u_1)_{s1}(u_2)_{s2} - (u_1)_{s2}(u_2)_{s1}} \tag{2.9}$$

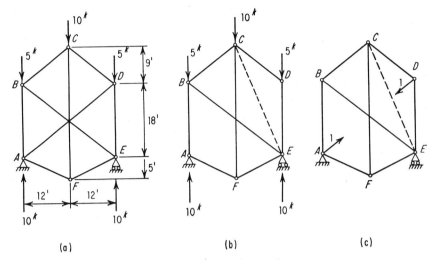

Figure 2-20. Analysis of Complex Truss

The complex truss in Figure 2-20(a) is now analyzed. The forces F' and u, corresponding to Figure 2-20(b) and Figure 2-20(c), respectively, are found, by the method of joints, to be the following:

Bar	F'	u
AB	-10.00	-0.933
AF	0	-0.867
EF	0	-0.867
CF	0	$+0.667$
BE	$+4.17$	$+0.777$
BC	-4.17	-0.777
CD	0	-1.000
DE	-5.00	-1.200
CE	-8.21	$+0.438$

From Equation (2.7),

$$X = -\frac{-8.21}{0.438} = +18.74 \text{ kips}$$

This is the force in bar AD. All bar forces in the actual complex truss can now be obtained by means of Equation (2.6). For example,

$$AB = -10.00 + 18.74(-0.933) = -27.49 \text{ kips}$$

$$AF = 0 + 18.74(-0.867) = -16.25 \text{ kips}$$

Sometimes it is possible to analyze a complex truss without recourse to the use of substitute members or the solution of a large number of joint equations. For example, in Figure 2-20(a) it can be seen that if the horizontal component of force in AF is called $+H$, the horizontal component of EF is also $+H$. Therefore, force FC is $-\frac{5}{6}H$. From joint C, the vertical component of force in bars BC and CD is (assuming a tension) $\frac{1}{2}(\frac{5}{6}H - 10)$. The horizontal component is $\frac{2}{3}(\frac{5}{6}H - 10)$. Now pass a vertical section through the truss, to the right of

CF, and isolate the portion to the left. By taking moments about the inter-section of the long interior bars, we obtain

$$\sum M = 10(12) - 5(12) - 14H + \tfrac{2}{3}(\tfrac{5}{6}H - 10)18 = 0$$

$$H = -15 \text{ kips}$$

All bar forces can now be determined.

2.10 Critical Form and Instability

Geometrical instability of trusses was discussed in Section 2.5. The designa-tion *critical form* is often used to describe a configuration that results in a geometrically unstable truss, whereas adjacent configurations are stable. As with usual geometric instability, no unique solution is possible for a critical form.

The complex truss in Figure 2-21 is geometrically unstable unless one of the distances labeled h is changed. The fact that the truss is of critical form can be

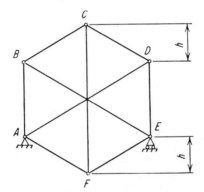

Figure 2-21.   Critical Form

shown quite readily by passing a vertical section through the truss to the right of CF and isolating either position. If there is no load applied at C or F, it is obvious that the forces in CD and FE are identical, and no resistance can be developed to moment about the intersection of the interior bars.

Strictly speaking, critical form as here defined has meaning only in certain complex trusses. A properly supported structure that satisfies the definition of Section 2.4 for a simple truss or a compound truss has no critical form and a unique solution will exist.

Geometric instability, whether of the usual kind or whether involving critical form, can always be finally demonstrated by attempting an analysis. For an unstable structure the results will be inconsistent or indeterminate. If simultaneous joint equations are written, it is not necessary to solve the equations, as explained in what follows.

The solution of a set of simultaneous equations such as

$$a_1 x + b_1 y + c_1 z = k_1$$

$$a_2 x + b_2 y + c_3 z = k_2$$

$$a_3 x + b_3 y + c_3 z = k_3$$

can be written as follows:

$$x = \frac{D_x}{D}; \qquad y = \frac{D_y}{D}; \qquad z = \frac{D_z}{D} \qquad\qquad \textbf{(2.10)}$$

In Equations (2.10), D is the determinant of the coefficients of the system and includes all coefficients, even though they are zero. It is independent of any loading and depends only on the configuration of the truss. The symbol D_x represents the same array of coefficients except that all coefficients of x are replaced by the constants, any of which may be zero, on the right-hand side of the equations. Similarly, D_y and D_z are equivalent to D except that all coefficients of y and all coefficients of z, respectively, are replaced. The values of D_x, D_y, and D_z are dependent on the loading.

To check stability, determine whether D is equal to zero. If it is equal to zero, this indicates that the equations are either inconsistent or dependent. In either case, no unique solution is possible, and the structure is unstable.

The preceding discussion suggests a simple method (the zero-load test) of testing for critical form. With no load on the truss, assume any force in a bar. Now compute the forces in the other bars. If these are compatible, any number of solutions is possible, and the form of the truss is critical. Thus, for Figure 2-21 we can see that for any force assumed in EF, we will obtain compatible bar forces, satisfying equilibrium at all joints.

The zero-load test is also a test for statical indeterminateness. No compatible bar forces are possible in an unloaded statically determinate truss. However, if a force is induced (say by turnbuckle), in a statically indeterminate truss, other bars will be stressed. The number of solutions possible are infinite, depending on the magnitude of the force induced, exactly as for critical form. We can, therefore, conclude that a truss of critical form is always statically indeterminate. Unique solutions for statically indeterminate trusses are considered in Chapter 8.

2.11 Trussed Arches

A three-hinged trussed arch is shown in Figure 2-22(a). The arch is free to rotate at L_0, L_3, and L_6. In an actual structure, members are fastened rigidly to each other at each joint by rivets, bolts, or welding. Therefore, pins, or hinges, are provided at L_0, L_3, and L_6 so as to permit rotation. However, either member U_2U_3 or U_3U_4 (shown by dashed line), or both must be left free to move horizontally at one end. Otherwise, even with a hinge at L_3, moment can be resisted at the crown and the structure will act as a two-hinged arch, which is statically indeterminate. As a matter of fact, two-hinged trussed arches are generally erected as three-hinged arches and act as two-hinged arches only after the top chord members over the crown hinge are securely fastened.

The four reaction components were calculated, exactly as in Section 2.2, by taking moments about L_6 to determine V_0, moments about L_0 to determine V_6, and moments about L_3 of the forces on either side of this point to determine H_0 or H_6. From $\sum F_x = 0$, $H_0 = H_6$. The following results were obtained:

$$V_0 = 13.00 \text{ kips}$$

$$V_6 = 5.00 \text{ kips}$$

$$H_0 = H_6 = 13.9^k$$

Of course, the reactions could also be determined graphically. In this case, since there is no load between the crown hinge at L_3 and the support at L_6, the pressure line to the right of L_3 is a straight line passing through L_3 and L_6. Therefore $H_6 = \frac{75}{27} V_6$.

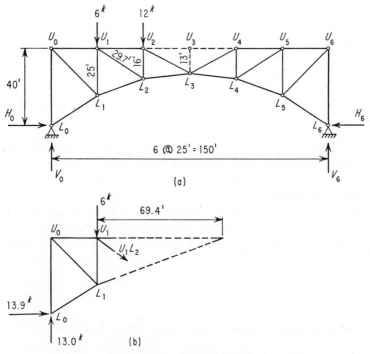

Figure 2-22. *Trussed Arch*

Bar forces can now be determined exactly as before. For example, a joint-by-joint analysis can commence at L_0 or L_6, remembering to include the horizontal component of reaction. Or bar forces can be found independently by the method of sections. For instance, considering the portion of the structure shown in Figure 2-22(b), force U_1U_2 and force L_1L_2 can be computed by taking moments about L_2 and U_1 respectively. To determine force U_1L_2, take moments about the intersection, i, of the line of action of U_1U_2 and L_1L_2. Assuming U_1L_2 as a tension,

$$\sum M_i = 13.0(94.4) - 13.9(40) - 6(69.4) - \tfrac{16}{29.7} U_1L_2(69.4) = 0$$

$$U_1L_2 = +6.8 \text{ kips}$$

The bottom-chord panel points of the arch in Figure 2-22 lie on a parabola. Suppose the structure were subjected to equal vertical loads at each top-chord panel point or each bottom-chord panel point, or split between top and bottom. The simple-beam moment diagram would be a polygon, each of whose apexes would lie on a parabola. That is, it would be identical in shape to the bottom chord of the structure in Figure 2-22. Consequently, for uniform load the pressure line, which must pass through the three hinges, would coincide with the bottom chord. This means only the members of the bottom chord would be subjected to force if all load were applied at the bottom-chord panel points. The horizontal component of force would be constant and could be obtained by means of Equation (2.1). If load were applied at the upper-chord panel points, then, in addition to the bottom-chord members, the vertical bars would be subjected to a force, and this would be equal to the panel load at the top chord.

Problems

2.1. Compute the reactions for the three-hinged frame and draw the shear and moment diagrams. (*Ans.*: $H_A = 3.18$ kips to right.)

2.2. Draw the pressure line for a vertical load of 5 kips at C in Figure 2-3 and determine the reactions.

2.3. Draw the pressure line for a vertical load of 5 kips at C in Figure 2-4 and determine the reactions.   Check values using equations of equilibrium.

2.4. Compute the forces in bars a and b by using Sections 1-1 and 2-2, respectively. (*Ans.*: $b = 42.2$ kips.)

2.5. Compute all bar forces.

2.6. Compute all bar forces.

2.7. Compute all bar forces.

2.8. Compute forces in bars a, b, and c. (*Ans.*: $c = -6.25$ kips.)

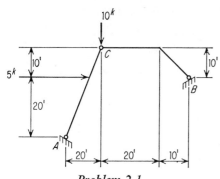

Problem 2-1

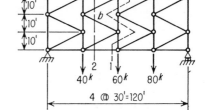

Problem 2-4

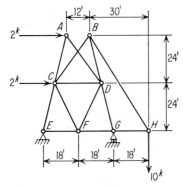

Problem 2-5

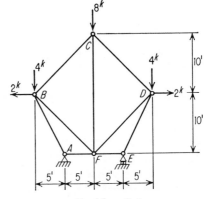

Problem 2-6

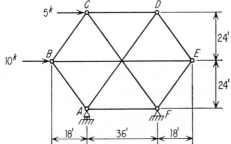

Problem 2-7

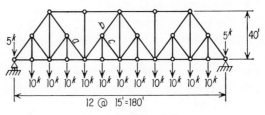

Problem 2-8

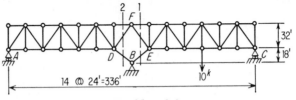

Problem 2-9

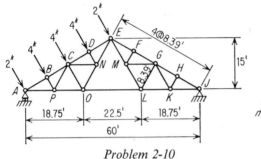

Problem 2-10

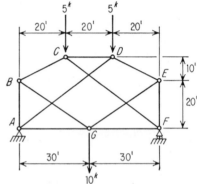

Problem 2-12

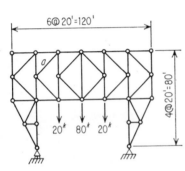

Problem 2-13

Problem 2-14

2.9. Determine the reactions. The Wichert truss is statically determinate (see Section 2.5). *Hint:* Take moments about *F* of all forces to the right of Section 1-1, and then do the same for forces to the left of Section 2-2, obtaining force components of bars *BE* and *BD* in terms of the reactions at *C* and *A*, respectively. Reaction at *B* is then known in terms of those at *C* and *A*. Apply $\Sigma F_y = 0$ and $\Sigma M = 0$ to the entire structure to obtain reactions. (*Ans.* $R_c = 4.30$ kips, acting upwards.)

2.10. Compute forces in all bars.

2.11. Do Problem 2.10 graphically.

2.12. Determine bar forces graphically, and check results analytically. (*Ans.:* $a = -143$ kips.)

2.13. Determine bar forces graphically. (*Ans.:* $a = -42.3$ kips.)

2.14. Compute all bar forces, using Henneberg's method. Check answers joint by joint.

2.15. In Figure 2-22, compute all bar forces when equal panel loads of 5 kips each are applied at all lower-chord panel points.

Chapter 3

Influence Lines for
Statically Determinate Structures

The effects of loading that is fixed in position were considered in Chapters 1 and 2. Attention is now turned to the effects of movable and moving loads. The concept of the influence line is introduced for positioning live loads so as to obtain maximum values of force, shear, or moment.

3.1 Moving Loads and Influence Lines

In order to design properly any element of a structure, it is necessary to know the maximum stress to which it will be subjected. The maximum moment, shear, or force in a particular section or member of a structure will vary with the location of the live loads on the structure.

The effects of loads placed in various positions can be studied conveniently by means of diagrams called influence lines. An influence line shows, for a particular section or member of a structure, the variation in shear, moment, reaction, force, or other direct function due to a unit load moving across the structure.

The student must clearly understand the distinction between, say, a moment diagram and an influence line for moment. A moment diagram shows the variation in moment all along a structure due to a particular load position. An influence line for moment shows the variation of moment *at a particular section* of the structure due to a unit load placed anywhere along the structure.

3.2 Types of Influence Lines

It follows from the definition that an influence line can be constructed by plotting successive values of the function under consideration as a unit load is moved across the structure. Consider the beam in Figure 3-1(a). The influence line for reaction at support A is shown in (b). Each ordinate of this influence line represents the reaction at A due to a unit load placed on the beam at a point corresponding to the particular influence ordinate. Since the reaction at A increases linearly as a unit load is moved from B to A, the influence line is a straight line. The unit ordinate at end A definitely establishes the influence line.

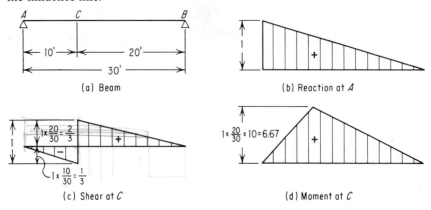

(a) Beam

(b) Reaction at A

(c) Shear at C

(d) Moment at C

Figure 3-1.   Influence Lines

The influence line for shear at point C in the beam is shown in Figure 3-1(c). Each ordinate represents the shear at C due to a unit load placed on the beam at a point corresponding to the particular influence ordinate. The shear at C due to unit load placed anywhere between C and B is equal to the reaction at A and is positive. Consequently, the portion of the influence line between C and B is identical to the corresponding portion of the influence line for reaction, shown above it in (b). Similarly, the shear at C due to unit load placed anywhere between A and C is equal to the reaction at B but with a minus sign to indicate negative shear, in accordance with the sign convention adopted in Section 1.6. The portion of the influence line between A and C is identical, but with negative ordinates, to the corresponding portion of an influence line for reaction at B.

The student will have observed that the sloping lines of the influence line in (c) must be parallel. All possible influence lines for shear can be obtained by drawing two sloping lines, which represent plus reaction at A and minus reaction at B, and then connecting them with vertical lines at the points for which influence lines are desired.

The influence line for moment at C, shown in Figure 3-1(d), is obtained by plotting values of moment at C due to unit load at different positions along the structure. For any location of the unit load, the moment at C is positive. It increases linearly as the unit load moves from B to C and decreases linearly as the load moves from C to A. One influence value, at C, is enough to establish the influence line.

For statically determinate structures, all influence lines for shear, moment, and reaction are composed of straight-line segments. This is also true of influence lines for bar forces in trusses, which are considered in Section 3.9. In Chapter 7 it will be seen that influence lines for statically indeterminate structures are curved.

A number of influence lines for a beam with overhang are shown in Figure 3-2. Span AB is identical to the span in Figure 3-1. Therefore, the portions of the influence lines between A and B in Figure 3-2 are identical to the corresponding influence lines in Figure 3-1. Note in (e) and (f) of Figure 3-2 that when a load is placed in span AB no moment can be developed at B and no shear can be developed at any location, such as E, along the overhang. Observe also that shear at E is constant for load placed anywhere to the right of E.

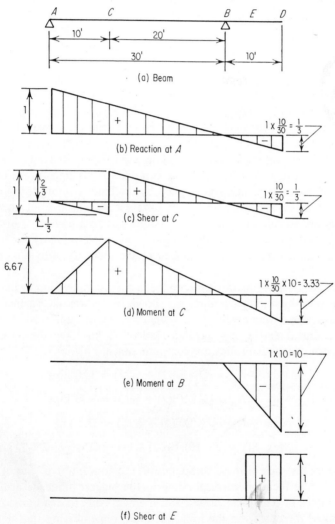

Figure 3-2.   *Influence Lines for Beam with Overhang*

A word about units is in order. In influence lines for reaction or shear, the ordinates represent pounds per pound, kips per kip, and so forth. In influence lines for moment, the units are foot-pounds per pound, foot-kips per kip, and so forth.

3.3   Properties of Influence Lines

Influence lines serve two purposes, one qualitative and one quantitative. They can be used qualitatively to determine the position of the live loads that will lead to maximum effects. For such use it is not necessary to compute any influence values. Only shape of influence line is required. For example, for the beam of Figure 3-2, to get maximum upward reaction at A, place loads between A and B. To get maximum downward reaction at A, place loads between B and D. To get maximum positive shear at C, place loads between C and B. To get maximum negative shear at C, place loads between A and C and between B and D. Once the loads have been placed, maximum values of reaction, shear, and moment can be computed in the usual manner.

On the other hand, influence lines can be used quantitatively in order to obtain maximum values directly by making use of computed influence values. The value of a function due to any concentrated load is equal to the influence ordinate at the load position multiplied by the load. If more than one concentrated load is applied, the values obtained for each load considered separately are added. The value of a function due to a uniformly distributed load is equal to the area under the influence line, corresponding to the loaded portion of the structure only, multiplied by the intensity of loading per unit length.

Assume that it is required to determine the maximum live-load values of the functions for which influence lines are shown in Figure 3-2. Further assume that the movable or moving live-load system consists of a uniformly distributed load of 2 kips/ft and a concentrated load of 15 kips. On the basis of the previous discussion, the following computations are obvious:

$$\text{Max.} + R_A = \tfrac{1}{2}(1)(30)(2) + 1(15) = 45.0 \text{ kips}$$

$$\text{Max.} - R_A = \tfrac{1}{2}(\tfrac{1}{3})(10)(2) + \tfrac{1}{3}(15) = 8.33 \text{ kips}$$

$$\text{Max.} + V_C = \tfrac{1}{2}(\tfrac{2}{3})(20)(2) + \tfrac{2}{3}(15) = 23.3 \text{ kips}$$

$$\text{Max.} \; M_B = \tfrac{1}{2}(-10)(10)(2) + (-10)(15) = -250 \text{ ft-kips}$$

Observe that for each of these computations the concentrated load of 15 kips is placed at the location corresponding to the biggest influence ordinate. If desired, values of reactions, shears, and moments due to dead load can also be computed directly from the influence lines, remembering that dead load extends over the entire structure.

3.4   Virtual Displacements and Müller-Breslau's Principle

A beam with overhang and concentrated load W placed arbitrarily along its length is shown in Figure 3-3(a). In (b) the beam has been given a very small (virtual) displacement Δ (see Section 1.14) at A. The displacement is of infinitesi-

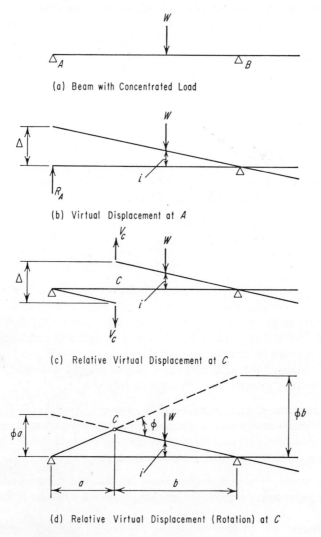

(a) Beam with Concentrated Load

(b) Virtual Displacement at *A*

(c) Relative Virtual Displacement at *C*

(d) Relative Virtual Displacement (Rotation) at *C*

Figure 3-3.   Virtual Displacements

mal magnitude but is grossly exaggerated for pictorial purposes. It is considered so small that horizontal displacements can be assumed equal to zero, without error.

The virtual work done is

$$R_A \Delta - Wi = 0$$

If Δ and W are each made equal to one, then

$$R_A = i$$

and an influence line for reaction at A has been constructed.

In Figure 3-3(c) the beam is cut at C and a very small relative displacement is introduced. Such a small movement can occur along the cut at C only if the displaced segments AC and CB are parallel. The equation of virtual work is

$$V_C \Delta - Wi = 0$$

With unit values of Δ and W, we obtain

$$V_C = i$$

and thus have constructed an influence line for shear at C.

In Figure 3-3(d) it is assumed that a hinge has been inserted at C. A very small rotation equal to ϕ is freely imposed by means of equal and opposite couples M_C. The resulting equation of virtual work is

$$M_C \phi - Wi = 0$$

With unit values of ϕ and W, we obtain

$$M_C = i$$

and the displaced position represents an influence line for moment at C. Since ϕ is an infinitesimally small angle, any vertical distance such as ϕa or ϕb can be obtained as the product of the angle and a horizontal distance. With $\phi = 1$, the vertical distance is equal to a or b, and any ordinate, y, to the influence line can be determined by ratio.

On the basis of the preceding discussion a general statement, known as Müller-Breslau's principle, can be made as follows:

If any function—such as reaction, shear, moment, axial force—is allowed to produce freely a very small corresponding displacement Δ at a section of an elastic structure, the resulting displacements of the load line of the structure represent influence ordinates multiplied by Δ.

In other words, if a unit displacement is produced corresponding to the function under consideration, the resulting deflected structure is the influence line.

The student should now reexamine Figures 3-1 and 3-2. Application of Müller-Breslau's principle in (b) and (c) of each figure is obvious. In (d) a unit angle at C would lead to a vertical distance at B, corresponding to ϕb in Figure 3-3(d), of $1(20) = 20$. By ratio, the ordinate at C would be

$$\tfrac{10}{30}(20) = 6.67$$

exactly as previously obtained by computations of statics.

The influence line in Figure 3-2(e) would be obtained by introducing a unit angle at B. Then the ordinate at B is $1(10) = 10$. Introducing a unit relative displacement at E in Figure 3-2(f) results in movement of segment ED only since segment AE is restrained from tilting because it rests on two supports. As we have seen, the displaced segments must remain parallel. Therefore, displaced segment ED is horizontal.

The Müller-Breslau principle is particularly advantageous when applied to more complicated structures, such as the cantilever structure in Figure 3-4. Each of the influence lines "draws itself" when the corresponding unit displacement is applied. Because of the two hinges, the load line in any case is

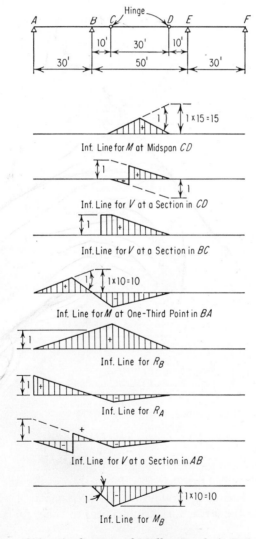

Figure 3-4. Application of Müller–Breslau's Principle

deflected in no more than two spans. The student should check all influence lines in Figure 3-4 by the elementary method of moving a unit load along the beam.

3.5   Girders with Floor System

Beams that support other beams are generally called girders. Figure 3-5(a) shows a girder that supports floor beams at several points, commonly referred to as panel joints. The portion of the girder between two adjacent panel points

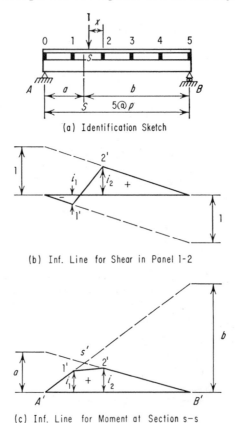

(a) Identification Sketch

(b) Inf. Line for Shear in Panel 1-2

(c) Inf. Line for Moment at Section s–s

Figure 3-5.   Girder with Floor Beams

is called a panel. The floor beams support stringers which are parallel to the girder, and a load applied to a stringer can be transmitted to the girder only at the panel points. This in no way affects the reactions at A and B, and the influence lines for these reactions are identical to those for a beam loaded directly.

Since loads are transmitted to the girder only at the panel points, for any loading the shear is constant throughout a given panel. Therefore, we speak of panel shear and influence lines for panel shear. The influence line for shear in panel $1 - 2$ is shown in Figure 3-5(b). The portion to the right of panel point 2 is identical to the corresponding portion of the influence line for reaction at A. The portion to the left of panel point 1 is identical to the corresponding portion of the influence line for reaction at B. If we assume that each stringer is simply supported at each panel point, a unit load in panel $1 - 2$ will result in panel point loads (reactions of stringer $1 - 2$) of x/p at 1, and $(p - x)/p$ at 2. The influence ordinate between points 1 and 2 is then

$$ i = \frac{x}{p} i_1 + \frac{p - x}{p} i_2 \qquad (3.1) $$

This is the equation of a straight line. Thus, we draw a straight line between $1'$ and $2'$ in (b).

Influence lines for shear in the other panels can all be shown in Figure 3-5(b). The one for shear in panel $0 - 1$ will have no negative ordinates because $0'$ will be identical to 0 and $0' - 1'$ will not cross below the horizontal base line.

Contrary to what is true for shear, bending moment varies throughout a panel. Nevertheless, since load can be transmitted to the girder only at the panel points, Equation (3.1) is applicable, and the influence line for moment at a section $s - s$ is determined in a manner similar to that for panel shear. Thus, in Figure 3-5(c), $A's'B'$ is the influence line for moment that would occur at $s - s$ if the load were applied directly on the girder, and $i_1 = (\frac{1}{3})b$ and $i_2 = (\frac{2}{3})a$. To obtain the influence line for moment at $s - s$ in the actual girder with floor beams, connect points $1'$ and $2'$ with a straight line.

Generally, we are interested only in moment at the panel points, because maximum moment under any loading will always occur at such a point. An influence line for moment at a panel point is identical to that for a beam that is loaded directly.

3.6   Analysis for Moving Loads

The determination of maximum reactions, shears, and bending moments resulting from a moving live-load system was considered briefly in Section 3.3. In that section the load system consisted of a concentrated load and a uniformly distributed load. We now consider a system of moving concentrated loads.

Figure 3-6(a) shows a girder and a system of three concentrated loads, assumed to move from right to left across the structure. A load system of this type can consist of many concentrated loads, such as those corresponding to the wheels of a train. On the other hand, such a complicated load system is

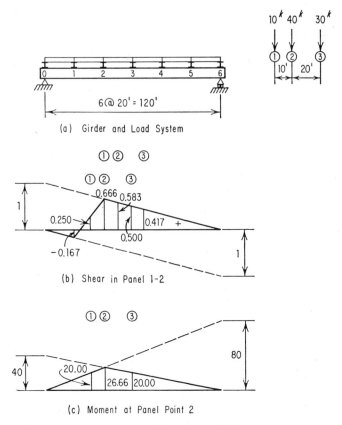

(a) Girder and Load System

(b) Shear in Panel 1-2

(c) Moment at Panel Point 2

Figure 3-6. *Determination of Maximum Values*

sometimes simulated by means of a so-called equivalent uniformly distributed load or uniform load plus concentrated load.

The influence line for shear in panel $1 - 2$ is shown in Figure 3-6(b). As wheel 1 approaches panel point 2, the influence line indicates that the shear in panel $1 - 2$ will keep increasing. With wheel 1 on point 2, the value of the shear will be

$$10(0.666) + 40(0.583) + 30(0.417) = 42.49 \text{ kips}$$

If the movement of the load system to the left is continued, the influence ordinates corresponding to successive positions of wheel 1 will decrease linearly whereas the ordinates corresponding to the positions of wheels 2 and 3 will increase. This will continue until wheel 2 reaches panel point 2. The panel shear will then be

$$10(0.250) + 40(0.666) + 30(0.500) = 44.14 \text{ kips}$$

The increase in shear due to wheels 2 and 3 overbalanced the decrease due to wheel 1.

If the movement to the left is continued, it is obvious that the decrease in shear due to wheels 1 and 2 will be greater than the increase due to wheel 3.

78

As a matter of fact, wheels 1 and 2 will both contribute negative shear when wheel 3 is at panel point 2.

It should be obvious that maximum shear will occur in a panel when one of the leading wheels (generally the first or second) is placed at the panel point adjoining the panel in question. Similarly, from consideration of the influence line in Figure 3-6(c) for moment at panel point 2, it should be obvious that maximum moment will occur when one of the wheels is placed at panel point 2. It is further obvious in this case that this will occur when wheel 2 is at panel point 2, and the maximum moment will be

$$10(20.00) + 40(26.66) + 30(20.00) = 1,866 \text{ ft-kips}$$

If desired, one can, from the slopes of the influence line segments, compute only the increase or decrease of a function for successive wheel positions. When a decrease occurs, the movement should not have been made, and the maximum value is computed for the previous position of the loads.

Special criteria are available for determining maximum values of shear and moment. These also involve successive trial positions and are based on the phenomena we have observed as the wheels are moved. The authors do not recommend their use.

Even for a loading system consisting of many wheels, it is not necessary to try many positions. What we are after is the maximum sum of the products of load intensities and corresponding influence ordinates. By eye it is generally possible to start with a load position close to that which yields a maximum value.

3.7 Absolute Maxima

In the preceding section maximum shears and moments due to moving concentrated live loads were determined *for particular locations*. The question sometimes arises as to the *absolute maximum* value of shear and moment that can occur in a structure.

Absolute maximum shear will always occur at a section or panel immediately adjacent to one of the supports. For a simple beam or girder with end supports, this will be at a section or panel immediately adjacent to an end support. If, however, we do not have a beam or girder with just end supports, the absolute maximum live-load shear must be computed for each side or panel immediately adjacent to a support. The greatest of these values is the absolute maximum live-load shear.

Absolute maximum moment due to uniformly distributed live load or single concentrated live load occurs at midspan for a simply supported beam and at the panel point nearest midspan for a girder. In cantilever construction, maximum moment can occur at a support.

The case of a simply supported beam subjected to a system of moving concentrated live loads is of special interest. The absolute maximum bending moment will occur under one of the concentrated loads during the passage of the system of loads. The load under which absolute maximum moment will occur must be determined by trial. For any particular wheel, however, it is possible to determine a position such that maximum moment under that wheel will result. This is done for several wheels, and the greatest of the maximum moments obtained is the absolute maximum.

Figure 3-7 shows a system of concentrated loads on a beam. It is desired to

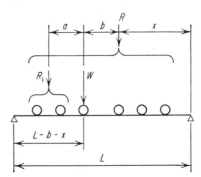

Figure 3-7. Identification Sketch

determine the position of load W that will result in maximum moment under that load. Let R represent the resultant of all loads on the beam, and R_1 represent the resultant of all loads in front of W but still on the beam. The bending moment under W is

$$M = \frac{Rx}{L}(L - b - x) - R_1 a$$

As long as all loads stay on the span, we can obtain a maximum value of M by setting dM/dx equal to zero, as follows:

$$\frac{dM}{dx} = \frac{R}{L}(L - b - 2x) = 0$$

Then

$$L - b - x = x \qquad\qquad \textbf{(3.2)}$$

This equation states that in order to obtain maximum bending moment under any given concentrated load of a group, the distance from one beam support to the wheel should be equal to the distance from the other support to the resultant of all the concentrated loads on the span. Or, to put it another way, *maximum moment under a concentrated load occurs when the centerline of the span bisects the distance between this load and the resultant of all concentrated loads on the span.*

Notice that for a single concentrated load, this criterion leads to placing the load at midspan. When more than one load is on the beam, maximum moment no longer occurs at midspan, but under a wheel placed in accordance with the criterion. In general, since the section of absolute maximum moment is always near midspan, such moment will occur under the load that is closest to the resultant of all loads on the span. This is generally the load that is placed at midspan for maximum moment there, or a load adjacent to it.

The determination of absolute maximum moment is illustrated in connection with Figure 3-8. The beam and load system are shown in (a). The influence line for maximum moment at midspan is shown in (b). It should be obvious that maximum moment at midspan will occur when wheel 3 is placed there. Therefore, absolute maximum moment will almost certainly occur under the same wheel.

In Figure 3-8(c), wheel 3 is placed in accordance with the criterion for maximum moment under a wheel. The moment under wheel 3 is

$$M_3 = \frac{90(19.722)^2}{40} - 20(5) - 10(15) = 625.15 \text{ ft-kips}$$

If the maximum moment under wheel 2 and under wheel 4 are computed, they

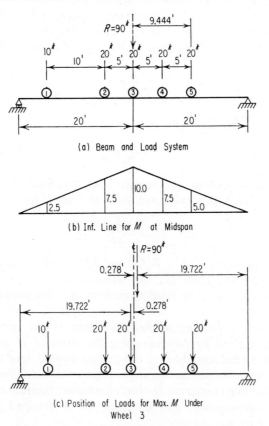

(a) Beam and Load System

(b) Inf. Line for M at Midspan

(c) Position of Loads for Max. M Under Wheel 3

Figure 3-8.   Absolute Maximum Moment

will be found to be less than the value obtained for wheel 3. Therefore, the moment of 625.15 ft-kips is the absolute maximum and it occurs under wheel 3 when it is placed 0.278 ft to the left of midspan.

It is of interest to compare the absolute maximum moment with the maximum moment that can occur at midspan. Making use of the influence line in Figure 3-8(b), this moment is

$$10(2.5) + 20(7.5) + 20(10) + 20(7.5) + 20(5.0) = 625.00 \text{ ft-kips}$$

Notice the extremely small difference between maximum moment at midspan and absolute maximum moment. The difference is always relatively small, but particularly so in this specific case.

3.8   Influence Lines for Three-Hinged Arches

A three-hinged arch rib is shown in Figure 3-9(a). The vertical components of reaction, R_A and R_B, due to any vertical loading will be identical to those in a simply supported beam of the same span. Consequently, influence lines for end reaction in the arch are identical to those for end reaction in the beam.

If a unit load is applied anywhere to the right of C, and AC is treated as a free body,

$$H = \frac{R_A L}{2h} \tag{3.3a}$$

Similarly, for load to the left of C,

$$H = \frac{R_B L}{2h} \tag{3.3b}$$

These two equations define two straight lines that form the influence line, shown in (b), for H, with a maximum value at C equal to

$$H_{max} = \frac{L}{4h} \tag{3.4}$$

Observe that, in Equations (3.3), $R_A L/2$ and $R_B L/2$ represent the simple-beam bending moment at C. Therefore, the influence line for H is identical to the influence line for simple-beam bending moment at C, but with all ordinates of the latter divided by h.

Influence lines for bending moment and shear in the arch rib can most readily be constructed by superimposing the effect of H on simple-beam influence lines. An influence line for bending moment at D of Figure 3-9(a) is shown in (c). It is obtained in two steps. First an influence line is drawn for simple-beam bending moment at D. Next an influence line for bending moment due to H is superimposed. This influence line is obtained by multiplying ordinates in (b) by y_D.

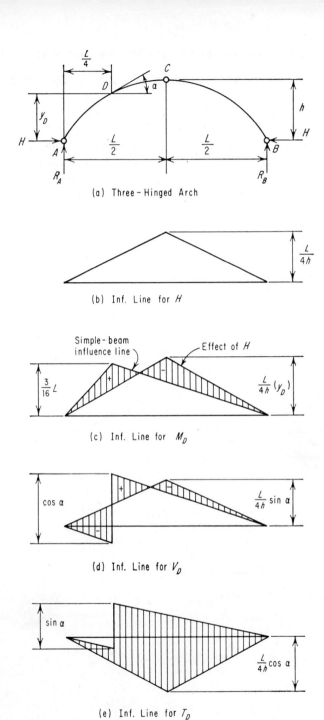

(a) Three-Hinged Arch

(b) Inf. Line for H

(c) Inf. Line for M_D

(d) Inf. Line for V_D

(e) Inf. Line for T_D

Figure 3-9. *Influence Lines for Symmetrical Arch*

83

If the arch in Figure 3-9(a) is parabolic, then $y_D = \frac{3}{4}h$, and, in Figure 3-9(c),

$$\frac{L}{4h}(y_D) = \frac{3}{16}L$$

which is identical to the maximum influence ordinate for simple-beam moment at D. The total influence area in (c) is then equal to zero, and thus no bending moment will result at D (or any other point in the arch) due to a uniformly distributed horizontal load over the entire span. This agrees with what we have said in Section 2.3.

To obtain the influence line for shear at D, shown in Figure 3-9(d), we first draw the influence line for shear due to vertical reaction only. This is identical to the simple-beam influence line for shear, except that all ordinates are multiplied by $\cos \alpha$ to account for the fact that shear, by definition, is measured perpendicular to the arch axis. On this influence line we superimpose the contribution of H to the shear, which is obtained by multiplying influence line ordinates for H by $\sin \alpha$.

In Figure 3-9(e), the influence line for thrust at D is obtained in a similar manner, but the effect of H is plotted below the horizontal line because H produces a thrust of the same sense.

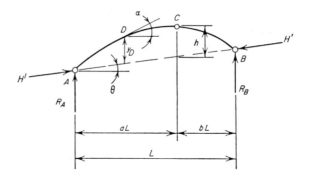

Figure 3-10.   Unsymmetrical Arch

An unsymmetrical arch is shown in Figure 3-10. If the reactions are resolved into vertical components, R_A and R_B, and into components, H', along line AB, Equations (3.3) become

$$H = H' \cos \theta = \frac{R_A a L}{h} \tag{3.5a}$$

and

$$H = H' \cos \theta = \frac{R_B b L}{h} \tag{3.5b}$$

Also, Equation (3.4) becomes

$$H_{\max} = \frac{abL}{h} \tag{3.6}$$

Equations (3.5) and (3.6) are general expressions, of which Equations (3.3) and (3.4) are special cases. For the same value of h and y_D, influence lines for H and for bending moment in the arch of Figure 3-10 have ordinates identical to those in Figure 3-9, providing $a = b$. This is not true for influence lines for shear and thrust.

The shear at a section D, for unit load to the right, is (see Figure 3-10)

$$V_D = R_A \cos \alpha - H' \sin (\alpha - \theta)$$

$$V_D = R_A \cos \alpha - H \frac{\sin (\alpha - \theta)}{\cos \theta} \tag{3.7}$$

The thrust at section D is

$$T_D = R_A \sin \alpha + H' \cos (\alpha - \theta)$$

$$T_D = R_A \sin \alpha + H \frac{\cos (\alpha - \theta)}{\cos \theta} \tag{3.8}$$

From Equations (3.7) and (3.6) it is seen that the maximum ordinate for shear at D due to H only will be

$$\frac{abL}{h} \frac{\sin (\alpha - \theta)}{\cos \theta}$$

From Equation (3.8) it is seen that the maximum ordinate for thrust at D due to H only will be

$$\frac{abL}{h} \frac{\cos (\alpha - \theta)}{\cos \theta}$$

For the common case of a symmetrical arch, θ is zero and a and b are each $\frac{1}{2}$. Thus we get the ordinates shown in Figure 3-9.

Often loads are not transmitted directly to the arch rib, but rather through floor beams, as, for example, in bridges. Influence lines for such cases are modified in a manner similar to that used for girders with floor beams.

3.9 Influence Lines for Trusses

Figure 3-11(a) shows a through-type truss for which it is desired to construct some influence lines. In such a truss all loads are applied to the panel points of the lower chord by means of floor beams that frame into them.

An influence line for bar force in any truss can be obtained by the fundamental method of placing a unit load at successive panel points of the loaded chord and computing the corresponding bar force. As with girders, however, no more than one or two such computations are necessary to fix the influence line.

Force in member $L_2 L_3$ can be determined directly by cutting section $1 - 1$ and isolating either portion of the truss. Force $L_2 L_3$ is equal to the moment

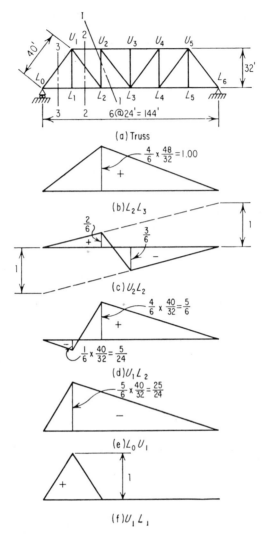

Figure 3-11. Influence Lines for Pratt Truss

about U_2 divided by the perpendicular distance of 32 ft. Moment (and bar force) increase linearly until the unit load is placed at L_2, directly below the moment center, U_2. Considering the portion of the truss to the left of section 1 – 1, the reaction at L_6 is $\frac{4}{6}$, and the moment about U_2 is $(\frac{4}{6})(48)$. Dividing by 32 ft, we obtain the influence ordinate of 1.00 in Figure 3-11(b). This ordinate represents the force in bar L_2L_3 due to a unit load placed at L_2. Similarly, for all other chord members of this parallel-chord truss the influence line for bar force is identical to the influence line for moment at the opposite panel point, but with ordinates divided by 32.

Using section 1 – 1 again, it can be seen that the force in U_2L_2 is always equal to the shear in panel L_2L_3 but with opposite sign. Therefore the influence line in (c) is identical to the influence line for shear in panel L_2L_3 but with signs reversed.

Force in member U_1L_2 can be found directly by cutting section $2-2$. The vertical component of this force will always be equal to the shear in panel L_1L_2, and the bar force will be equal to the vertical component multiplied by the ratio of bar length to its vertical projection. Consequently, the influence line in (d) is identical to that for shear in panel L_1L_2 but with all ordinates multiplied by $\frac{40}{32}$.

Vertical component of force in bar L_0U_1 is numerically equal to the shear in panel L_0L_1. Values of panel shear are multiplied by $\frac{40}{32}$ in Figure 3-11(e) in order to obtain influence ordinates for bar force Force L_0U_1 can also be computed by taking moments about L_1, considering the portion of the truss to the left of section $3-3$. Notice that the influence line in (e) has the shape of an influence line for shear (in an end panel) and also the shape of an influence line for moment about L_1.

Force in hanger U_1L_1 is equal to the end reaction of the floor beam framing into L_1. This bar is stressed only when load is applied on the floor system between L_0 and L_2 The influence line for force in U_1L_1 is shown in (f).

A truss with nonparallel chords is shown in Figure 3-12(a). Influence lines for force in the bottom chord members and for force in members L_0U_1 and

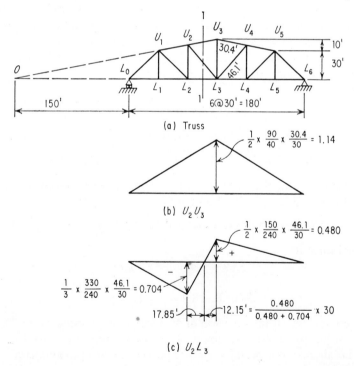

(a) Truss

$$-\frac{1}{2} \times \frac{90}{40} \times \frac{30.4}{30} = 1.14$$

(b) U_2U_3

$$-\frac{1}{2} \times \frac{150}{240} \times \frac{46.1}{30} = 0.480$$

$$\frac{1}{3} \times \frac{330}{240} \times \frac{46.1}{30} = 0.704$$

$$17.85' \qquad 12.15' = \frac{0.480}{0.480 + 0.704} \times 30$$

(c) U_2L_3

Figure 3-12.   Influence Lines for Pratt Truss with Curved Chord

U_1L_1 can be obtained just as for the truss in Figure 3-11. The influence line for U_2U_3 is shown in (b). With a unit load placed at L_3, and considering the portion of the truss to the left (or right) of section $1 - 1$, the end reaction is $\frac{1}{2}$, and the moment about L_3 is $(\frac{1}{2})(90)$. Instead of dividing this moment by the perpendicular distance from L_3 to U_2U_3, it is convenient to resolve U_2U_3 into horizontal and vertical components at U_3, directly above the moment center, L_3. The horizontal component of force is then $(\frac{1}{2})(90)/40$. To obtain the force in U_2U_3, we then multiply the horizontal component by the ratio of length of bar to horizontal projection.

The force in bar U_2L_3 is not now equal to the shear in panel L_2L_3 because bar U_2U_3 has a vertical component of force also. The influence line for force in U_2L_3 can be constructed indirectly by subtracting the vertical component of force in U_2U_3 from the panel shear, but it can also be obtained directly.

The influence line for force U_2L_3 is determined directly, in (c), by making use of section $1 - 1$ and taking moments about the intersection, O, of the other two members cut by the section. With a unit load at L_3, consider the portion of the truss to the left of section $1 - 1$. The only external force acting on this portion is the reaction of $\frac{1}{2}$ at L_0. Taking moments about O, the vertical component of force in U_2L_3 is $(\frac{1}{2})(\frac{150}{240})$. By resolving force U_2L_3 into components at L_3, which is 240 ft from O, the horizontal component does not enter the computation. The vertical component is then multiplied by $\frac{46.1}{30}$ to obtain the force in U_2L_3. With a unit load at L_2, isolate the portion of the truss to the right of section $1 - 1$ and proceed in a similar manner.

Suppose the live load consisted of a moving uniform load of 2 kips per ft and a roving concentrated load of 10 kips. The maximum live-load tension in bar U_2L_3 would be

$$\tfrac{1}{2}(0.480)(102.15)(2) + 0.480(10) = +53.9 \text{ kips}$$

The maximum live-load compression would be

$$\tfrac{1}{2}(-0.704)(77.85(2) + (-0.704)(10) = -61.8 \text{ kips}$$

Dead-load force can also be found with the aid of the influence line. Thus, if the dead load is 3 kips/ft, the dead-load force in U_2L_3 is

$$\tfrac{1}{2}(0.480)(102.15)(3) + \tfrac{1}{2}(-0.704)(77.85)(3) = -8.4 \text{ kips}$$

The total force is

$$53.9 - 8.4 = +45.5 \text{ kips}$$

or

$$-61.8 - 8.4 = -70.2 \text{ kips}$$

A stress reversal, from a tension of 45.5 kips to a compression of 70.2 kips occurs during passage of the loads. This is an important consideration in design because stress reversal magnifies fatigue effects in the material.

There are, of course, many types of trusses, both simple and compound.

Influence lines can be constructed for any bar of these trusses by the fundamental method, provided one can compute forces correctly.

10   Influence Lines for Arch Trusses

Influence lines for bar forces in three-hinged trussed arches can also be determined by computing bar forces for successive positions of a unit load. Generally, however, they can be more readily obtained by superimposing the effect of H on the influence line that would result if the structure were simply supported ($H = 0$).

A three-hinged arch truss is shown in Figure 3-13(a). The influence line shown in (b) is for force in $U_1 U_2$ with the truss considered to be simply

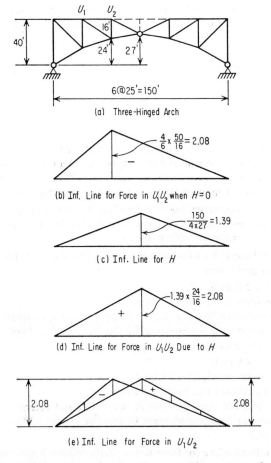

(a)   Three-Hinged Arch

(b) Inf. Line for Force in $U_1 U_2$ when $H = 0$

$$-\frac{4}{6} \times \frac{50}{16} = 2.08$$

(c) Inf. Line for H

$$-\frac{150}{4 \times 27} = 1.39$$

(d) Inf. Line for Force in $U_1 U_2$ Due to H

$$-1.39 \times \frac{24}{16} = 2.08$$

(e) Inf. Line for Force in $U_1 U_2$

Figure 3-13.   Influence Line for Bar Force in Three–Hinged Arch Truss

supported. The influence line for H is shown in (c). The ordinate at the intermediate hinge is, from Equation (3.4), $L/4h$. The effect of H on force in $U_1 U_2$ is shown in (d). Ordinates represent force (compression) in $U_1 U_2$ due to H only. The influence lines in (b) and (d) are superimposed in (e) to obtain the influence line for bar force $U_1 U_2$ in the three-hinged arch.

Notice that the maximum ordinates of the triangles in (b) and (d) are identical in magnitude but opposite in sign. Therefore, the areas under these influence lines are equal but of opposite sign, and the resulting area under the influence line in (e) is zero, indicating zero force in $U_1 U_2$ for a uniformly distributed load. This results from the fact that the bottom chord panel points, which are moment centers for computing force in the upper chord members, lie on a parabola. For uniform load the pressure line is also a parabola and passes through the crown hinge, and consequently through the panel points of the lower chord. It follows that the moment at these panel points is equal to zero, and thus the force in the upper chord members is zero. As a result, for uniform load, only the verticals and the bottom chord members are acting.

Problems

3.1. Draw the influence line for shear immediately to the right of support B, and the influence line for moment at the midpoint of span BC. From the influence ordinates determine the maximum values of the shear and moment resulting from the system of moving loads. (*Ans.:* $V = 21.25$ kips; $M = 425$ ft-kips.)

3.2. Determine the maximum possible bending moment caused by the system of moving loads. How does it compare with the maximum moment at midspan? (*Ans.:* Max. possible $M = 402$ ft-kips.)

3.3. Draw the influence lines for moment, shear, and thrust at the quarterpoint of the three-hinged frame.

3.4. Dead load $= 2$ kips/ft.
Moving uniform live load $= 1$ kip/ft.
Draw the influence line for force in bar $L_2 U_3$ and compute the maximum possible tension and compression in the bar. (*Ans.:* Max. tension $= 110.3$ kips; max. compression $= 0$.)

3.5. Dead load $= 3$ kips/ft.
Moving uniform live load $= 2$ kips/ft.
Roving concentrated live load $= 18$ kips.
Draw the influence line for force in bar $U_1 M_2$ and determine the maximum possible tension and compression in the bar. (*Ans.:* Max. compression $= -37.59$ kips.)

3.6. Draw the influence line for force in bar $U_1 U_2$. Why is it not triangular?

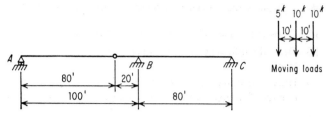

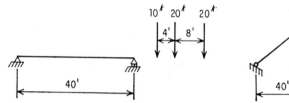

Problem 3-1

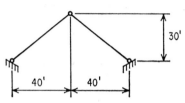

Problem 3-2   Problem 3-3

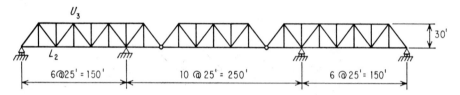

Problem 3-4

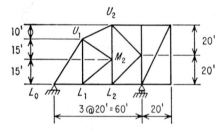

Problem 3-5

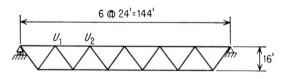

Problem 3-6

91

3.7. Draw the influence lines for force in bars L_4L_6, U_4M_5, M_5L_6, U_4L_4, and U_8L_8.

3.8. Draw the influence lines for force in bars a, b, and c of the three-hinged trussed frame.

3.9. Draw the influence lines for force in the diagonal member and lower-chord member framing into the crown hinge of the arch of Figure 3-13.

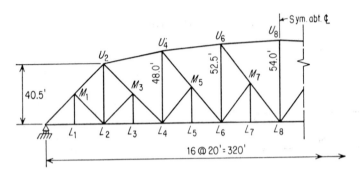

Problem 3-7

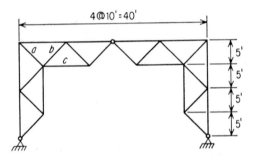

Problem 3-8

Chapter 4

Three-Dimensional Trussed Frameworks

Methods for three-dimensional, but statically determinate, trussed frameworks are considered in this chapter. Practically all engineering structures are three-dimensional, but it is usually possible to resolve them into component coplanar systems. However, in some three-dimensional structures the interaction of the elements is such that an analysis cannot be based on the use of component coplanar systems.

The force and displacement methods of analysis presented in Chapter 7 can be used to analyze statically indeterminate space structures, whether trusses or flexural systems. Matrix formulation, considered in Chapter 9, is particularly useful in conjunction with a digital computer.

4.1   Space Statics

As was the case with the coplanar systems previously considered, it is usually assumed that the members of a three-dimensional trussed framework are pin-connected in such a manner that all members can carry only axial forces. Since we are dealing with stressed members oriented in any direction in space, it is convenient to resolve the bar forces into components parallel to each of three coordinate axes.

In Figure 4-1 a space vector, P, is shown. The projections of the force are P_x, P_y, and P_z in the X-, Y-, and Z-directions, respectively. The angles α, β,

93

and γ are equal to the angles AOC, GOC, and EOC, respectively. Therefore

$$P_x = P \cos \alpha; \qquad P_y = P \cos \beta; \qquad P_z = P \cos \gamma \qquad (4.1)$$

The cosine terms are called the direction cosines of the force P. With coordinates A, G, and E known, the direction cosines can be expressed in terms of

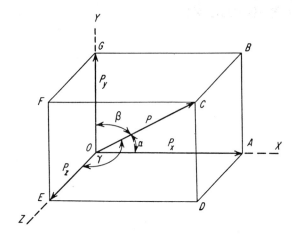

Figure 4-1.   Space Force Vector

the sides of the parallelepiped and the length, r, of its diagonal. Equations (4.1) then become

$$P_x = P\left(\frac{OA}{r}\right); \qquad P_y = P\left(\frac{OG}{r}\right); \qquad P_z = P\left(\frac{OE}{r}\right) \qquad (4.2)$$

where

$$r = \sqrt{\overline{OA}^2 + \overline{OG}^2 + \overline{OE}^2}$$

Also from Eqs. (4.1),

$$P_x^2 + P_y^2 + P_z^2 = P^2(\cos^2 \alpha + \cos^2 \beta + \cos^2 \gamma)$$

or

$$P = \sqrt{P_x^2 + P_y^2 + P_z^2} \qquad (4.3)$$

If the sums of components of all forces along the axes are $\sum F_x$, $\sum F_y$, and $\sum F_z$, the resultant of the forces, from Equation (4.3), is

$$R = \sqrt{\sum F_x^2 + \sum F_y^2 + \sum F_z^2} \qquad (4.4)$$

The direction of the resultant is defined by its direction cosines:

$$\cos \phi_x = \frac{\sum F_x}{R}; \qquad \cos \phi_y = \frac{\sum F_y}{R}; \qquad \cos \phi_z = \frac{\sum F_z}{R} \qquad (4.5)$$

The conditions of equilibrium for the general case of a system of non-coplanar forces can be stated as follows:

$$\sum F_x = 0; \qquad \sum F_y = 0; \qquad \sum F_z = 0 \qquad \textbf{(4.6)}$$
$$\sum M_x = 0; \qquad \sum M_y = 0; \qquad \sum M_z = 0$$

For a concurrent system of forces, only three of these equations are independent and any three can be used to obtain a solution.

The three force equations are used to determine the bar forces in the tripod shown in Figure 4-2. Lengths of the members have been computed in the figure. The force of 50 kips at D lies in a plane parallel to the XY-plane and acts at an angle of $30°$ to a plane parallel to the XZ-plane. All members are assumed to be in tension. As a result, compression forces will be indicated by

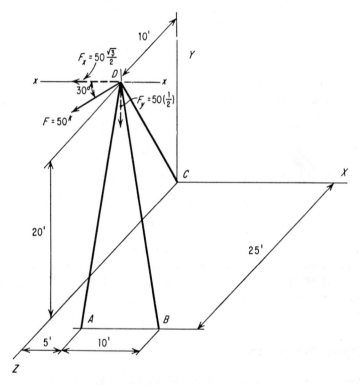

Member Lengths :

$$AD = \sqrt{\overline{5}^2 + \overline{20}^2 + \overline{15}^2} \;=\; 25.50$$
$$BD = \sqrt{\overline{15}^2 + \overline{20}^2 + \overline{15}^2} \;=\; 29.15$$
$$CD = \sqrt{\overline{0}^2 + \overline{20}^2 + \overline{10}^2} \;=\; 22.36$$

Figure 4-2.   Tripod

negative signs in the solution of the equations of equilibrium. Applying Equations (4.6) at point D in the tripod:

$$\sum F_x = \frac{5}{25.50}AD + \frac{15}{29.15}BD \qquad - 50(\frac{\sqrt{3}}{2}) = 0$$

$$\sum F_y = \frac{20}{25.50}AD + \frac{20}{29.15}BD + \frac{20}{22.36}CD + 50(\frac{1}{2}) = 0$$

$$\sum F_z = \frac{15}{25.50}AD + \frac{15}{29.15}BD - \frac{10}{22.36}CD \qquad = 0$$

Solution of the three simultaneous equations yields

$$AD = -129.54 \text{ kips}; \qquad BD = +133.51 \text{ kips}; \qquad CD = -16.77 \text{ kips}$$

The three moment expressions of Equation (4.6) can be used in an alternate solution for the bar forces in the tripod of Figure 4-2. Again, all unknown bar forces are assumed to be tension. The force in member CD is found directly by taking moments about AB.

$$\sum M_{AB} = 50(\frac{1}{2})(15) + CD\frac{20}{22.36}(25) = 0$$

$$CD = -16.77^k$$

Taking moments about a Z-axis through point B,

$$\sum M_{B_z} = -50(\frac{\sqrt{3}}{2})(20) - 50(\frac{1}{2})(15) + 16.77\frac{20}{22.36}(15) - AD\frac{20}{25.50}(10) = 0$$

$$AD = -129.54^k$$

Finally, taking moments about a X-axis through point C,

$$\sum M_{C_x} = 50(\frac{1}{2})(10) - 129.54\frac{20}{25.50}(25) + BD\frac{20}{29.15}(25) = 0$$

$$BD = +133.51^k$$

In the preceding problem, bar forces were determined first through use of force equations only and then through use of moment equations only. Any combination of three equations can be used. The student should rework the problem using such a combination.

4.2   Stability and Determinacy

Equations (4.6) provide six relationships which may be used to calculate external reaction components. It follows that a necessary, although not sufficient, requirement for statical determinacy of a three-dimensional framework with respect to its external forces is that the total number of reaction components equal six. If it is desired to maintain external statical determinacy, care must be taken to limit the number of reaction components to six. This may require the introduction of devices at the supports of a structure to restrict the number of reaction components that can be developed at various supports. A three-force connection results from the use of a ball-and-socket type of support. A roller restrained in one direction provides a two-force connection, and a spherical ball provides a one-force connection.

It is possible for a space framework to have six reaction components and still be unstable. The reactions must be oriented in such a manner that they can resist translation along, and rotation about, each of the three coordinate axes.

For each joint in a frame, three independent equations of statics can be written. Therefore, if both external reaction forces and internal bar forces are considered, a necessary, but not sufficient, condition for statical determinacy of a three-dimensional framework is that the total number of bars, b, plus the total number of independent reaction components, r, must be equal to three times the number of joints, j. Stated mathematically,

$$b + r = 3j \qquad (4.7)$$

In this expression, each support point is counted as a joint.

If $(b + r) > 3j$, the framework is statically indeterminate. If $(b + r) < 3j$, the structure is unstable since one or more joints are not constrained.

A given framework may satisfy Equation (4.7) and still be unstable unless each joint is rigidly constrained against movement in all directions. Because of the complexity of some space frameworks, great care must be taken so as not inadvertently to select an unstable structure. Each joint must be retrained by at least three bars whose far ends are connected to previously constrained joints in order to insure stability.

4.3 Special Theorems

A considerable saving in the amount of computational time required to analyze a three-dimensional framework may result if note is taken of the following theorems. Each of these relationships follows directly from a consideration of the static equilibrium of a joint.

1. If at a joint all bars except one lie in the same plane, the force component normal to the plane of the single bar not in the plane is equal to the component normal to the same plane of the external load or loads applied at the joint.
2. With the same type of bar arrangement, if no external force acts on the joint, the force in the bar not in a plane is equal to zero.
3. If three noncoplanar bars meet at a joint, and no external force acts on the joint, all bars have zero force unless two of the bars are colinear.
4. If all but two bars at a joint have zero stress and these two are not colinear, the force in each bar is zero if no external force acts on the joint.

4.4 Reactions and Bar Forces

If a space framework is statically determinate with respect to its external forces, all reactions components can be computed by applying any six equations of equilibrium to the structure as a whole. If not, it is usually necessary to determine some or all of the bar forces before reaction components can be evaluated.

The framework in Figure 4-3 is supported at *A*, *B*, and *C*, and can develop two reaction components at each support with the directions assumed as

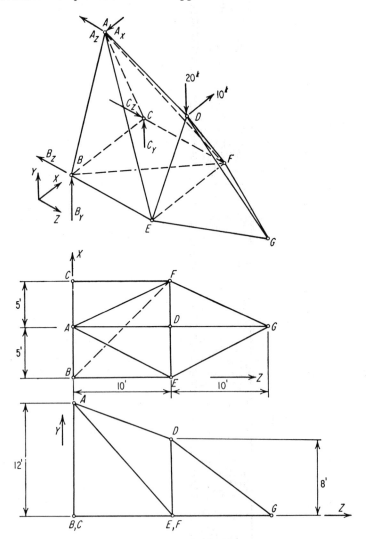

Figure 4-3. Space Framework

shown in the figure. The six reaction components are determined by considering the structure as a whole, as follows:

$$\sum M_{BC} = 20(10) - 12A_z = 0$$
$$A_z = 15.6667^k$$

$$\sum F_x = A_x = 10.0000^k$$

$$\sum M_{Cy} = 10(10) - 16.667(5) - 10B_z = 0$$
$$B_z = 1.6667^k$$

$$\sum M_{By} = 10(10) + 16.6667^k(5) - 10C_z = 0$$
$$C_z = 18.3333^k$$

$$\sum M_{BE} = 20(5) + 10(8) - 10(12) - 10C_y = 0$$
$$C_y = 6.0000^k$$

$$\sum M_{CF} = 20(5) + 10(12) - 10(8) - 10B_y = 0$$
$$B_y = 14.0000^k$$

Since all results are positive, the reactions act as shown in Figure 4-3.

Application of the special theorems of Section 4.3 reveals that the forces in all bars meeting at joint G are equal to zero. The forces in all other bars are computed in what follows by starting at a joint C in which there are only three bars and then proceeding from joint to joint in such a sequence that there are no more than three unknown bar forces at each new joint. All bars are assumed to be in tension. The required geometric properties of the bars are shown in Table 4-1.

TABLE 4-1 Geometric Properties of Bars of Framework in Figure 4-3

	x	y	z	Length	cos. x	cos. y	cos. z
AB	5	12	0	13.000	0.3846	0.9231	0
AC	5	12	0	13.000	0.3846	0.9231	0
BC	10	0	0	10.000	1.0000	0	0
AD	0	4	10	10.770	0	0.3714	0.9285
BE	0	0	10	10.000	0	0	1.0000
CF	0	0	10	10.000	0	0	1.0000
BF	10	0	10	14.142	0.7071	0	0.7071
AE	5	12	10	16.401	0.3049	0.7317	0.6097
AF	5	12	10	16.401	0.3049	0.7317	0.6097
DE	5	8	0	9.434	0.5300	0.8479	0
DF	5	8	0	9.434	0.5300	0.8479	0
EF	10	0	0	10.000	1.0000	0	0

At Joint C:

$$\sum F_y = 0.923AC + 6.000 = 0$$
$$AC = -6.50^k$$

$$\sum F_z = 1.000CF + 18.333 = 0$$
$$CF = -18.33^k$$

$$\sum F_x = 1.000BC + 0.385(-6.50) = 0$$
$$BC = 2.50^k$$

At Joint B:

$$\sum F_y = 0.923AB + 14.000 = 0$$
$$AB = -15.17^k$$

$$\sum F_x = 0.707BF + 0.385(-15.17) + 1.000(2.50) = 0$$
$$BF = 4.72^k$$

$$\sum F_z = 1.000BE + 0.707(4.72) - 1.667 = 0$$
$$BE = -1.67^k$$

At Joint D:

$$\sum F_z = 0.928AD + 0 = 0$$
$$AD = 0$$

$$\sum F_y = 0.848DE + 0.848DF + 20.000 = 0$$
$$\sum F_x = -0.530DE + 0.530DF + 10.000 = 0$$
$$DE = -2.36^k; \qquad DF = -21.23^k$$

At Joint E:

$$\sum F_y = 0.732AE + 0.848(-2.36) = 0$$
$$AE = 2.73^k$$

$$\sum F_z = 0.610(2.73) - 1.67 = 0$$
$$\sum F_x = 1.000EF + 0.305(2.73) + 0.530(-2.36) = 0$$
$$EF = 0.42^k$$

At Joint F:

$$\sum F_y = 0.732AF + 0.848(-21.23) = 0$$
$$AF = 24.59^k$$

$$\sum F_x = 0.42 + 0.305(+24.59) + 0.530(-21.23)$$
$$+ 0.707(4.72) = 0$$

In this example all computations were made by the method of joints. It is emphasized, however, that in many cases a combination of the method of joints and the method of moments will lead to the most expeditious solution.

If a digital computer is available, the easiest approach may involve the solution of a set of linear equations, composed of three equations of statics at each joint, in order to obtain bar forces and reactions. These equations can be written rather easily, and standard programs are generally available for the computer solution. The use of a digital computer should be considered in particular if the framework to be analyzed has a large number of bars. Alternatively, a computer solution could be made using the displacement method and inverting the stiffness matrix (see Chapter 9). This procedure is advantageous when many loading conditions must be considered.

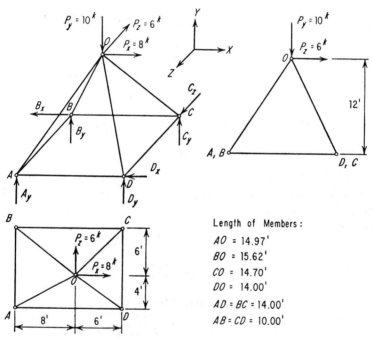

Length of Members:

$AO = 14.97'$
$BO = 15.62'$
$CO = 14.70'$
$DO = 14.00'$
$AD = BC = 14.00'$
$AB = CD = 10.00'$

Figure 4-4.   Space Framework

The frame in Figure 4-4 has seven external reactions, assumed acting in the directions shown. The seven reactions are one more than can be computed directly by use of the six available equations of statics. However, the frame is statically determinate as a whole since Equation (4.7) is satisfied. That is:

$$8 \text{ bars} + 7 \text{ reactions} = 3 \times 5 \text{ joints}$$

Since the seven reactions cannot be determined directly, use will be made of the internal statics equations to supply the extra condition necessary to evaluate them. To begin the solution for reactions and bar forces, one reaction is assumed to be known. For this example, A_y is taken as a known quantity. The other reactions are computed in terms of A_y, as follows:

$$\sum F_z = C_z - 6.00 = 0$$

$$C_z = 6.00^k$$

$$\sum M_{C_y} = 10.00D_x + 6.00(6) - 8.00(6) = 0$$

$$D_x = 1.20^k$$

$$\sum F_x = 8.00 - 1.20 - B_x = 0$$

$$B_x = 6.80^k$$

$$\sum M_{CD} = 8.00(12) - 10.00(6) + 14A_y + 14B_y = 0$$

$$B_y = 2.57 - A_y$$

$$\sum M_{BC} = 6.00(12) - 10.00(6) + 10A_y + 10D_y$$

$$D_y = -1.20 - A_y$$

$$\sum F_y = A_y + (-2.57 - A_y) + (-1.20 - A_y) + C_y - 10.00$$

$$C_y = A_y + 13.77$$

To determine the actual value of A_y, we write an expression for bar force AD at each of joints A and D, and then equate these expressions. In all that follows, all bar forces are assumed to be tensile.
At joint A:

$$\sum F_y = A_y + AD(\tfrac{12.00}{14.97}) = 0$$

$$AO = -\tfrac{14.97}{12.00}A_y$$

$$\sum F_x = AD + AD(\tfrac{8.00}{14.97}) = 0$$

$$AD = \tfrac{14.97}{12.00}(A_y)\tfrac{8.00}{14.97} = \tfrac{2}{3}A_y$$

At joint D, using $D_y = (-1.20 - A_y)$:

$$\sum F_y = (-1.20 - A_y) + DO(\tfrac{12.00}{14.00}) = 0$$

$$DO = (1.20 + A_y)\tfrac{14.00}{12.00}$$

$$\sum F_x = -AD + DO(\tfrac{6.00}{14.00}) - 1.20 = 0$$

$$AD = -(1.20 + A_y)(\tfrac{14.00}{12.00})(\tfrac{6.00}{14.00}) - 1.20$$

$$= -1.80 - \tfrac{1}{2}A_y$$

Equating the expressions for AD,

$$\tfrac{2}{3}A_y = -1.80 - \tfrac{1}{2}A_y$$
$$A_y = -1.54^k$$

which indicates that A_y acts downward rather than upward as assumed.

With the value of A_y determined, the values of B_y, D_y, and C_y are

$$B_y = -2.57 - (-1.54) = -1.03^k$$
$$D_y = -1.20 - (-1.54) = 0.34^k$$
$$C_y = -1.54 + 13.77 = 12.23^k$$

The negative sign for B_y indicates it acts downward rather than upward as assumed.

The analysis can now be completed by proceeding from joint to joint. At joint A, using the expressions previously developed:

$$AO = -\tfrac{14.97}{12.00}(-1.54) = 1.93^k$$
$$AD = \tfrac{2}{3}(-1.54) = -1.03^k$$

Similarly, at joint D:

$$DO = (1.20 - 1.54)\tfrac{14.00}{12.00} = -0.40^k$$

At joint C:

$$\sum F_y = 12.23 + CO(\tfrac{12.00}{14.70}) = 0$$
$$CO = -14.98^k$$

$$\sum F_z = 6.00 + CD + (-14.98)(\tfrac{6.00}{14.70}) = 0$$
$$CD = 0.11^k$$

$$\sum F_x = -CB - (-14.98)(\tfrac{6.00}{14.70}) = 0$$
$$CB = 6.11^k$$

At joint B:

$$\sum F_y = -1.03 + BO(\tfrac{12.00}{15.62}) = 0$$
$$BO = 1.34^k$$

$$\sum F_z = BA + 1.34(\tfrac{6.00}{15.62}) = 0$$
$$BA = -0.51^k$$

Since all bar forces were assumed as tensions, a negative sign for bar force indicates it is compression.

A matrix analysis of the loaded truss shown in Figure 4-4 is performed in Section 9.10.

4.5   Compound and Complex Frameworks

The space truss in Figure 4-5(a) satisfies Equation (4.7) and is therefore statically determinate. In addition, that part of the framework labeled *DEFG* forms an independent simple truss connected by six bars to the support points *A*, *B*, and *C*. A system that includes one or more independent stable trusses is commonly called a *compound* framework (see also sections 2.4 and 2.7).

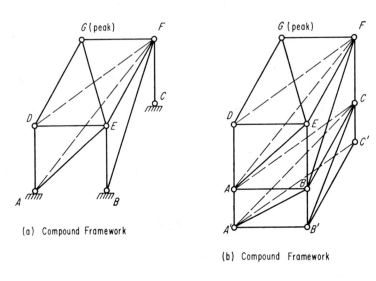

(a) Compound Framework

(b) Compound Framework

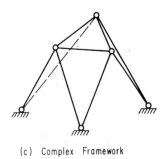

(c) Complex Framework

Figure 4-5.   Compound and Complex Frameworks

The analysis usually can be simplified by considering the independent truss as a rigid body, restrained in space by the compounding bars, and first computing the forces in these bars. After the forces in the compounding bars are determined, the forces in the independent truss (or trusses) can be found.

In Figure 4-5(b), the points *ABC* are supported by a second independent framework *A'B'C'ABC*. For this compound framework with two independent truss systems, the solution for bar forces will be expedited by treating the two truss systems as free bodies and computing the forces in the compounding bars *AD*, *BD*, *EB*, *BF*, *FC*, and *AF* as a first step.

For certain configurations a compound framework can be formed by connecting two independent trusses to each other by means of three bars and a space pin capable of resisting three components of force. Such a system can again be analyzed by first considering the two independent trusses as rigid bodies.

All space frameworks considered previously can be analyzed without the necessity of solving sets of simultaneous equations if the methods of joints and moments are carefully applied. Many important types of space frameworks, including domes and towers without internal cross members, may be statically determinate but can only be analyzed by solution of a set of simultaneous linear equations or by special methods (see Section 2.9). Space systems of this type are called *complex* frameworks. An example of a comlpex system is shown in Figure 4-5(c). The bar forces can be computed by solving nine simultaneous equations.

As has been indicated for the framework of Figure 4-3, the solution of simultaneous equations presents no unusual difficulty if a digital computer and standard programs for solution of equations are available. See Chapter 9 for solution by inversion of a stiffness matrix.

4.6   Domes

Framed domes are complex structures which can be analyzed by solution of a large set of simultaneous equations. Many of the framed dome forms in use are statically indeterminate. The Schwedler-type dome, which has been extensively investigated by C. M. Spofford,[1] is an example of a statically determinate dome framework. A two-tiered, hexagonal-shaped Schwedler dome is illustrated in Figure 4-6. It is supported at each of the base points by a vertical reaction and by a horizontal reaction acting in a direction perpendicular to a radius to the point. The structure is statically determinate since

$$42 \text{ bars} + 12 \text{ reactions} = 3 \times 18 \text{ joints}$$

For the single vertical load at *A*, shown in Figure 4-6, application of the theorems of Section 4.3 reveals that all the bars shown as broken lines carry no force. At joint *F*, members *FE*, *FL*, and *FM* lie in a single plane. As no external loads act on the joint, the force in member *FA* is equal to zero. Following the same reasoning, the force in members *FE*, *ED*, *DC*, and *CB* is equal to zero. Returning to joint *F*, with zero force in *FA* and *FE*, *FL* and *FM*

[1] C. M. Spofford, *Theory of Structures* (4th ed.; New York: McGraw-Hill 1939), chap. XVI.

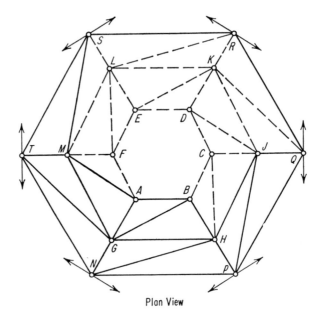

Plan View

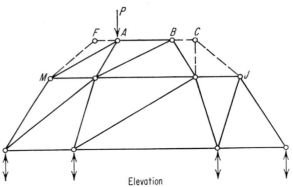

Elevation

Figure 4-6. Schwedler Dome

become two bars at a joint with no applied load. Consequently, force *FL* = force *FM* = 0. In a like manner, forces in *EL*, *EK*, *DK*, *DJ*, *CJ*, and *CH* can be shown to be equal to zero. At joint *L*, with force *EL* = *FL* = 0, and no external load, *ML* is unstressed since it is the only bar not in the plane of *LK*, *LR*, and *LS*. Similarly, forces *LK* and *KJ* are equal to zero. At joint *L*, bars *LS* and *LR* are unstressed because they are the only two remaining members and no external load acts at joint *L*. Members *KR* and *KQ* also carry zero force.

Application of the method of joints successively to *A*, *B*, *M*, *G*, *H*, and *J* yields values for the forces in all stressed members except those in the base ring. Values for all vertical reactions are determined by summing the vertical components of forces at each point of support.

The forces in the bars of the base ring and the horizontal reactions can be computed in the following manner. Assume some bar force as known, say *PN*, and proceed around the base ring expressing all bar forces and horizontal reactions in terms of *PN*. If the procedure is started at joint *N* and continued clockwise around the base, the statics closure equations at joint *P* can be solved for the force in *PN* and the horizontal reaction at *P*.

If the Schwedler dome is symmetrically loaded with a vertical load at every joint, it can be shown that all diagonals, such as *LF*, carry no force. For this condition the dome may be analyzed by the method of joints without the necessity of solving laige sets of simultaneous equations.

For more general loading conditions it becomes necessary to solve a set of 54 simultaneous equations (3 × 18 joints) to determine bar forces and reactions in the dome in Figure 4-6. Solution can also be made through inversion of a 42 × 42 stiffness matrix. The size of the stiffness matrix results from three degrees of freedom at each joint except the support points plus one degree of freedom at the support points. After the bar forces are determined, the twelve reactions can be computed by a consideration of static equilibrium at each support.

If the direction of the horizontal reactions in Figure 4-6 were not restricted as shown, six additional reaction components would result, making the structure statically indeterminate. This would hardly complicate the analysis by means of a stiffness matrix. The 42 × 42 matrix for the statically determinate structure would become a 48 × 48 matrix for the statically indeterminate structure.

4.7   Towers

The legs of the tower shown in Figure 4-7 have a constant slope over the entire height. As a result, this framework can be analyzed by treating each side of the tower as a planar truss. This method of analysis follows from the special theorems of Section 4.3.

In Figure 4-7 an arbitrary load *P* acts at the upper joint *A*. This force can be resolved into three components, P_{AE}, P_{AB}, and P_{AD}. These act, respectively, along the column line *AE*, in the plane of truss *ABEF*, and in the plane of truss *ADEH*. Application of the theorems of Section 4.3 reveals that all the members shown as broken lines in Figure 4-7 are unstressed. For example, members *BC* and *CD* frame into joints *B* and *D*, respectively, where no external loads are applied and where all other members at the joint are coplanar. Therefore, members *CD* and *BC* must have zero force.

The fact that only the members represented by solid lines in Figure 4-7 are stressed is consistent with the usual assumption that trusses resist only forces in their plane. It should be noted that the total force in column *AE* is the algebraic sum of P_{AE} and of the forces due to P_{AD} acting on truss *ADMJ* and P_{AB} acting on truss *ABKJ*.

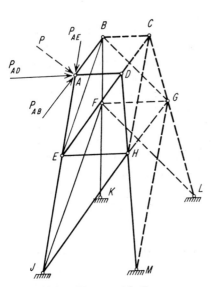

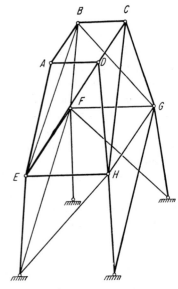

Figure 4-7. Tower with Constant
Slope of Columns

Figure 4-8. Tower with Variable
Slope of Columns

The two-tiered tower of rectangular cross-section shown in Figure 4-8 cannot be analyzed using component coplanar trusses because the legs do not have a constant slope over the entire height of the tower. The fullest possible use should be made of the theorems of Section 4.3 to facilitate the solution for bar forces. Bar forces in the four members forming a horizontal ring such as $ABCD$ or $EFGH$ can be computed by assuming one bar force as known and proceeding round the ring in a manner similar to that explained in Section 4.6 for the base ring of the Schwedler dome.

It is common practice to have secondary bracing in the horizontal plane where the slopes of the legs change. In some instances such bracing is used at each tier level. Any horizontal bracing of this kind makes the structure statically indeterminate. However, such redundant bracing is generally assumed to carry no primary forces, thereby permitting an analysis by use of the principles of statics only.

Problems

4.1. Calculate the values of all bar forces. The 10-kip load is in the YZ-plane, the 5-kip load is in the XZ-plane.

4.2. Compute the forces in members AE and BE. (Ans.: $AE = -4.4^k$; $BE = +5.40^k$.)

4.3. Determine the values of all reactions and bar forces in the space structure. (Ans.: $AC = -50^k$; $CF = +122.5^k$.)

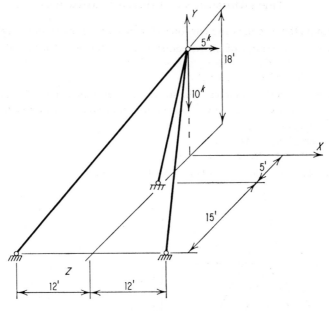

Problem 4-1

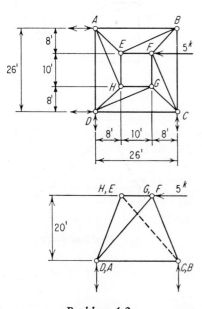

Problem 4-2

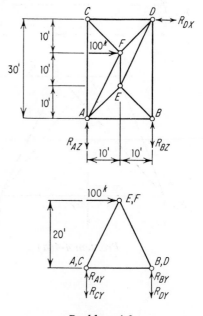

Problem 4-3

109

4.4. Compute the reactions and bar forces for each of the space frameworks.

4.5. Calculate the values of all reactions and bar forces. (*Ans.:* $AB = -33.3^k$; $BC = -33.3^k$; $CD = +16.7^k$; $AE = -81.5^k$; $BE = +81.5^k$; $CE = +50.0^k$; $DE = -50.0^k$; $DA = +33.3^k$.)

4.6. By means of a sketch indicate the stressed and unstressed bars of the Schwedler dome of Figure 4-6 due to the following concentrated vertical loadings:
   (a) single load at E;
   (b) single load at M;
   (c) loads at G, H, J, K, L, and M.

4.7. Determine the values of all bar forces for the tower.

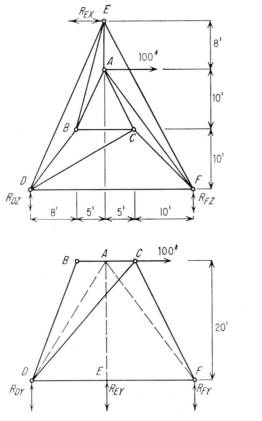

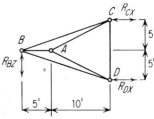

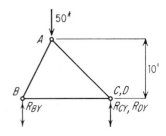

Problem 4-4(a)   Problem 4-4(b)

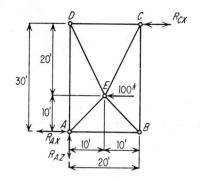

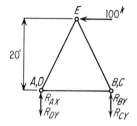

Problem 4-5

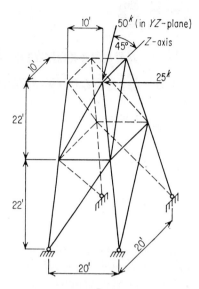

Problem 4-7

Chapter **5**

Approximate Analysis of
Statically Indeterminate Structures

In this chapter attention is turned to some satically indeterminate structures, but consideration is limited to qualitative and approximate procedures. In the following chapters the concepts and procedures necessary for exact analysis are developed.

5.1 Exact and Approximate Solutions

Results of an analysis may be exact with reference to an idealized structure or mathematical model (for example, a truss with frictionless pins) but be inexact with reference to the real structure. The discrepancy between mathematical model and real structure may be one of form or one of properties of material, dictated by limitations of the analytical tools or by inadequate knowledge. The problem of "exactness" occurs in all scientific and engineering endeavor. Solutions may be precise but not exact in the true sense of the word. Nevertheless, we classify precise solutions, using acceptable methods, as exact in order to differentiate them from approximate solutions.

By approximate solutions we mean those obtained considering the same idealized structure as in exact analysis, but using a simplified or less precise scheme of analysis. An approximate study may be made in order to obtain quick results for use in preliminary design, or because an exact solution is impossible or too difficult, or because it is desired to check an exact solution.

The ability to obtain quick approximate solutions cannot be overemphasized. It is difficult to conceive of a great designer without such ability. Its importance to the designer or analyst is quite possibly even greater now as the result of the widespread use of electronic computers. The engineer without the ability to visualize and assess the action of a structure, even though quite roughly, is more than ever at the mercy of numbers.

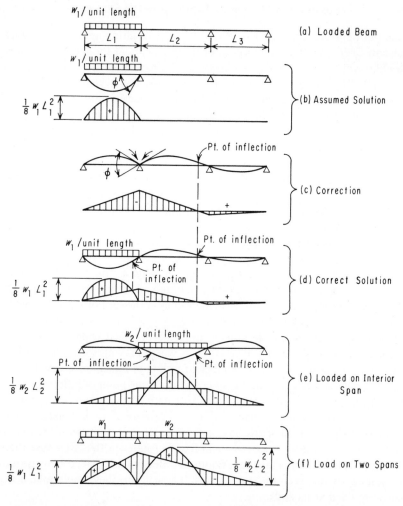

w_1 / unit length

(a) Loaded Beam

w_1 / unit length

$\frac{1}{8} w_1 L_1^2$

(b) Assumed Solution

Pt. of inflection

ϕ

(c) Correction

w_1 / unit length

Pt. of inflection

Pt. of inflection

$\frac{1}{8} w_1 L_1^2$

(d) Correct Solution

w_2 / unit length

Pt. of inflection

Pt. of inflection

$\frac{1}{8} w_2 L_2^2$

(e) Loaded on Interior Span

w_1

w_2

$\frac{1}{8} w_1 L_1^2$

$\frac{1}{8} w_2 L_2^2$

(f) Load on Two Spans

Figure 5-1. Moment Diagrams by Sketching the Deflected Structure

5.2 The Deflected Structure: Continuous Beams

Figure 5-1(a) shows a three-span continuous beam. This structure is statically indeterminate in the second degree since there are two supports beyond those required for statical equilibrium.

In (b) it is assumed that the continuous beam has been cut at the first interior support, thus making the loaded span statically determinate, and resulting in the deflected structure and moment diagram shown. The displacements of the deflected structure have been grossly exaggerated for clarity.

Continuity is restored in (c) by applying equal and opposite moments at the cut ends so that they are rotated relative to each other through an angle

113

equal but opposite to that in (b). Notice that the resulting moment diagram is linear in each span, but magnitudes of the moments at the interior supports are unknown. These moments are the indeterminate quantities, which cannot be obtained by computations of statics alone, and their values must be those necessary to satisfy the requirements of geometry (continuity).

We are not yet prepared for an exact analysis, but we can approximate the required quantities by proceeding as in (d). First, sketch the deflected structure, grossly exaggerating the displacements for convenience. In the usual structure such movements are so small that it would be impossible to show them to scale on a sketch. Once the deflected structure has been sketched, the moment diagram can be obtained by superimposing the correction moment diagram in (c) on the moment diagram in (b) in such a way that zero moment is indicated at the points of inflection.

In Figure 5-1(e) the load has been placed on the interior span. After sketching the deflected structure, the moment diagram can be obtained immediately by superimposing the linear correction diagram on the simple-beam moment. The moment diagram in (f) was obtained simply by combining the moment diagrams in (d) and (e), with the values at the supports determined by adding algebraically the values in (d) and (e).

As the values of the indeterminate moments obtained depend directly on the location of the points of inflection, it is worth making some observations concerning the latter. The total number of points of inflection is equal to the degree of indeterminacy. A loaded span will have one point of inflection if it is an exterior span with extreme end free to rotate. It will have two points of inflection if it is an interior span or if it is an exterior span with extreme end restrained. All unloaded spans have one point of inflection, with the exception of exterior spans with extreme end free to rotate. In the latter case there is no point of inflection in the span. Points of inflection in a loaded span are located somewhere between the support and the positions they would take if the span were fixed at its ends.

To the extent that points of inflection can be accurately located, the indeterminate moments will approach exact values. Results obtained by exact methods of analysis differ from those of the approximate method illustrated in Figure 5-1 only in the accuracy with which the indeterminate values are obtained.

The student should, by ignoring the statements made regarding the location of points of inflection, attempt to draw a moment diagram based on a different distribution among spans of the points of inflection. Remembering that the superimposed diagram for correction moments must consist of straight lines intersectioning at the supports, it will be found impossible to obtain a final moment diagram that is consistent with this requirement, with the curvature of the assumed deflected shape, and with the support conditions. Only one combination of deflected structure and corresponding moment diagram is possible, and that is the correct one.

End shears and reactions can be obtained in the same manner as bending moments were obtained in Figure 5-1—that is, by combining corrections with the known simple-beam values of the assumed solution. A loaded beam and the resulting moment diagram are shown in (a) and (b) of Figure 5-2. In the top line in (c) we compute the end shears for the assumed simply supported loaded span. In the following line we determine the end shears corresponding to the correction moments. These are computed for each span by combining the moments at the ends of the span and dividing by the span length. Thus,

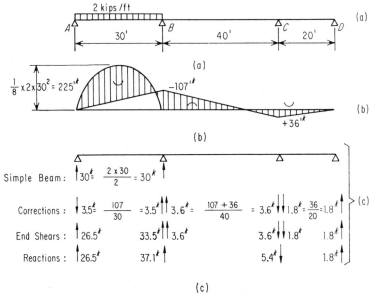

Figure 5-2.   *Shears and Reactions*

isolating span AB, the moment at A is zero and the moment at B is 107 ft-kips, clockwise. Consequently, a counterclockwise external couple of 107 ft-kips is necessary to satisfy the requirements of equilibrium. This is furnished by a downward force of 3.5 kips at A and an upward force of 3.5 kips at B.

In span BC, there is a counterclockwise moment of 107 ft-kips at B and a counterclockwise moment of 36 ft-kips at C. A balancing couple is furnished by an upward force of 3.6 kips at B and a downward force of 3.6 kips at C. The clockwise moment at C for span CD results in forces of 1.8 kips at C and D. The corrections are combined with the simple-beam values to obtain the end shears. Finally, end shears are combined to obtain reactions.

The degree of accuracy of the shears and reactions in Figure 5-2 depends on the accuracy with which the indeterminate moments at B and C were determined. If these moments are exact, then the shears and reactions in (c) are also exact.

A three-span beam with two hinges is considered in Figure 5-3. This structure is statically determinate because of the two hinges. With load on the

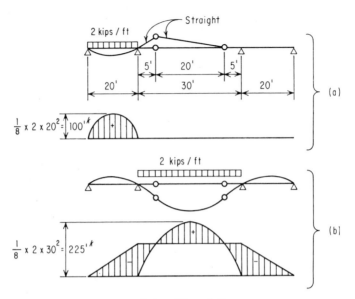

Figure 5-3.   Hinged Beam

exterior span, as shown in (a), bending moment occurs only in the loaded span. With load in the middle span, as in (b), bending moment occurs throughout, except at the hinges. The hinges are treated exactly as were the points of inflection in Figure 5-1(e). If the hinges in Figure 5-3 were located in the same position as the points of inflection in Figure 5-1, then for the same spans and the same loading intensity the moment diagrams would be identical.

Practice in sketching the deflected structure is recommended to the student not so much for obtaining approximate results as for sharpening his feel for structural behavior. As will be seen in Chapter 7, the powerful method of moment distribution lends itself to quick approximation, as well as precise determination, of the indeterminate moments.

5.3   The Deflected Structure: Rigid Frames

A two-hinged rigid frame, or bent, and the moment diagram corresponding to the deflected structure are shown in Figure 5-4(a). Moments that cause compression in the outer fibers are called positive. Because of the requirements of statical equilibrium, the horizontal reactions at A and D must be equal and opposite. This means that if the heights of legs AB and CD are equal, then the moment at C must be equal to the moment at B. If the legs are not of equal height, then the moments at B and C adjust accordingly so as to maintain equal horizontal reactions.

The moment diagram for the "equivalent" beam in Figure 5-4(b) is identical to that in (a). However, since the horizontal reactions in (a) are now vertical, the interior reactions of the beam are increased.

116

To make the horizontal reactions of the hingeless frame in Figure 5-4(c) equal, $(M_A + M_B)$ must equal $(M_C + M_D)$. If the legs are unequal in length, the moments at A, B, C, and D adjust accordingly so as to maintain equal horizontal reactions.

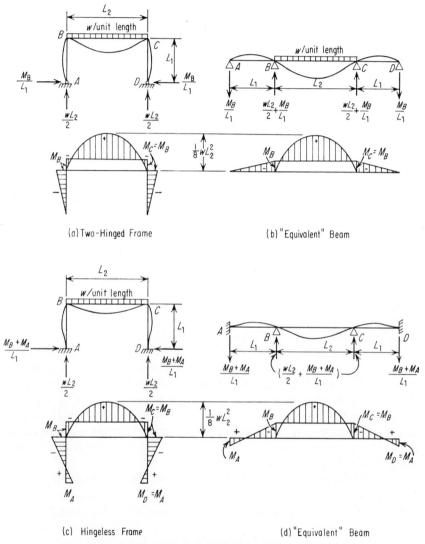

(a) Two-Hinged Frame   (b) "Equivalent" Beam

(c) Hingeless Frame   (d) "Equivalent" Beam

Figure 5-4. Rigid Frames: Symmetrical Case

An unsymmetrically loaded, two-hinged rigid frame is shown in Figure 5-5(a). As a result of the dissymmetry, joints B and C are displaced laterally an equal amount. Such a movement is commonly referred to as *sidesway*. It must take place in order to make $M_B = M_C$, and thus result in fulfilling the requirement $H_A = D_D$.

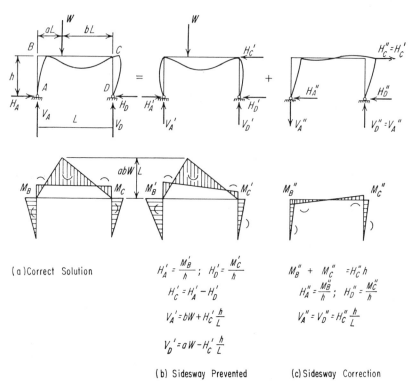

(a) Correct Solution

$$H_A' = \frac{M_B'}{h}; \quad H_D' = \frac{M_C'}{h}$$

$$H_C' = H_A' - H_D'$$

$$V_A' = bW + H_C'\frac{h}{L}$$

$$V_D' = aW - H_C'\frac{h}{L}$$

$$M_B'' + M_C'' = H_C''h$$

$$H_A'' = \frac{M_B''}{h}; \quad H_D'' = \frac{M_C''}{h}$$

$$V_A'' = V_D'' = H_C''\frac{h}{L}$$

(b) Sidesway Prevented   (c) Sidesway Correction

Figure 5-5.   Two-Hinged Frame: Unsymmetrical Case

Frames involving dissymmetry can be analyzed by superimposing corrections, to account for sidesway, on values determined by assuming that no sidesway occurs. Thus the deflected structure and moment diagram in Figure 5-5(b) results in $H_A' \neq H_D'$. Such a solution is possible if an external lateral force of $H_C' = H_A' - H_D'$ can be developed. Under this condition the analysis is complete. If, as is generally the case, there is no external restraint to the lateral movement of BC, it is necessary to correct the results in (b) for the effect of removing the holding force. This is done in (c) by applying a force H_C'' that is equal and opposite to H_C'. For legs of equal length and identical composition, $H_A'' = H_D'' = \frac{1}{2}H_C''$ exactly. Consequently, $M_B'' = M_C''$, and the point of inflection is at the midpoint of BC.

Except for the girder in (a) and (b), the moment diagrams have been drawn on the tension side of the member. If desired, the moment diagrams for the girder can be redrawn in the same way, using a horizontal base line, but there is no need for this.

The final moment diagram in Figure 5-5(a) is obtained by superimposing values in (c) on values in (b). Vertical and horizontal components of reaction are obtained in the same way. If desired, the identical values of vertical and horizontal components of reaction can be obtained directly from (a) by a consideration, respectively, of member BC and the legs. Observe that the moment corrections in (c) are automatically such as to result in $M_B = M_C$

118

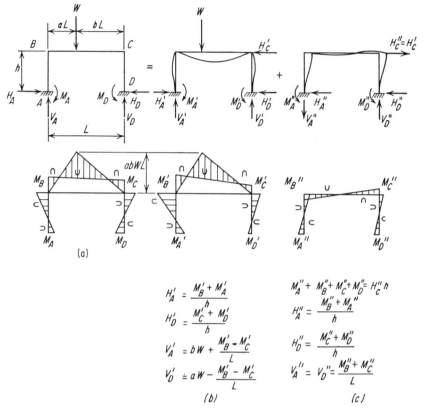

$$H_A' = \frac{M_B' + M_A'}{h}$$

$$H_D' = \frac{M_C' + M_D'}{h}$$

$$V_A' = bW + \frac{M_B' - M_C'}{L}$$

$$V_D' = aW - \frac{M_B' - M_C'}{L}$$

(b)

$$M_A'' + M_B'' + M_C'' + M_D'' = H_C'' h$$

$$H_A'' = \frac{M_B'' + M_A''}{h}$$

$$H_D'' = \frac{M_C'' + M_D''}{h}$$

$$V_A'' = V_D'' = \frac{M_B'' + M_C''}{L}$$

(c)

Figure 5-6. Hingeless Frame: Unsymmetrical Case

for legs of equal length. In any event, M_B and M_C must have values that will result in $H_A = H_D$. Results in Figure 5-5 depend only upon the accuracy with which moments are determined in (b) and (c).

Results for the frame in Figure 5-6, with supports at A and D fixed against rotation, are obtained in a similar manner. To determine horizontal components of reaction in (b), it is necessary to consider moments at both ends of each leg. As will be seen in Chapter 7, for members of constant section, $M_A' = \frac{1}{2}M_B'$, and $M_D' = \frac{1}{2}M_C'$. Vertical components of reaction in (b) are now more readily found by isolating member BC and applying corrections, due to end moments, to the simple-beam reactions.

If the legs of the frame are identical, then in Figure 5-6(c) the point of inflection in BC is at midspan. The point of inflection in the columns would be at midheight if no rotation occurred at B and C—that is, if BC were infinitely stiff. Since some rotation does occur at B and C, the point of inflection in the legs is somewhat above midheight. Except for quite flexible girders, however, the position of the point of inflection is always close to midheight.

Since it is difficult to fix the bases at A and D perfectly, it is recommended that for approximate analyses the points of inflection of the columns in (c) be

119

taken at midheight. In any event, the corrections in (c) are small compared to the values in (b), and great precision in determining the former is hardly necessary.

Once the location of the point of inflection in each column is assumed, it is possible to isolate the upper portion, which can then be treated as the two-hinged frame in Figure 5-5(c). This has been done in Figure 5-7 by assuming

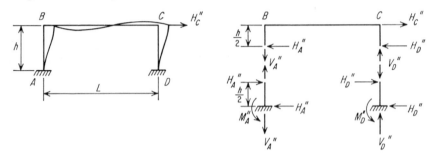

Figure 5-7.   Hingeless Frame

points of inflection at midheight. H_C'' may represent a correction force, as in Figure 5-6, or an actual applied force. The bending moments at A and B are each equal to $H_A''h/2$. Those at C and D are $H_D''h/2$. The vertical reactions can be obtained conveniently as

$$V_A'' = V_D'' = \frac{H_c''(h/2)}{L}$$

If the columns are identical, then $H_A'' = H_D'' = \tfrac{1}{2}H_C''$, and the bending moments at A, B, C, and D are each equal to $(H_C''/2)(h/2) = H_C''h/4$.

A multispan frame such as that in Figure 5-8 can be analyzed approximately by assuming the location of the points of inflection in the girders and the distribution of shear to the columns. (If the frame were fixed at its supports, it would also be necessary to assume points of inflection in the columns.) When lateral load is applied to the knee of a frame, the points of inflection are generally in the neighborhood of the midpoint of each girder (and column, if fixed at its base), and the interior columns are subjected to greater shear than are the exterior columns. This tendency for greater shear in the interior columns is accentuated by the fact that they usually are designed to carry greater vertical load than the exterior columns, and thus are heavier (and stiffer).

The location of points of inflection and the distribution of shear to the columns must be compatible in order to satisfy requirements of statics. A compatible set of assumptions consists of assuming points of inflection at mid-length of the girders (and at midheight of the columns if they are fixed at their bases) and assuming that the shear resisted by each interior column is two times that resisted by each exterior column. This has been done in Figure 5-8.

In Figure 5-9 lateral load is applied to one of the legs rather than at a knee

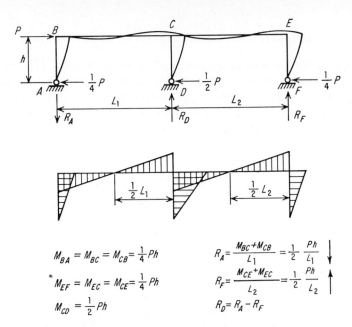

$$M_{BA} = M_{BC} = M_{CB} = \tfrac{1}{4} Ph \qquad R_A = \frac{M_{BC} + M_{CB}}{L_1} = \tfrac{1}{2} \frac{Ph}{L_1} \;\downarrow$$

$$M_{EF} = M_{EC} = M_{CE} = \tfrac{1}{4} Ph \qquad R_F = \frac{M_{CE} + M_{EC}}{L_2} = \tfrac{1}{2} \frac{Ph}{L_2} \;\uparrow$$

$$M_{CD} = \tfrac{1}{2} Ph \qquad\qquad R_D = R_A - R_F$$

Figure 5-8.   Two–Span Rigid Frame

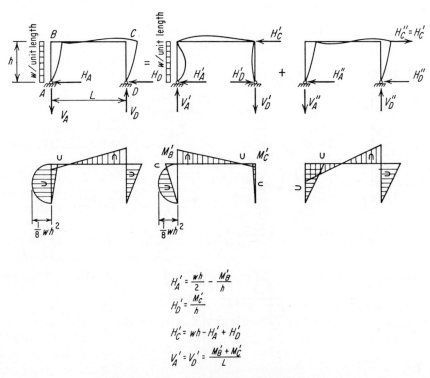

$$H_A' = \frac{wh}{2} - \frac{M_B'}{h}$$

$$H_D' = \frac{M_C'}{h}$$

$$H_C' = wh - H_A' + H_D'$$

$$V_A' = V_D' = \frac{M_B' + M_C'}{L}$$

Figure 5-9.   Laterally Loaded Frame

of the frame. The loading could represent the effect of wind. The analysis is made in the same manner as before, by adding corrections to a solution obtained by preventing sidesway. The student should see clearly that H_C' is not equal to the thrust in member BC. The thrust in BC is equal to $wh - H_A'$, whereas H_C' includes the value of H_D'.

5.4 Trussed Frames

The frame in Figure 5-10(a) is analyzed in a manner similar to the frame in Figure 5-7. Because of the great relative stiffness of the truss, the point of inflection of each column is assumed to be located at one half the distance from

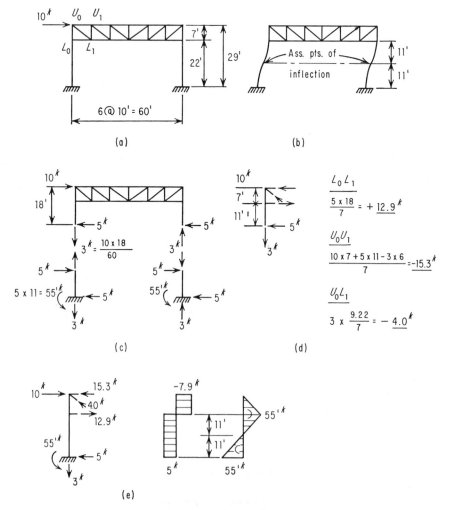

Figure 5-10.   Trussed Frame

column base to bottom of truss, as shown in (b). The resisting forces and moments developed in the columns are shown in (c). With the shear and axial force in the columns determined, bar forces in the truss can be computed as in Chapter 2, considering the structure above the points of inflection of the columns. Forces in three of the bars are determined in (d). Shear and moment diagrams for the left-hand column are shown in (e). Note that the shear of -7.9 kips at the top of the column is equal to the algebraic sum of the 10-kip load, the force in $U_0 U_1$, and the horizontal component of force in $U_0 L_1$.

The student should draw the shear and moment diagrams for the right-hand column. They will be identical to those in (e) even though the forces in the adjacent bars are somewhat different.

The reactions in Figure 5-10, as well as the shear and moment diagrams for the portion of the columns below the lower chord of the truss, are identical to those that would be obtained for the rigid frame in Figure 5-7 with $H_C'' = 10$ kips, $h = 22$ ft, and $L = 60$ ft. The portions of the shear and moment diagrams between truss chords follow from a consideration of the adjacent bar forces. In a similar manner, approximate results for a fixed or hinged trussed frame loaded as in Figure 5-9 can be obtained by modifying a solution such as that in Figure 5-9.

The magnitude of the moments in a column of a frame considered fixed at its bases can be greatly altered by slight rotations at the bases. Theoretical solutions for rotation of the bottom of a support are readily possible by the methods of Chapter 7. However, the sensitivity alluded to above, together with the inherent inaccuracies in predicting the behavior of foundation materials, makes any accurate determination of the effects of imperfect fixity extremely difficult. If in a fixed-end frame there is doubt as to actual fixity, a conservative procedure would be to bracket the actual case by obtaining results for a hinged frame as well.

5.5 Multilevel Frames

By sketching the deflected structure, it can be seen that maximum positive live-load moment in a span occurs when that span plus alternate adjacent spans are loaded. This is the so-called checker board pattern of loading. On the other hand, maximum negative live-load moment at a support occurs when the spans immediately adjacent to the support are loaded and alternate spans beyond are also loaded. There is, of course, no choice with respect to placing dead load. All spans are loaded.

Consider a multistory, rigid frame building, such as that shown in Figure 5-11(a), with fairly uniform span lengths (adjacent spans not differing by more than, say, 20 or 25 per cent). For uniformly distributed live load that does not exceed approximately three times the dead load, the moment coefficients shown in (b) will yield reasonable approximate results for maximum moments. The coefficients can be used for all floors. To obtain bending moments, the

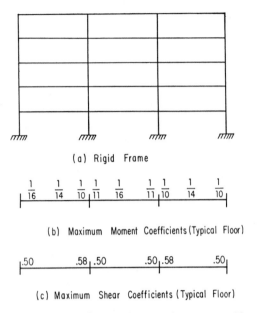

(a) Rigid Frame

$\frac{1}{16}$ $\frac{1}{14}$ $\frac{1}{10}\frac{1}{11}$ $\frac{1}{16}$ $\frac{1}{11}\frac{1}{10}$ $\frac{1}{14}$ $\frac{1}{10}$

(b) Maximum Moment Coefficients (Typical Floor)

.50   .58 .50   .50 .58   .50

(c) Maximum Shear Coefficients (Typical Floor)

Figure 5-11.   Coefficients for Rigid Frame Buildings

coefficients are multiplied by wL^2, in which w is the dead load plus live load per unit length and L is the span of the particular beam. The maximum shear coefficients, shown in Figure 5-11(c), are multiplied by wL.

The sum of the column moments at a joint must be equal and opposite to the beam moments. At the interior joints, with adjacent spans loaded to obtain maximum compression in the column, as well as maximum negative bending moment in the beams, the bending moment shared by the two columns is quite small $(\frac{1}{10}wL^2 - \frac{1}{11}wL^2)$. In all cases, moment is shared by the two columns at a joint in proportion to their relative stiffnesses (I/h).

The multistory rigid frame in Figure 5-12(a) is subjected to lateral loads applied at the level of each row of horizontal members. An approximate analysis is made by application of the so-called portal method used previously. It is again assumed that points of inflection are located at the midpoint of each member, and that the interior columns resist twice as much shear as the exterior columns.

The uppermost portion of the frame has been isolated by passing a section through the points of inflection of the columns, and it is shown in (b). The shear is distributed among the columns in accordance with the assumptions made. The moments shown then follow on the basis of the shears in the columns and the assumption of points of inflection at the midlength of each horizontal member.

The axial force in each column is equal to the sum of the end shears in the adjoining beams. At A only one beam frames into the column, and its end shear, 0.3 kip, is found as the sum of its end moments at A and B divided by its span length. At B the end shear in BC is equal and opposite to the end shear

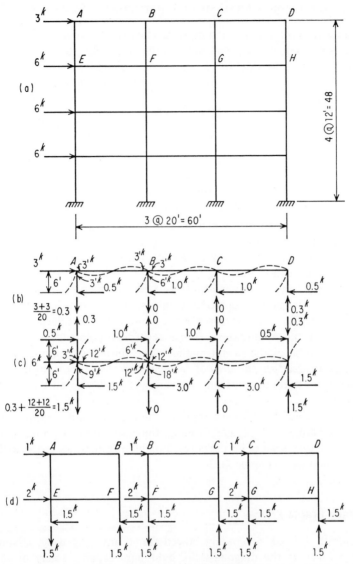

Figure 5-12. Portal Method

in *BA*. Therefore, there is no axial force in the interior column. This will be true for all interior columns when the beam lengths are all equal. As a result, the axial forces in the exterior columns can also be computed by dividing the external moment by the distance between columns. Thus, axial force is equal to $3(6)/60 = 0.3$ kip.

The second level from the top, between points of inflection of the columns above and below, is shown in Figure 5-12(c). The shears and axial loads from (b) are shown in the opposite direction on the upper columns. The shears in the lower columns are obtained by dividing the total shear $(3 + 6)$ in accordance with the original assumption. The axial force in the lower exterior columns is now equal to the end shear in the girder plus the axial force in the upper column. Or, the axial force can be found directly by taking moments of all external forces about an axis in the plane of contraflexure of the lower columns. Thus

$$3(18) = 54 \text{ ft-kips}$$
$$6(6) \ = \underline{36}$$
$$ 90 \text{ ft-kips}$$

and

$$\tfrac{90}{60} = 1.5 \text{ kip.}$$

Identical results will be obtained if the frame is considered to consist of three separate portals, as in (d). When results from these individual portals are combined, the shears of the interior columns become twice those of the exterior columns. Similarly, for equal beam lengths, the axial forces in the interior columns cancel out.

Variations of the portal method, as well as other methods have been proposed for determining approximate forces and moments in multilevel rigid frames. One of the better known ones is the so-called cantilever method, for which two of the assumptions (those regarding points of inflection) are identical to those of the portal method. The third assumption, however, is that the axial stress *per unit area* of each column of a story is proportional to the distance of that column from the center of gravity of all the columns of the story.

Results obtained by different approximate methods can vary quite widely. For low buildings with regular framing, the easily applied portal method is fairly satisfactory for design purposes. For high frames, an exact analysis is recommended (see Chapter 7).

5.6 Diagonally Braced Frames

A laterally loaded, diagonally braced frame, one bay wide, is shown in Figure 5-13(a). If the diagonals are light bars capable solely of resisting tension, only the diagonals sloping down from right to left will act when the

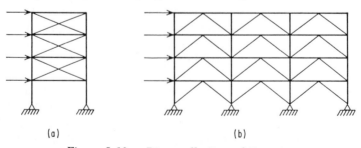

(a)   (b)

Figure 5-13.   Diagonally Braced Frames

forces are applied in the direction shown. The resulting vertical truss is statically determinate.

If both diagonals are capable of acting as compression members as well as tension members, then both will act, one in compression and one in tension. The vertical truss is now statically indeterminate, but an acceptable approximate analysis can be made by assuming that each of the two diagonals resists one half of the story shear.

A braced frame more than one bay wide, such as that in Figure 5-13(b), is always statically indeterminate. An approximate analysis is made possible by assuming that the shear is divided equally among adjoining bays. For equal bay widths, the axial force in an interior column is equal to zero and the entire overturning moment at any story level is resisted by the exterior columns.

Problems

5.1. By sketching the deflected structure, obtain the moment diagrams when a uniformly distributed load of 2 kips/ft is placed, successively, on each span. (*Exact Ans.:* For load on AB, $M_B = -104$ ft-kips and $M_C = +30$ ft-kips. For load on BC, $M_B = M_C = -176$ ft-kips.)

5.2. Using exact answers from Problem 5.1, obtain, by superposition, the exact moment diagram for a uniformly distributed load of 1 kip/ft placed along the entire structure.

5.3. Determine the end shears and reactions corresponding to the loading in Problem 5.2.

5.4. From a consideration of the deflected structure, obtain the moment diagrams when a uniformly distributed load of 2 kips/ft is placed, successively, on spans AB and BC.

5.5. Repeat Problem 5.4, but with concentrated loads of 10 kips placed simultaneously 5 ft to the right of B and 10 ft to the left of C.

5.6. With sidesway prevented, $M_B = 334$ ft-kips, $M_C = 275$ ft-kips, $M_A = 167$ ft-kips, and $M_D = 138$ ft-kips. The sidesway corrections are $M_B = M_C = 20$ ft-kips, and $M_A = M_D = 24$ ft-kips. Draw the final moment diagram and compute the final reactions. (*Ans.:* $V_A = 60.4$ kips.)

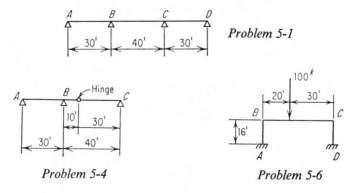

Problem 5-1

Problem 5-4

Problem 5-6

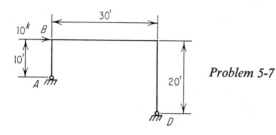

10^k B
|← 30' →|
10'
20'
A
D

Problem 5-7

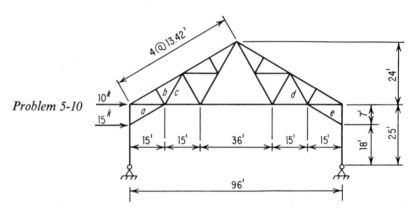

Problem 5-10

4@13.42'
24'
10^k
15^k
a b c d e
7'
15' 15' 36' 15' 15'
18'
25'
96'

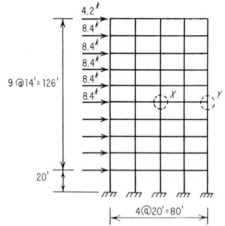

4.2^k
8.4^k
8.4^k
8.4^k
8.4^k
8.4^k
9 @14'= 126'
X Y
20'
4@20'=80'

Problem 5-11

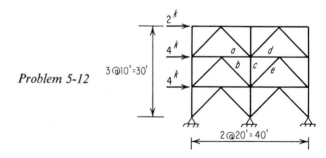

Problem 5-12

2^k
4^k
4^k
3@10'=30'
a d
b c e
2@20'= 40'

5.7. In the unsymmetrical two-hinged frame, assume that $H_A = 7.3$ kips and $H_D = 2.7$ kips. Sketch the deflected structure and determine the moment diagram and V_A and V_D.

5.8. Repeat Problem 5.7, assuming ends A and D fixed and points of inflection at midheight of each column.

5.9. Repeat Problem 5.8, assuming points of inflection in columns at 4 ft from B and 8 ft from C.

5.10. Determine reactions, draw shear and moment diagrams for the columns, and compute forces in the marked bars.   (*Ans.:* $a = +32.9$ kips.)

5.11. Through use of the portal method find the bending moments and shears in the columns and girders framing into joints X and Y. Sketch the deflected joints. In addition, compute the axial forces in the columns at Y.   (*Ans.:* $M = 80.0$ ft-kips in lower column at X.)

5.12. On the assumption that the shear is divided equally between the two bays, compute the force in each marked bar.   *Hint:* See Figure 5-12(d).

Chapter **6**

Deformations and Deflections of Elastic Systems

Procedures are developed in this chapter for determining displacements in beams, frames, and trusses. Computation of displacements is important to the engineer for two principal reasons. He may wish to predict the movements of a structure due to specific loads. Second, he may use the relative magnitudes of certain imaginary movements in the analysis of statically indeterminate structures. The use of deflection computations in the analysis of indeterminate structures will be considered in Chapters 7 and 8.

As will be seen, expressions for beam and frame displacements due to bending contain the product, EI, of the modulus of elasticity in tension and compression and the moment of inertia of the section. Computed values of deflections can only be as precise as the values of EI used.

The value of E for some materials, such as steel, is practically constant in the commonly used stress range. In other materials, such as concrete, this ratio varies with both the magnitude and duration of stress. The value of I for a steel section can be computed as the moment of inertia of the area of the cross section. In reinforced concrete such a computation is not strictly valid because stresses are not proportional to strains and because of uncertainties as to the effective section resisting bending. Additional complications can arise because of shrinkage, creep, cracking, and bond slip. One should proceed cautiously and conservatively in predicting deflections of reinforced concrete structures.

Uncertainties as to the value of EI are of much less importance in deflection calculations used in the analysis of continuous structures (Chapter 7). It is generally not necessary to know the absolute values of EI along the structure. It is necessary, however, to know the relative values.

6.1 Geometry of Small Angles

A closed traverse and an open traverse are shown, respectively, in Figures 6-1 and 6-2. These traverses differ from those of the land surveyor in that the deflection angles will be considered to be very small. By this is meant that they

130

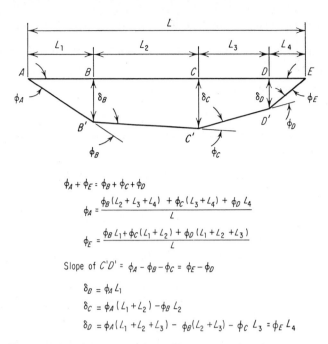

$$\phi_A + \phi_E = \phi_B + \phi_C + \phi_D$$

$$\phi_A = \frac{\phi_B(L_2 + L_3 + L_4) + \phi_C(L_3 + L_4) + \phi_D L_4}{L}$$

$$\phi_E = \frac{\phi_B L_1 + \phi_C(L_1 + L_2) + \phi_D(L_1 + L_2 + L_3)}{L}$$

Slope of $C'D' = \phi_A - \phi_B - \phi_C = \phi_E - \phi_D$

$$\delta_B = \phi_A L_1$$

$$\delta_C = \phi_A(L_1 + L_2) - \phi_B L_2$$

$$\delta_D = \phi_A(L_1 + L_2 + L_3) - \phi_B(L_2 + L_3) - \phi_C L_3 = \phi_E L_4$$

Figure 6-1.   Geometry of Small Angles, Closed Traverse

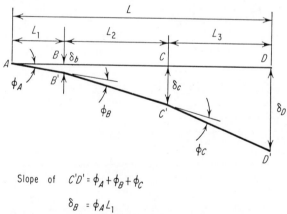

Slope of $C'D' = \phi_A + \phi_B + \phi_C$

$$\delta_B = \phi_A L_1$$

$$\delta_C = \phi_A(L_1 + L_2) + \phi_B L_2$$

$$\delta_D = \phi_A(L_1 + L_2 + L_3) + \phi_B(L_2 + L_3) + \phi_C l_3$$

Figure 6-2.   Geometry of Small Angles, Open Traverse

can be expressed as ratios of two linear distances. For example, in either figure $\phi_A = \delta_B/AB = \delta_B/AB'$. All angles, ϕ, and consequently displacements, δ, are grossly exaggerated in Figures 6-1 and 6-2 because it would be impossible to plot them to the same scale as the sides of the traverses.

131

For the closed traverse of Figure 6-1 the requirements of geometry can be stated as follows:

1. The traverse angles must balance, or

$$\phi_A + \phi_E = \phi_B + \phi_C + \phi_D$$

2. The sum of the products of angles and distances to a vertical axis through A or E must balance, or

$$\phi_A L = \phi_B(L_2 + L_3 + L_4) + \phi_C(L_3 + L_4) + \phi_D L_4$$

and

$$\phi_E L = \phi_B L_1 + \phi_C(L_1 + L_2) + \phi_D(L_1 + L_2 + L_3)$$

The expressions in Figure 6-1 follow from the above requirements of a closed circuit and from the definition of a small angle. In an open circuit, such as that

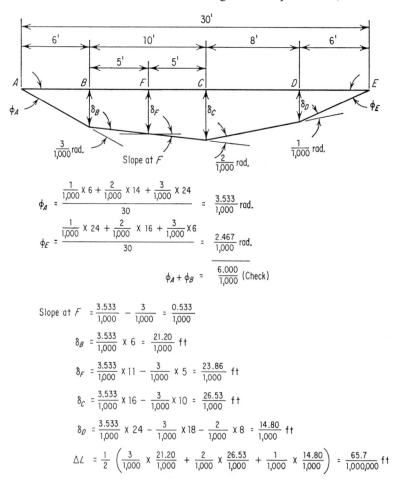

$$\phi_A = \cfrac{\dfrac{1}{1,000} \times 6 + \dfrac{2}{1,000} \times 14 + \dfrac{3}{1,000} \times 24}{30} = \dfrac{3.533}{1,000} \text{ rad.}$$

$$\phi_E = \cfrac{\dfrac{1}{1,000} \times 24 + \dfrac{2}{1,000} \times 16 + \dfrac{3}{1,000} \times 6}{30} = \dfrac{2.467}{1,000} \text{ rad.}$$

$$\phi_A + \phi_B = \dfrac{6.000}{1,000} \text{ (Check)}$$

$$\text{Slope at } F = \dfrac{3.533}{1,000} - \dfrac{3}{1,000} = \dfrac{0.533}{1,000}$$

$$\delta_B = \dfrac{3.533}{1,000} \times 6 = \dfrac{21.20}{1,000} \text{ ft}$$

$$\delta_F = \dfrac{3.533}{1,000} \times 11 - \dfrac{3}{1,000} \times 5 = \dfrac{23.86}{1,000} \text{ ft}$$

$$\delta_C = \dfrac{3.533}{1,000} \times 16 - \dfrac{3}{1,000} \times 10 = \dfrac{26.53}{1,000} \text{ ft}$$

$$\delta_D = \dfrac{3.533}{1,000} \times 24 - \dfrac{3}{1,000} \times 18 - \dfrac{2}{1,000} \times 8 = \dfrac{14.80}{1,000} \text{ ft}$$

$$\Delta L = \dfrac{1}{2} \left(\dfrac{3}{1,000} \times \dfrac{21.20}{1,000} + \dfrac{2}{1,000} \times \dfrac{26.53}{1,000} + \dfrac{1}{1,000} \times \dfrac{14.80}{1,000} \right) = \dfrac{65.7}{1,000,000} \text{ ft}$$

Figure 6-3.   Displacements Due to Small Angles, Closed Traverse

in Figure 6-2, there are no requirements of geometry corresponding to those for closed circuit. The slope of any segment is equal to the sum of the angles from point A to that segment. The expressions for displacements in Figure 6-2 follow from the definition of a small angle.

If $AB'C'D'E$ in Figure 6-1 is considered a new shape of $ABCDE$, then, with point A assumed fixed in position, point E of the circuit $AB'C'D'E$ will lie to the left of the original point E. However, since all displacements δ are small compared to the length L, the change in length AE will be extremely small and may be considered a secondary movement due to the primary displacements δ. This horizontal movement, ΔL, can be computed in a manner similar to that used for determining vertical displacements. However, as line $ABCDE$ is displaced from its original position to its new position, the vertical distances and deflection angles are both increasing. Therefore, the horizontal movement is

$$\Delta L = \tfrac{1}{2}(\phi_B\delta_B + \phi_C\delta_C + \phi_D\delta_D)$$

Two examples of computations involving small angles are shown in Figures 6-3 and 6-4. Observe that for the closed traverse in Figure 6-3 the horizontal displacement, ΔL, of E is about $\frac{2.5}{1,000}$ of the vertical displacement at C or $\frac{2.2}{1,000,000}$ of the length AE.

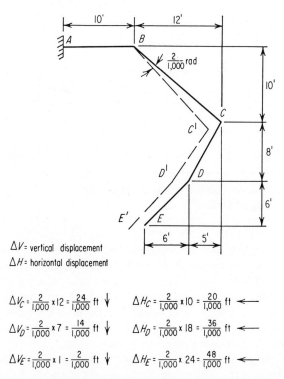

ΔV = vertical displacement
ΔH = horizontal displacement

$\Delta V_C = \frac{2}{1,000} \times 12 = \frac{24}{1,000}$ ft $\downarrow$ $\Delta H_C = \frac{2}{1,000} \times 10 = \frac{20}{1,000}$ ft $\leftarrow$

$\Delta V_D = \frac{2}{1,000} \times 7 = \frac{14}{1,000}$ ft $\downarrow$ $\Delta H_D = \frac{2}{1,000} \times 18 = \frac{36}{1,000}$ ft $\leftarrow$

$\Delta V_E = \frac{2}{1,000} \times 1 = \frac{2}{1,000}$ ft $\downarrow$ $\Delta H_E = \frac{2}{1,000} \times 24 = \frac{48}{1,000}$ ft $\leftarrow$

Figure 6-4.   Displacements Due to Small Angles, Open Traverse

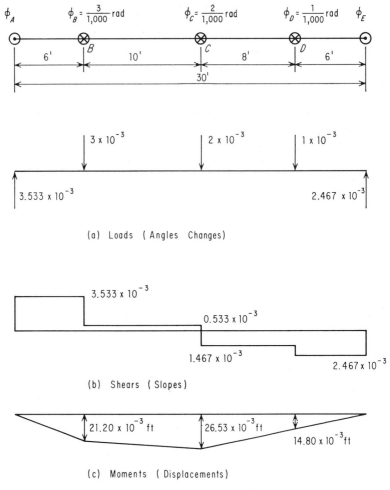

(a) Loads (Angles Changes)

(b) Shears (Slopes)

(c) Moments (Displacements)

Figure 6-5. Slopes and Displacements by Analogy

6.2 Relationships between Computations of Geometry and Computations of Statics

An examination of the expressions in Figure 6-1 and the computations in Figure 6-3 reveals that they are similar to those used for the determination of reactions, shears, and moments in a simply supported beam subjected to a series of concentrated loads. This is a result of similarity of the requirements of geometry and the requirements of statical equilibrium. The requirement of geometry is that *for any closed traverse the angles and displacements must balance*. The requirement of statical equilibrium is that *for any structure or part thereof the forces and moments must balance*.

A problem in geometry involving small angle changes can be solved as a problem in statics if the angle changes are treated as forces. The reactions and

134

shears resulting from the application of these "forces" are the actual slopes, and the moments are the actual displacements. This analogy between slopes and shears, and between displacements and moments enables us to solve problems of geometry involving small angles by performing familiar computations of statics.

The geometrical problem solved in Figure 6-3 is reexamined in Figure 6-5 by treating the angle changes as forces acting along their axes of rotation—that is, as loads normal to the page, as shown in the upper sketch in (a). For convenience, this sketch has been rotated 90 degrees in the lower sketch in (a). The reactions (end shears) resulting from the applied "loads" are equal to the end slopes, ϕ_A and ϕ_E, of Figure 6-3. The shears in Figure 6-5(b) are equal to the slopes of the segments in Figure 6-3. Finally, the moments in Figure 6-5(c) are equal to the displacements, δ, in Figure 6-3. To determine ΔL, the angle changes are applied as forces *normal to the paper* and at the displaced positions of B, C, and D.

It is emphasized that all computations made by treating angle changes as forces are identical to those made from a strict consideration of geometry only. It is also emphasized that angle changes are treated as forces *along* their axis of rotation.

If in the problem of Figure 6-4 the angle change at B is treated as a force, a displacement is equal to the moment of this force about the axis of displacement. For example, the vertical displacement of D, ΔV_D, is equal to the product of the force and its distance to a vertical axis through D. The horizontal displacement of D, ΔH_D, is equal to the product of the force and its distance to a horizontal axis through D. If additional angle changes had been imposed, all such angles would be treated as forces, and all such forces between A and the point under consideration would be included in taking moments about an axis through the point.

Addition examples of the computation of rotation sand displacements due to small angle changes are shown in Figures 6-6 and 6-7 for a three-hinged frame. Angle changes are treated as loads acting normal to the paper. Increase of interior angles is considered positive, and decrease is considered negative. In Figure 6-6 the reactions at the hinges (normal to the plane of the structure) due to a concentrated angle load of -0.003 rad at point D are computed. These reactions are equal to the hinge rotations. Displacements are then computed as moments due to the angle loading.

In Figure 6-7 a relative horizontal displacement of 0.20 ft between A and B of the framework of Figure 6-6 is introduced. The sign convention is the same as that used in Figure 6-6. The rotation of hinge C can be computed as the force necessary to produce a moment of 0.20 about axis AB. Resulting rotations at A and B are then computed as reactions due to a force at C equal to the rotation of $+0.005$ rad at C. The sum of the rotations at A, B, and C must equal zero.

The vertical and horizontal components of displacement of C in Figure 6-7 are computed as moments about the vertical and horizontal lines of displacement, considering angle changes as forces. As in any computations involving statical equilibrium, these moments may be computed using the forces acting on *either* side of C. Of course the answers are identical, as shown. Observe that the displacement (analogous moment) of 0.20 enters the equation of moments when working with the right-hand portion of the structure.

In Figure 6-7 the entire 0.2-ft displacement has been considered to take place at B. If one half the movement occurs at A, the hinge rotations are the same. However, the displacement of point C would be changed. Taking moments at C due to ϕ_A,

$$\Delta H_C = 0.100 - 0.0015(40) = 0.04\,\text{ft}$$

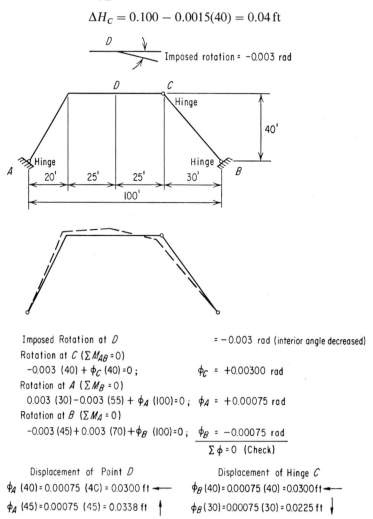

Imposed Rotation at D $= -0.003$ rad (interior angle decreased)
Rotation at C ($\Sigma M_{AB} = 0$)
   $-0.003\,(40) + \phi_C\,(40) = 0$; $\phi_C = +0.00300$ rad
Rotation at A ($\Sigma M_B = 0$)
   $0.003\,(30) - 0.003\,(55) + \phi_A\,(100) = 0$; $\phi_A = +0.00075$ rad
Rotation at B ($\Sigma M_A = 0$)
   $-0.003\,(45) + 0.003\,(70) + \phi_B\,(100) = 0$; $\phi_B = -0.00075$ rad
                                                   $\Sigma\phi = 0$ (Check)

Displacement of Point D   Displacement of Hinge C
$\phi_A\,(40) = 0.00075\,(40) = 0.0300$ ft ←—— $\phi_B\,(40) = 0.00075\,(40) = 0.0300$ ft ←——
$\phi_A\,(45) = 0.00075\,(45) = 0.0338$ ft ↑ $\phi_B\,(30) = 0.00075\,(30) = 0.0225$ ft ↓

Figure 6-6.   Frame Displacement Due to a Small Imposed Rotation

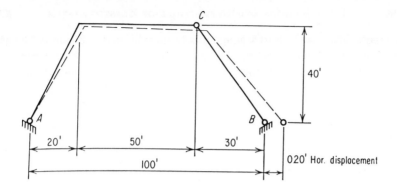

$$\phi_C = \frac{0.2}{40} = +0.005 \text{ rad}$$

$$\phi_A = \frac{0.005 \times 30}{100} = -0.0015 \text{ rad}$$

$$\phi_B = \frac{0.005 \times 70}{100} = -0.0035 \text{ rad}$$
$$\text{Total} = 0 \quad \text{(Check)}$$

$\Delta V_C = 0.0015 \times 70 = 0.105\,\text{ft} \downarrow \quad \Delta V_C = 0.0035 \times 30 = 0.105\,\text{ft} \downarrow$

$\Delta H_C = 0.0015 \times 40 = 0.060\,\text{ft} \rightarrow \quad \Delta H_C = 0.20 - 0.0035 \times 40 = 0.06\,\text{ft} \rightarrow$

Figure 6-7.   Frame Displacements Due to a Small Imposed Displacement

or, working with ϕ_B,

$$\Delta H_C = 0.0035(40) - 0.100 = 0.04 \text{ ft}$$

If a vertical displacement of 0.20 ft is imposed at B and no horizontal displacement is imposed, there is no "moment" about axis AB, and therefore zero rotation at hinge C. The structure rotates only about hinge A to take its new position. This rotation at A can be computed as the force necessary to produce a moment of 0.20 about a vertical axis through B. That is,

$$\phi_A = \frac{0.20}{100} = 0.002 \text{ rad}$$

6.3   Beam Deflections: Angle Changes and Moment Areas

The treatment in Sections 6.1 and 6.2 of systems subjected to small angle changes was limited to cases involving a finite number of angle changes. Structures are generally subjected to an infinite number of angle changes resulting from bending due to load or other causes. In order to determine rotations and displacements in such structures, it is necessary to derive expressions for angle change in a differential length, ds.

137

Figure 6-8 shows a short segment of a beam subjected to bending. The usual assumption that plane sections before bending remain plane after bending is made—that is, shear distortions are neglected. The broken lines AB show the

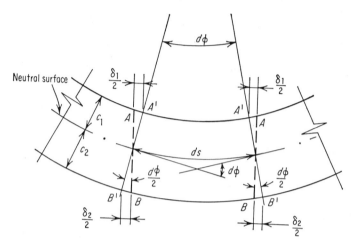

Figure 6-8.   Geometry of a Bent Beam Segment

position on the originally straight beam of two right sections a very short distance, ds, apart. These sections take positions $A'B'$ after bending. Since the angle $d\phi$ is small,

$$d\phi = \frac{\delta_1}{c_1} = \frac{\delta_2}{c_2}$$

The strains in the extreme fibers are

$$\varepsilon_1 = \frac{\delta_1}{ds}; \qquad \varepsilon_2 = \frac{\delta_2}{ds}$$

Therefore,

$$d\phi = \frac{\varepsilon_1}{c_1} ds = \frac{\varepsilon_2}{c_2} ds$$

and, in general,

$$d\phi = \frac{\varepsilon}{c} ds \qquad (6.1)$$

This is an equation of geometry, depending only on the assumption of planarity of strains.

If, in addition, the usual assumption that stress is proportional to strain is made, then

$$d\phi = \frac{\sigma\, ds}{Ec} \qquad (6.2)$$

where σ is the stress at the extreme fiber and E is the proportionality constant. Since σ can be taken as equal to Mc/I,

$$d\phi = \frac{M\,ds}{EI} \tag{6.3}$$

in which M represents the bending moment and I represents the moment of inertia of the cross-sectional area.

Equation (6.1) is a fundamental expression depending only on the assumption of plane sections remaining plane after bending. It is purely an equation of geometry. Equations (6.2) and (6.3) follow from Equation (6.1) if the material behaves in accordance with Hooke's Law. These equations relate geometry, $d\phi$, to statics, M or σ, through the defined properties, EI. Knowing any two of these quantities, the third can be computed. If stress is not proportional to strain, angle changes can still be calculated if the relationship is known between the actual moment and angle change at each section along the structure. In other words, a quantity corresponding to EI of the elastic case must be known.

Figure 6-9 shows a simply supported beam of constant EI loaded with a concentrated load P. Since the angle change at any section is equal to M/EI,

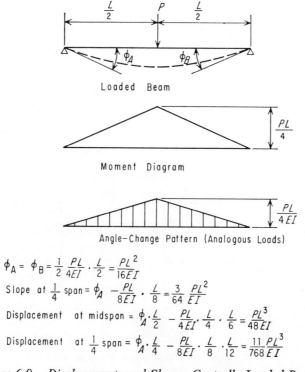

$$\phi_A = \phi_B = \frac{1}{2}\frac{PL}{4EI}\cdot\frac{L}{2} = \frac{PL^2}{16EI}$$

$$\text{Slope at }\tfrac{1}{4}\text{ span} = \phi_A - \frac{PL}{8EI}\cdot\frac{L}{8} = \frac{3}{64}\frac{PL^2}{EI}$$

$$\text{Displacement at midspan} = \phi_A\cdot\frac{L}{2} - \frac{PL}{4EI}\cdot\frac{L}{4}\cdot\frac{L}{6} = \frac{PL^3}{48EI}$$

$$\text{Displacement at }\tfrac{1}{4}\text{ span} = \phi_A\cdot\frac{L}{4} - \frac{PL}{8EI}\cdot\frac{L}{8}\cdot\frac{L}{12} = \frac{11}{768}\frac{PL^3}{EI}$$

Figure 6-9. Displacements and Slopes, Centrally Loaded Beam

the pattern of angle changes is represented by an M/EI diagram. For a member with constant EI over its entire length, the M/EI diagram has the same shape as the M diagram. The analogous load is equal to M/EI per unit length, and the total load (angle change) between two sections is equal to the area of the M/EI diagram between these sections. The end slopes, ϕ_A and ϕ_B, are found as the end shears or reactions due to a total load equal to the area under the M/EI diagram. The slope at the quarter-point is found as the shear at that section, which is the difference between the reaction at A and the angle-change load between A and the quarter-point. The deflection at a section is equal to the moment at the section due to all angle loads acting on one side of the section. If numerical results are required, all units must be consistent. For example, if E and I are expressed in pounds per square inch and (inches)^4, respectively, then P must be given in pounds and L in inches.

The angle-change loading patterns commonly encountered in slope and deflection computations in beams and frames consist in whole or in part of triangles, rectangles, trapezoids, or parabolas. To facilitate the computations, expressions for areas and centroids for such figures are given in Figure 6-10. Of course the triangle and trapezoid shown can each be replaced by two triangles.

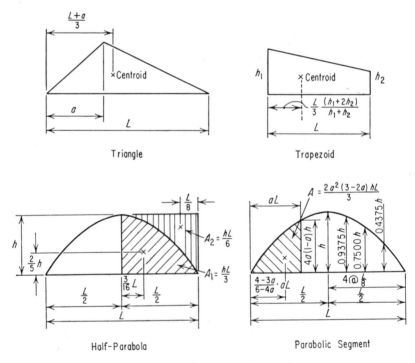

Figure 6-10.   Geometric Properties

The beam of Figure 6-11 illustrates the procedure of dividing the angle-change pattern into figures of known properties and working with resultant loads applied at the centroids. Since EI is constant throughout the length of the beam, the analogous loading, M/EI, is of the same shape as the moment

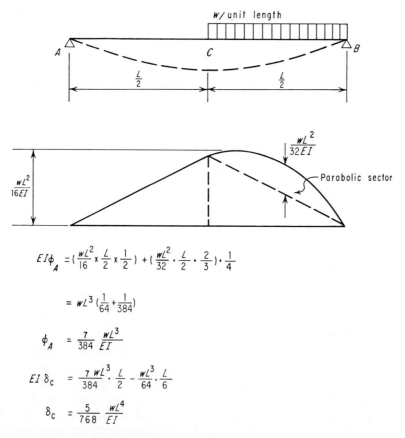

$$EI\phi_A = (\frac{wL^2}{16} \times \frac{L}{2} \times \frac{1}{2}) + (\frac{wL^2}{32} \cdot \frac{L}{2} \cdot \frac{2}{3}) \cdot \frac{1}{4}$$

$$= wL^3 (\frac{1}{64} + \frac{1}{384})$$

$$\phi_A = \frac{7}{384} \frac{wL^3}{EI}$$

$$EI\delta_c = \frac{7}{384} \frac{wL^3}{.} \cdot \frac{L}{2} - \frac{wL^3}{64} \cdot \frac{L}{6}$$

$$\delta_c = \frac{5}{768} \frac{wL^4}{EI}$$

Figure 6-11. Slope and Deflection, Unsymmetrically Loaded Beam

diagram. The M/EI diagram is divided into two equal triangles and a parabolic sector, and angle changes concentrated at their centroids in the calculations. Again, end slopes and deflection are computed as the reactions and moment, respectively, in a beam loaded with the angle changes.

In Figure 6-12 the end deflection of a cantilever beam is computed. As in Figures 6-2 and 6-4 for an open traverse, the deflection is determined as the moment of all the angle changes between A and B about B. As there is no rotation at A, this is the same as taking moments of the M/EI diagram about B. With the loads in kip units and the length in feet, it is necessary to introduce

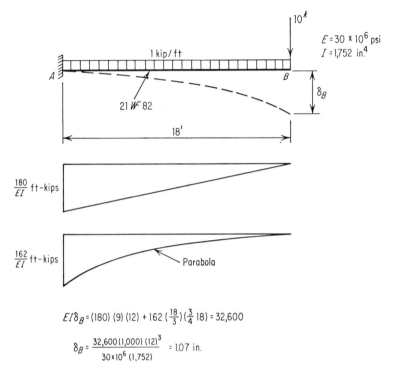

$$EI\delta_B = (180)\,(9)\,(12) + 162\left(\frac{18}{3}\right)\left(\frac{3}{4}\,18\right) = 32{,}600$$

$$\delta_B = \frac{32{,}600\,(1{,}000)\,(12)^3}{30\times10^6\,(1{,}752)} = 1.07 \text{ in.}$$

Figure 6-12.   Deflection of a Cantilever Beam

a constant of $1000(12)^3$ to obtain δ_B in inches since E and I are in lb/in.^{2} and in.^{4}, respectively.

Deflections of a beam with an overhang are computed in Figure 6-13. Between the supports A and B the deflection curve forms a closed circuit with the undisplaced position AB. Therefore this section of beam is treated exactly as in Figures 6-9 and 6-11. For clarity, the moment curve has been drawn in two parts: positive due to the uniform load, and negative due to the 5-kip concentrated load. The slopes at A and B are found as the end reactions of a beam AB subjected to the angle loading marked ① and ②. The deflection at C was found as the moment about C of all angle forces between B and C. The displacement at the 5-kip load is equal to the moment about D of the concentrated angle, ϕ_A, and of the triangular load ③ between A and D.

A beam with variable section is considered in Figure 6-14. In this instance the angle-change diagram is not the same shape as the moment diagram. The bending moments in CB have been divided by 3 in order to obtain angle changes in terms of EI.

It should be clear that since we deal with areas and moments of an M/EI diagram, slopes and deflections can be found by use of the integral calculus. In cases where the moment of inertia varies along the beam continuously in a known manner which can be easily expressed mathematically, it may be

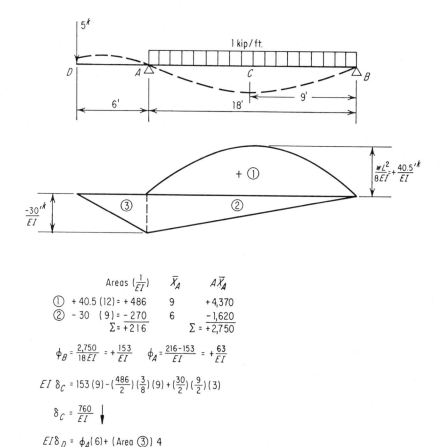

$$\phi_B = \frac{2{,}750}{18EI} = +\frac{153}{EI} \qquad \phi_A = \frac{216-153}{EI} = +\frac{63}{EI}$$

$$EI\,\delta_C = 153\,(9) - \left(\frac{486}{2}\right)\left(\frac{3}{8}\right)(9) + \left(\frac{30}{2}\right)\left(\frac{9}{2}\right)(3)$$

$$\delta_C = \frac{760}{EI}\;\downarrow$$

$$EI\delta_D = \phi_A(6) + (\text{Area } ③)\,4$$

$$= 63\,(6) - 90\,(4)$$

$$\delta_D = \frac{-18}{EI}\;\uparrow$$

Figure 6-13.   Deflections of a Beam with Overhang

expedient to determine slopes and deflections by writing algebraic expressions and then integrating. In many cases, however, the variation in section is such that use of calculus is not feasible. The beam can be divided into segments of finite length, and resultant angle changes used. For most practical purposes, acceptable answers can be obtained by dividing the beam into relatively few segments.

The continuous beam in Figure 6-15 has a moment of inertia in the center span which is 50 per cent greater than that in the side spans. The distribution of moments is given, having been found by methods to be discussed in Chapter 7. Angle changes for the central and side spans are computed by dividing moments by 1.5EI and EI, respectively. The displacement curve in

143

each span is a closed traverse. Therefore, any span can be isolated, and slopes and deflections for that span computed as if the remaining two spans did not exist. For example, the slopes at A and B are the reactions at A and B for span AB considered simply supported and loaded with a triangular pattern of angle changes. The slope at B can also be found as the reaction at B due to the angle loads (positive and negative) on simple span BC. With the slope at B known, the deflection at F can be computed as the moment at F due to the angle reaction at B and the angle loads between B and F. Deflections in span AB can be computed using ϕ_A (or ϕ_B) and the angle changes between A and B.

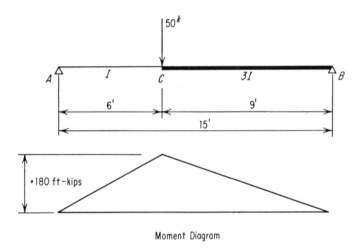

Moment Diagram

Angle Change Pattern

$$15\,\phi_A = \frac{180}{EI}\left(\frac{6}{2}\right)(11) + \frac{60}{EI}\left(\frac{9}{2}\right)(6)$$

$$\phi_A = \frac{504}{EI}$$

$$EI\,\delta_C = 504.6 - 180\left(\frac{6}{2}\right)(2) = 1,944$$

$$\delta_C = \frac{1944}{EI}$$

Figure 6-14. Deflections, Variable Section Beam

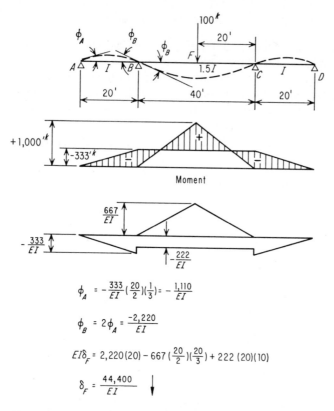

$$\phi_A = -\frac{333}{EI}(\frac{20}{2})(\frac{1}{3}) = -\frac{1,110}{EI}$$

$$\phi_B = 2\phi_A = \frac{-2,220}{EI}$$

$$EI\delta_F = 2,220(20) - 667(\frac{20}{2})(\frac{20}{3}) + 222(20)(10)$$

$$\delta_F = \frac{44,400}{EI} \quad \downarrow$$

Figure 6-15. Slopes and Deflections, Continuous Beam

5.4 Beam Deflections: Stress Areas

The beam deflection computations of the preceding article made use of the relationship between angle change and moment. It is sometimes convenient to compute deflections by making use of the relationship between angle change and stress in Equation (6.2).

In Figure 6-16 a uniformly loaded beam of constant cross section, 20 ft in length, has a maximum flexural stress level, σ, of 20,000 psi. The end slope is computed as the end reaction due to the angle-change loading, and the displacement as moment, exactly as in Section 6.3.

In general, we can write

$$\text{Slope} = \frac{K_1 \sigma L}{Ed} \tag{6.4}$$

$$\text{Deflection} = \frac{K_2 \sigma L^2}{Ed} \tag{6.5}$$

in which d is the beam depth. For any type of load, the constants K_1 and K_2

145

can be easily determined. Tables of deflections can then be prepared for given spans, depths, and working stresses.

The concept of stress areas provides a tool for making quick estimates of comparative slopes and deflections in beams of different materials since for a given span only σ, E, and possibly d of Equations (6.4) and (6.5) will change

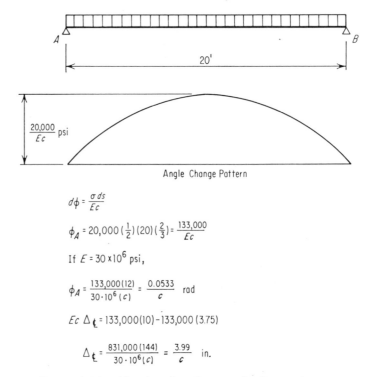

$$d\phi = \frac{\sigma \, ds}{Ec}$$

$$\phi_A = 20{,}000 \left(\tfrac{1}{2}\right)(20)\left(\tfrac{2}{3}\right) = \frac{133{,}000}{Ec}$$

If $E = 30 \times 10^6$ psi,

$$\phi_A = \frac{133{,}000(12)}{30 \cdot 10^6 (c)} = \frac{0.0533}{c} \quad \text{rad}$$

$$Ec \, \Delta_t = 133{,}000(10) - 133{,}000 \, (3.75)$$

$$\Delta_t = \frac{831{,}000 \, (144)}{30 \cdot 10^6 (c)} = \frac{3.99}{c} \quad \text{in.}$$

Figure 6-16.   Slopes and Deflections by Stress Areas

The ratio of working stress to modulus of elasticity and the ratio of length to depth determine relative slopes and deflections. A study of these ratios for different materials reveals that beams of such widely different materials as wood and steel have approximately the same deflections when working at their respective design stresses.

6.5   Deflections of Frames

Displacements of symmetrical frames subjected to a symmetrical loading pattern are computed exactly as for continuous beams (see Figure 6-15). If either the frame or loading is unsymmetrical, as in Figure 6-17 (unequal moments of inertia for the columns), the joints B and C will move laterally unless prevented by some external restraint. Because of this translation, the rotations at A and D cannot be determined as simple-beam reactions due to the angle loads on AB and CD, respectively. Rotations at hinges A and D must be computed as reactions normal to the plane of the frame due to *all* the angle loads applied normal to the frame. These calculations are made exactly as for the frame in Figures 6-6 and 6-7, except that the angle-change

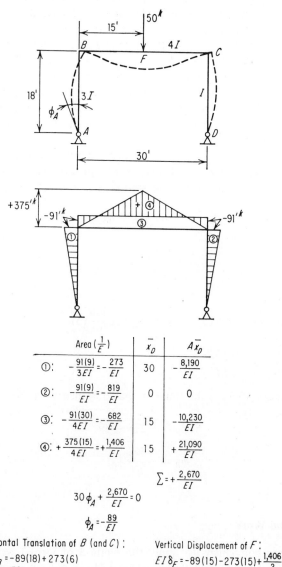

	Area $\left(\frac{1}{E}\right)$	$\overline{x}_D$	$A\overline{x}_D$
①:	$-\dfrac{91(9)}{3EI} = -\dfrac{273}{EI}$	30	$-\dfrac{8,190}{EI}$
②:	$-\dfrac{91(9)}{EI} = -\dfrac{819}{EI}$	0	0
③:	$-\dfrac{91(30)}{4EI} = -\dfrac{682}{EI}$	15	$-\dfrac{10,230}{EI}$
④:	$+\dfrac{375(15)}{4EI} = +\dfrac{1,406}{EI}$	15	$+\dfrac{21,090}{EI}$

$$\Sigma = +\frac{2,670}{EI}$$

$$30\,\phi_A + \frac{2,670}{EI} = 0$$

$$\phi_A = -\frac{89}{EI}$$

Horizontal Translation of B (and C):

$$EI\,\delta_B = -89(18) + 273(6)$$

$$\delta_B = \frac{36}{EI} \longrightarrow$$

Vertical Displacement of F:

$$EI\,\delta_F = -89(15) - 273(15) + \frac{1,406}{2}(5) - \frac{682}{2}(7.5)$$

$$\delta_F = -\frac{4,472}{EI} \downarrow$$

Figure 6-17.　Displacements of an Unsymmetrical Frame

loading is now a distributed one due to the M/EI pattern instead of a concentrated angle load.

In Figure 6-17 the moment diagram is given. The moments of inertia of CD, AB, and BC are in the ratio of 1, 3, 4. Moments are termed positive when the outer fibers of a member are in compression and negative when they are in tension. Signs of angle changes correspond to those of the moments producing them. Positive angle changes produce rotations and displacements opposite to those produced by negative angle changes.

In the calculation of ϕ_A, area ③ is the rectangle on BC and ④ is the entire positive triangle. The translation of BC is found as the moment about line BC of all angle "forces" between A and B—that is, ϕ_A times 18 ft minus the area ① times its moment arm of 6 ft. The movement of BC is small, but the rotation at A is quite different than it would have been if no translation occurred. The deflection of point F is computed as the moment about a vertical axis through F of all forces to the left of F.

The vertical deflection of point F can also be found by isolating BC and treating it as an independent closed traverse. Because of symmetry of angle changes along BC, ϕ_B is one of half the sum area ③ and area ④, or

$$EI\phi_B = -\frac{1}{2}(1{,}406 - 682)$$

$$\phi_B = -\frac{362}{EI}$$

and

$$EI\delta_F = -362(15) - \frac{682}{2}(7.5) + \frac{1{,}406}{2}(5) = -4{,}472$$

$$\delta_F = -\frac{4{,}472}{EI}$$

Of course the value of ϕ_B is the same as that obtained by adding the angle changes ① to ϕ_A,

$$EI\phi_B = -273 - 89$$

$$\phi_B = -\frac{362}{EI}$$

6.6 Method of Virtual Work

It is sometimes convenient to apply the method of virtual work to the calculation of beam and truss deflections. The following development is for a general rigid body but the resulting expressions may be interpreted as applying to beams, shafts, or truss members. The body in Figure 6-18 is subjected to an imaginary force F that is not a part of a real loading system. This is termed a virtual force. Now if the body undergoes a small change in shape due to some real cause such as real loads or temperature change, the virtual force F will move through a distance Δ in the direction of F. Consistent with the change in shape, internal distortions will be introduced. These may be bending, twisting, or shearing distortions, or change in axial length, depending on the nature of the system. Let δ be the real distortion of a differential element, and let u be the moment, torque, shear stress, or axial stress acting on the element when virtual force F is considered applied.

Since the virtual force F and the u stresses are assumed acting before the body changes shape, the external virtual work is $F\Delta$ and the internal virtual work is $u\delta$ for each differential element, with $\sum u\delta$ representing the total internal virtual work. Therefore,

$$F\Delta = \sum u\delta \qquad (6.6)$$

and if F is equal to unity,

$$\Delta = \sum u\delta \qquad (6.7)$$

To determine a displacement at any point, a unit load is applied at the point in the direction of the desired movement and Equation (6.7) solved for the

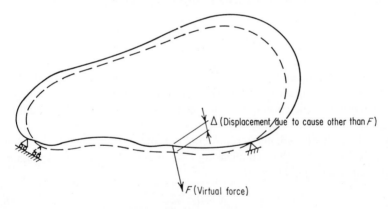

Δ (Displacement due to cause other than F)

F (Virtual force)

Figure 6-18. Virtual Force and Real Displacement

particular loading and structure involved. The movement of any point will be completely defined if displacements are calculated in two orthogonal directions.

The rotation of a point may be obtained by applying a virtual unit moment at the point. The external virtual work is $(1)(\theta)$ and the internal virtual work is $\sum u\delta$, where u is the axial stress, moment, torque, or shear stress due to the virtual unit moment. So,

$$\theta = \sum u\delta \qquad (6.8)$$

It is important to note that neither Equation (6.7) nor Equation (6.8) is dependent on the cause or type of distortions δ. The material may be elastic or plastic. If the distortions are known, displacements can be computed.

Equation (6.7) may be written in several forms, depending on the nature of the load and the structure. For axially loaded members, such as bars in a truss, u represents the virtual force in a bar, and δ represents the real change in length. Therefore, in the elastic range,

$$\Delta = \sum u \frac{FL}{AE} \tag{6.9}$$

where F now represents actual bar force, A represents bar cross-sectional area, and E is the modulus of elasticity.

In the case of flexural members, u is interpreted as the bending moment, m, at a section due to the unit virtual force, and δ represents the real angle change, $M \, ds/EI$, per differential length at the same section. Therefore,

$$\Delta = \int m \frac{M \, ds}{EI} \tag{6.10}$$

For a member subjected to torsion, u, represents the virtual twisting moment, t, and δ the real twist, $T \, ds/GJ$, in a differential length ds at the section. So,

$$\Delta = \int t \frac{T \, ds}{GJ} \tag{6.11}$$

where G is the shear modulus of elasticity and J is a factor such that GJ represents the moment necessary to twist a member through a unit angle per unit length. For the special case of a circular cross section, J is equal to the polar moment of inertia.

For shear displacements, u represents the total virtual shear, v, at a section and δ is $CV \, ds/AG$, the real shearing deformation in differential distance ds at the same section. Therefore

$$\Delta = \int v \frac{CV \, ds}{AG} \tag{6.12}$$

where A is the cross-sectional area and C a factor that accounts for the effects of a nonuniform distribution of shear across the section. C is approximately 1.2 for rectangular sections and 1.1. for circular sections. For wide-flange sections and plate girders, it is approximately equal to the ratio of the total area to the web area. Thus C can be taken as unity in Equation (6.12) if A is taken as the web area.

In a similar manner, from Equation (6.8), we can write equations for θ corresponding to Equations (6.9), (6.10), (6.11), and (6.12). They would differ only in that Δ is replaced by θ, and that values of u, m, t, and v are those due to a virtual unit moment.

6.7 Deflections of Beams and Frames by Method of Virtual Work

The deflection at the centerline of a beam carrying a load increasing uniformly to the center is determined in Figure 6-19. Because of symmetry, the virtual work integral is evaluated over one half the length and the result

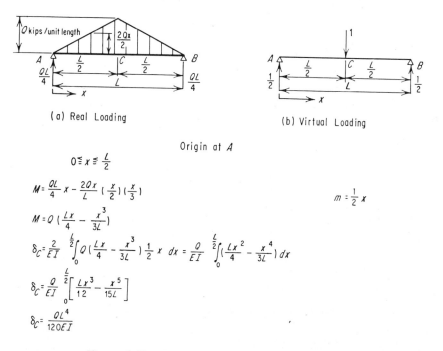

(a) Real Loading   (b) Virtual Loading

Origin at A

$$0 \leq x \leq \frac{L}{2}$$

$$M = \frac{QL}{4} x - \frac{2Qx}{L} \left(\frac{x}{2}\right)\left(\frac{x}{3}\right)$$

$$M = Q\left(\frac{Lx}{4} - \frac{x^3}{3L}\right)$$

$$m = \frac{1}{2} x$$

$$\delta_C = \frac{2}{EI} \int_0^{\frac{L}{2}} Q\left(\frac{Lx}{4} - \frac{x^3}{3L}\right)\frac{1}{2} x \, dx = \frac{Q}{EI} \int_0^{\frac{L}{2}} \left(\frac{Lx^2}{4} - \frac{x^4}{3L}\right) dx$$

$$\delta_C = \frac{Q}{EI} \left[\frac{Lx^3}{12} - \frac{x^5}{15L}\right]_0^{\frac{L}{2}}$$

$$\delta_C = \frac{QL^4}{120EI}$$

Figure 6-19. Beam Deflection by Virtual Work

doubled. In general there are alternate ways of setting up the integrals. Particular choices of origins for the x measurements may result in a saving of time for certain problems.

In Figure 6-20 a deflection calculation is made for a beam with an overhang. This is the same deflection, at D, found in Figure 6-13 by the angle-change procedure. The integral is evaluated between D and A, using D as the origin, and between B and A, using B as the origin. Any origin can be used to measure x in a given section but the same origin must be used in expressions for both the real moment and the virtual moment. Of course the virtual work must always be evaluated for the entire structure. The negative sign for δ_D indicates that the deflection is opposite in direction (upward) to the virtual load at D.

The end rotation, ϕ_B, of a uniformly loaded beam is computed in Figure 6-21. The procedure is the same as in the previous problems except that the

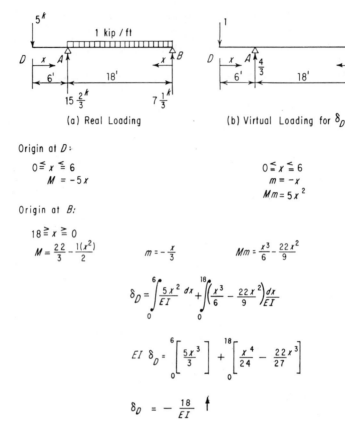

(a) Real Loading   (b) Virtual Loading for δ_D

Origin at D :

$0 \leq x \leq 6$
$M = -5x$

$0 \leq x \leq 6$
$m = -x$
$Mm = 5x^2$

Origin at B :

$18 \geq x \geq 0$
$M = \frac{22}{3} - \frac{1(x^2)}{2}$

$m = -\frac{x}{3}$

$Mm = \frac{x^3}{6} - \frac{22x^2}{9}$

$$\delta_D = \int_0^6 \frac{5x^2}{EI} \, dx + \int_0^{18} \left(\frac{x^3}{6} - \frac{22x^2}{9} \right) \frac{dx}{EI}$$

$$EI\,\delta_D = \left[\frac{5x^3}{3} \right]_0^6 + \left[\frac{x^4}{24} - \frac{22x^3}{27} \right]_0^{18}$$

$$\delta_D = -\frac{18}{EI} \uparrow$$

Figure 6-20 Beam Deflections by Virtual Work

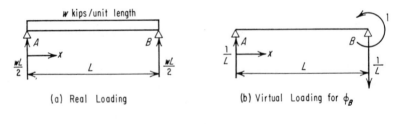

(a) Real Loading   (b) Virtual Loading for ϕ_B

Origin at A :

$M = \frac{wL}{2} \cdot x - \frac{wx^2}{2}$

$m = \frac{x}{L}$

$Mm = \frac{wx^2}{2} - \frac{wx^3}{2L}$

$$\phi_B = \frac{w}{2EI} \int_0^L \left(x^2 - \frac{x^3}{L} \right) dx$$

$$\phi_B = \frac{w}{2EI} \left[\frac{x^3}{3} - \frac{x^4}{4L} \right]_0^L = \frac{wL^3}{24EI}$$

Figure 6-21.   Beam Rotation by Virtual Work

virtual load is a unit moment at B. This moment was arbitrarily applied counterclockwise, and it induced reactions at A and B which produce an equal clockwise couple. Since the computed value of ϕ_B is found to be positive, this means that the rotation at B has the same sense (counterclockwise) as the applied virtual moment.

In Figure 6-22 the horizontal movement of one end of a statically deter-

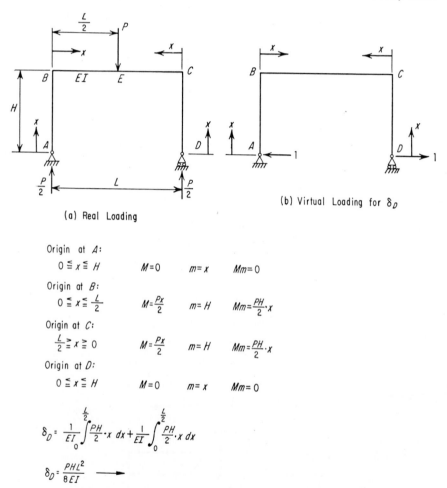

(a) Real Loading

(b) Virtual Loading for δ_D

Origin at A:

$$0 \leq x \leq H \qquad M = 0 \qquad m = x \qquad Mm = 0$$

Origin at B:

$$0 \leq x \leq \frac{L}{2} \qquad M = \frac{Px}{2} \qquad m = H \qquad Mm = \frac{PH}{2} \cdot x$$

Origin at C:

$$\frac{L}{2} \geq x \geq 0 \qquad M = \frac{Px}{2} \qquad m = H \qquad Mm = \frac{PH}{2} \cdot x$$

Origin at D:

$$0 \leq x \leq H \qquad M = 0 \qquad m = x \qquad Mm = 0$$

$$\delta_D = \frac{1}{EI} \int_0^{\frac{L}{2}} \frac{PH}{2} \cdot x \, dx + \frac{1}{EI} \int_0^{\frac{L}{2}} \frac{PH}{2} \cdot x \, dx$$

$$\delta_D = \frac{PHL^2}{8EI} \longrightarrow$$

Figure 6-22. Frame Displacement by Virtual Work

minate frame (support D on rollers) is computed. In this case only the horizontal member contributes to the displacement because M is equal to zero in each leg.

Figure 6-23(a) shows a plan view of an L-shaped structure. The load P acts downward, normal to the plane of the structure. Length CB is subjected only

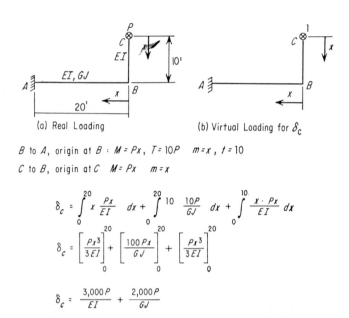

(a) Real Loading   (b) Virtual Loading for δ_c

B to A, origin at B : $M = Px$, $T = 10P$ $m = x$, $t = 10$

C to B, origin at C $M = Px$ $m = x$

$$\delta_c = \int_0^{20} x \frac{Px}{EI} \, dx + \int_0^{20} 10 \frac{10P}{GJ} \, dx + \int_0^{10} \frac{x \cdot Px}{EI} \, dx$$

$$\delta_c = \left[\frac{Px^3}{3EI} \right]_0^{20} + \left[\frac{100 Px}{GJ} \right]_0^{20} + \left[\frac{Px^3}{3EI} \right]_0^{20}$$

$$\delta_c = \frac{3,000 P}{EI} + \frac{2,000 P}{GJ}$$

Figure 6-23.   Deflection of a Cantilever Beam, Combined Flexure and Torsion

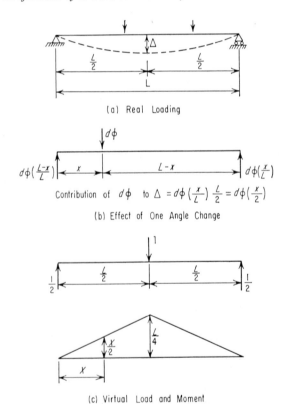

(a) Real Loading

Contribution of $d\phi$ to $\Delta = d\phi \left(\frac{x}{L} \right) \frac{L}{2} = d\phi \left(\frac{x}{2} \right)$

(b) Effect of One Angle Change

(c) Virtual Load and Moment

Figure 6-24.   Virtual Moments as a Scale for Deflections

to flexure while length BA is subjected to both torsion and flexure. This problem can also be solved readily by a direct consideration of angle changes.

The method of virtual work is in effect a procedure for prorating the contributions of individual distortions to displacement. This can be illustrated with the aid of Figure 6-24. The loading of Figure 6-24(a) results in a pattern of angle changes. In Figure 6-24(b) the angle change, $d\phi$, produced at a section a distance x from the left support is shown applied as a load. The resulting moment of $d\phi(x/2)$ at the center of the beam is the contribution of $d\phi$ to the displacement Δ. In Figure 6-24(c) this is also the value of the virtual moment at x. Therefore the diagram of virtual moments is an influence line for the deflection at the center due to angle changes.

6.8 Reciprocal Relationships

Assume that an arbitrary system of forces, F_A, is applied to a structure, and call the resulting movement of the point of application one of the forces in the direction of the force, Δ_{AA}. With the system F_A remaining on the structure, assume that a second force system, F_B, is added. Call the additional movement of the point of application of force F_A in the direction of F_A, Δ_{AB}. The subscript AB indicates that we are dealing with the displacement of the point of application of a force F_A caused by forces F_B. Let Δ_{BB} represent the movement of the point of application of one of the F_B forces in the direction of F_B, due to the same F_B system.

The external work done during the loading cycle consists of three parts: that due to the F_A system moving through the Δ_{AA} displacements, that due to the F_B system moving through the Δ_{BB} displacements, and that due to the F_A system moving through the Δ_{AB} displacements. The expressions for external work are, respectively, $\frac{1}{2}\sum F_A\Delta_{AA}$, $\frac{1}{2}\sum F_B\Delta_{BB}$, and $\sum F_A\Delta_{AB}$. Therefore, the total external work is

$$W_{A+B} = \tfrac{1}{2}\sum F_A\Delta_{AA} + \sum F_A\Delta_{AB} + \tfrac{1}{2}\sum F_B\Delta_{BB}$$

If the loading order is reversed, with the F_B system applied first, the total external work becomes

$$W_{B+A} = \tfrac{1}{2}\sum F_B\Delta_{BB} + \sum F_B\Delta_{BA} + \tfrac{1}{2}\sum F_A\Delta_{AA}$$

For small movements and elastic behavior, the order of loading does not affect the total external work. Thus

$$W_{A+B} = W_{B+A}$$

and

$$\sum F_A\Delta_{AB} = \sum F_B\Delta_{BA} \tag{6.13}$$

That is, the external work done by a system of forces F_A going through movements due to a force system F_B is equal to the external work done by the force system F_B moving through displacements due to a system of forces F_A. This general statement of reciprocal relationships is usually attributed to Betti.

Of particular interest in structural mechanics is Maxwell's theorem of reciprocal deflections. This can be obtained directly from Equation (6.13) by assuming that force system A consists of a single load F applied at point 1 in a direction ab, and by assuming that force system B consists of one force of the same magnitude F but applied at point 2 in the direction cd. If Δ_{12} is the displacement of point 1 in the direction ab due to the load F at point 2 in the direction cd, and if Δ_{21} is the displacement of point 2 in the direction cd due to the load F acting at point 1 in the direction ab,

$$F\Delta_{12} = F\Delta_{21}$$

and

$$\Delta_{12} = \Delta_{21} \tag{6.14}$$

Several reciprocal relationships can be written for beams and frames. For example, such relationships occur between rotations due to equal moments and between the displacement caused by a moment and the rotation due to a load arithmetically equal to the moment.

Equation (6.14) can be derived for a simple beam by use of virtual work. The product $\int m(M\,ds/EI)$ for Δ_{12} and Δ_{21} is identical since the product of virtual moment and real moment is the same for each and every point along the beam if the real and virtual loads are interchanged.

6.9 Castigliano's Theorem

Two theorems dealing with deflections are attributed to A. Castigliano. The first theorem will not be discussed in this book. His second theorem states that the first partial derivative of the strain energy with respect to any particular force is equal to the displacement of the point of application of that force in the direction of its line of action. It is assumed that the material is elastic and follows Hooke's law.

Castigliano's second theorem can be derived as follows. Assume that an arbitrary system of forces is to be applied gradually to a body such as shown in Figure 6-25, and let Δ_1, Δ_2, and Δ_3 represent the resulting displacements in the direction and sense of the corresponding forces. The total external work done by the forces is

$$W = \tfrac{1}{2}(F_1\Delta_1) + \tfrac{1}{2}(F_2\Delta_2) + \tfrac{1}{2}(F_3\Delta_3)$$

The displacements can be expressed as

$$\Delta_1 = F_1\delta_{11} + F_2\delta_{12} + F_3\delta_{13}$$
$$\Delta_2 = F_1\delta_{21} + F_2\delta_{22} + F_3\delta_{23}$$
$$\Delta_3 = F_1\delta_{31} + F_2\delta_{32} + F_3\delta_{33}$$

where δ_{11} = displacement of point 1 in the direction of Δ_1 due to a unit force at 1 in the direction of F_1, δ_{21} = displacement of point 2 in the direction of Δ_2 due to a unit force at point 1 in the direction of F_1, and so forth. Substituting in the equation for external work,

$$W = \tfrac{1}{2}(F_1{}^2\delta_{11} + F_2{}^2\delta_{22} + F_3{}^2\delta_{33} + F_1 F_2 \delta_{12} + F_1 F_3 \delta_{13} +$$
$$+ F_2 F_1 \delta_{21} + F_2 F_3 \delta_{23} + F_3 F_1 \delta_{31} + F_3 F_2 \delta_{32})$$

The external work W must be equal to the internal work of deformation, or strain energy, U. Taking the first partial derivative of $U(= W)$ with respect

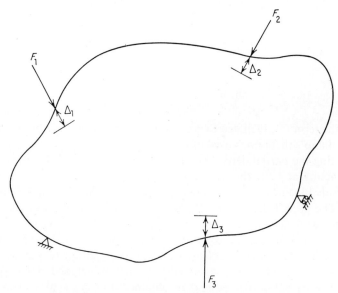

Figure 6-25.   Generalized Structure and Loading

to the successive forces, and using the reciprocal relationships $\delta_{12} = \delta_{21}$, and so forth,

$$\frac{\partial U}{\partial F_1} = F_1 \delta_{11} + F_2 \delta_{12} + F_3 \delta_{13} = \Delta_1$$

$$\frac{\partial U}{\partial F_2} = F_1 \delta_{21} + F_2 \delta_{22} + F_3 \delta_{23} = \Delta_2 \qquad\qquad \textbf{(6.15)}$$

$$\frac{\partial U}{\partial F_3} = F_1 \delta_{31} + F_2 \delta_{32} + F_3 \delta_{33} = \Delta_3$$

Similarly, the rotation of a point is

$$\theta = \frac{\partial U}{\partial M} \qquad\qquad \textbf{(6.16)}$$

where M is an external moment applied at the point under consideration.

Equations (6.15) and (6.16) are mathematical statements of Castigliano's second theorem.

The internal strain energy may result from axial loads, flexure, torsion, or shear. Since in each case the strain energy is equal to the area under the corresponding load-deformation diagram, the following expressions result:

$$\text{Axial loads}: \quad U = \frac{1}{2}\int \frac{F^2\,ds}{AE}$$

$$\text{Flexure}: \quad U = \frac{1}{2}\int \frac{M^2\,ds}{EI}$$

$$\text{Torsion}: \quad U = \frac{1}{2}\int \frac{T^2\,ds}{GJ}$$

$$\text{Shear}: \quad U = \frac{1}{2}\int \frac{CV^2\,ds}{GA}$$

Again, the term C is included to account for nonuniform distribution of shear.

Castigliano's theorem is used in Figure 6-26(a) to compute the deflection at C by taking the partial derivative of the strain energy, U, with respect to the load P acting at C. If the deflection at some other point, D, is required, a concentrated load P_D is assumed acting at D and is included in the expression for M. The partial derivative $\partial U/\partial P_D$ is evaluated and P_D set equal to zero to obtain the deflection.

In Figure 6-26(b) the end rotation θ_B in a uniformly loaded beam is determined. This is the same problem solved by the method of virtual work in Figure 6-21. A moment M_B is assumed acting and is included in the expression for M. The partial derivative is then obtained and M_B set equal to zero to obtain θ_B.

The expression for deflection at some point n of a flexural member always takes the form

$$\Delta_n = \frac{\partial U}{\partial P_n} = \int \frac{\partial M}{\partial P_n}\frac{M\,ds}{EI}$$

Comparison with Equation (6.10) shows that $\partial M/\partial P_n$ must be equal to m in the virtual work integral—that is, equal to the value of moment for $P_n = 1$. The student should check this in Figure 6-26(a) where $\partial M/\partial M = x/z$. Similarly, in Figure 6-26(b) the partial derivative of M with respect to M_B is equal to x/L, which is the moment for $M_B = 1$. Therefore, we can conclude that Castigliano's expressions for deflection and rotation are identical to those of the method of virtual work.

Deflection of a panel point in a truss can be obtained in the same manner provided the expression for strain energy resulting from axial force is used. Again, the expression becomes identical to that of the method of virtual work.

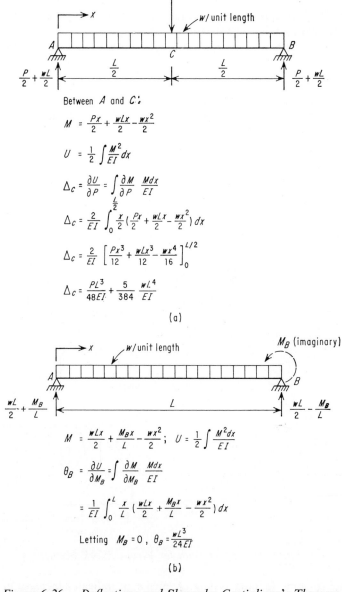

Between A and C:

$$M = \frac{Px}{2} + \frac{wLx}{2} - \frac{wx^2}{2}$$

$$U = \frac{1}{2} \int \frac{M^2}{EI} dx$$

$$\Delta_C = \frac{\partial U}{\partial P} = \int \frac{\partial M}{\partial P} \frac{Mdx}{EI}$$

$$\Delta_C = \frac{2}{EI} \int_0^{\frac{L}{2}} \frac{x}{2} \left(\frac{Px}{2} + \frac{wLx}{2} - \frac{wx^2}{2} \right) dx$$

$$\Delta_C = \frac{2}{EI} \left[\frac{Px^3}{12} + \frac{wLx^3}{12} - \frac{wx^4}{16} \right]_0^{L/2}$$

$$\Delta_C = \frac{PL^3}{48EI} + \frac{5}{384} \frac{wL^4}{EI}$$

(a)

$$M = \frac{wLx}{2} + \frac{M_B x}{L} - \frac{wx^2}{2}; \quad U = \frac{1}{2} \int \frac{M^2 dx}{EI}$$

$$\theta_B = \frac{\partial U}{\partial M_B} = \int \frac{\partial M}{\partial M_B} \frac{Mdx}{EI}$$

$$= \frac{1}{EI} \int_0^L \frac{x}{L} \left(\frac{wLx}{2} + \frac{M_B x}{L} - \frac{wx^2}{2} \right) dx$$

Letting $M_B = 0$, $\theta_B = \frac{wL^3}{24EI}$

(b)

Figure 6-26.   Deflections and Slopes by Castigliano's Theorem

6.10   Truss Deflections by Virtual Work

In this section and in Sections 6.11 and 6.12 three methods of computing truss deflections will be considered. These are: (1) virtual work; (2) angle

159

changes; (3) the displacement diagram. Each of these approaches has certain advantages for particular applications.

The general virtual work expression was shown to be Equation (6.7):

$$\Delta = \sum u\delta$$

For a truss, u represents a virtual bar force resulting from the application of an imaginary unit load at the point for which the displacement is required and in the direction of the displacement. The term δ represents the real change in length of each bar due to any cause. If this change of length is due to loading within the elastic range, $\delta = FL/AE$ and we obtain Equation (6.9):

$$\Delta = \sum u \frac{FL}{AE}$$

Figure 6-27(a) shows changes in length, $\delta = FL/AE$, of all members of a

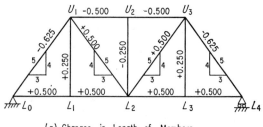

(a) Changes in Length of Members

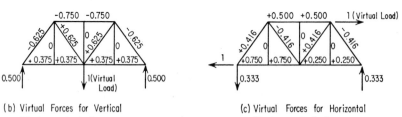

(b) Virtual Forces for Vertical Displacement of L_2

(c) Virtual Forces for Horizontal Displacement of U_3

Figure 6-27. Truss Data for Virtual Work Method

truss due to some loading system. A plus sign indicates increase in length. Figure 6-27(b) indicates the u forces required in a virtual work solution for the vertical displacement of L_2, and Figure 6-27(c) shows the u forces used in the calculation of the horizontal movement of U_3.

The vertical displacement of L_2 and the horizontal movement of U_3 of the truss in Figure 6-27 are determined in Table 6-1. The tabulated values of δ and u are taken from Figure 6-27. The virtual forces in Figure 6-27(b) are listed under the heading u_V, and those in Figure 6-27(c) are listed under the heading u_H. The vertical displacement of L_2 is determined as $\sum u_V \delta$, and the horizontal displacement of U_3 is determined as $\sum u_H \delta$. Positive answers indicate that the displacement in each case is in the direction of the virtual load.

To define completely the movement of a point, both the vertical and horizontal movement must be determined. Thus, in Figure 6-27, it would be necessary to determine, in addition to those in (b) and (c), virtual forces resulting from the application of a unit horizontal load at L_2 and a unit vertical load at U_3.

In (a) and (b) of Figure 6-27 there is symmetry of the changes in length and of the virtual forces with respect to L_2. Therefore, the vertical movement of L_2 can be obtained by doubling the result obtained by considering only one half the truss. If we were determining the vertical displacement of U_2, the virtual force in $U_2 L_2$ would not be zero, and this bar would have to be included in the summation, but only once.

TABLE 6-1 Truss (Figure 6-27) Displacement by Virtual Work

Member	$\delta (= \frac{FL}{AE})$	u_V	$u_V \delta$	u_H	$u_H \delta$
$L_0 L_1$	0.500	0.375	0.1875	0.750	0.375
$L_1 L_2$	0.500	0.375	0.1875	0.750	0.375
$L_2 L_3$	0.500	0.375	0.1875	0.250	0.125
$L_3 L_4$	0.500	0.375	0.1875	0.250	0.125
$L_0 U_1$	0.625	- 0.625	0.3906	0.416	- 0.260
$U_1 U_2$	0.500	- 0.750	0.3750	0.500	- 0.250
$U_2 U_3$	0.500	- 0.750	0.3750	0.500	- 0.250
$U_3 L_4$	0.625	- 0.625	0.3906	- 0.416	0.260
$U_1 L_2$	0.500	0.625	0.3125	- 0.416	- 0.208
$L_2 U_3$	0.500	0.625	0.3125	0.416	0.208
$U_1 L_1$	0.250	0	0	0	
$U_3 L_3$	0.250	0	0	0	
$U_2 L_2$	- 0.250	0	0	0	

$$\sum = 2.9062 \quad 0.500$$

Vertical Displacement of L_2 = 2.9062 $\downarrow$

Horizontal Displacement of U_3 = 0.500 $\longrightarrow$

Figure 6-28(a) shows a loaded truss for which it is desired to determine the vertical displacement at L_4 and the horizontal displacement at L_8. The virtual loadings are shown in (b) and (c). The displacements are obtained in Table 6-2,

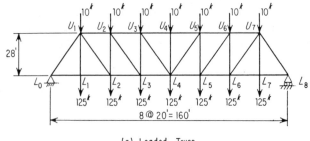

(a) Loaded Truss

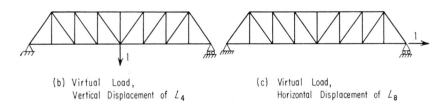

(b) Virtual Load,
Vertical Displacement of L_4

(c) Virtual Load,
Horizontal Displacement of L_8

Figure 6-28.   *Truss Data for Virtual Work Method*

using the given lengths and cross-sectional areas of the bars, as listed in columns 2 and 3 of the tabulation. As the modulus of elasticity, E, is 30×10^6 psi for all bars of the truss, for convenience it is omitted from all intermediate computations.

Displacements for statically indeterminate trusses, such as that in Figure

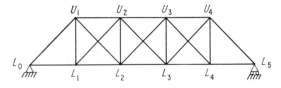

Figure 6-29.   *Statically Indeterminate Truss*

6-29, can be determined by virtual work or the methods explained in Sections 6.11 and 6.12. All calculations are based on the number of members required for static equilibrium. For example, for the truss of Figure 6-29, values $u\delta$ for members U_1L_2, L_2U_3, and L_3U_4 can be omitted from virtual work computations. Of course the changes in length of the bars included in the calculations must be those for the *actual truss with redundant members*. The determination

TABLE 6-2 Truss (Figure 6-28) Displacements by Virtual Work

Member	A (in.^{2})	L (in.)	L/A	F (kips)	FL/A	u_{L_4}	$u_{L_4} FL/A$	u_{L_8}	$u_{L_8} FL/A$
$L_0\,U_1$	50.	413.	8.26	-581.	-4,799.	-.614	2,947.	0.000	0.
$U_1\,U_2$	50.	240.	4.80	-579.	-2,779.	-.714	1,984.	0.000	0.
$U_2\,U_3$	60.	240.	4.00	-724.	-2,896.	-1.071	3,102.	0.000	0.
$U_3\,U_4$	60.	240.	4.00	-772.	-3,088.	-1.428	4,410.	0.000	0.
$U_4\,U_5$	60.	240.	4.00	-772.	-3,088.	-1.428	4,410.	0.000	0.
$U_5\,U_6$	60.	240.	4.00	-724.	-2,896.	-1.071	3,102.	0.000	0.
$U_6\,U_7$	50.	240.	4.80	-579.	-2,779.	-.714	1,984.	0.000	0.
$U_7\,L_8$	50.	413.	8.26	-581.	-4,799.	-.614	2,947.	0.000	0.
$L_0\,L_1$	30.	240.	8.00	338.	2,704.	.357	965.	1.000	2,704.
$L_1\,L_2$	30.	240.	8.00	338.	2,704.	.357	965.	1.000	2,704.
$L_2\,L_3$	50.	240.	4.80	579.	2,779.	.714	1,984.	1.000	2,779.
$L_3\,L_4$	60.	240.	4.00	724.	2,896.	1.071	3,102.	1.000	2,896.
$L_4\,L_5$	60.	240.	4.00	724.	2,896.	1.071	3,102.	1.000	2,896.
$L_5\,L_6$	50.	240.	4.80	579.	2,779.	.714	1,984.	1.000	2,779.
$L_6\,L_7$	30.	240.	8.00	338.	2,704.	.357	965.	1.000	2,704.
$L_7\,L_8$	30.	240.	8.00	338.	2,704.	.357	965.	1.000	2,704.
$U_1\,L_1$	20.	336.	16.80	125.	2,100.	0.000	0.	0.000	0.
$U_2\,L_2$	30.	336.	11.20	-212.	-2,374.	-.500	1,187.	0.000	0.
$U_3\,L_3$	20.	336.	16.80	-78.	-1,310.	-.500	655.	0.000	0.
$U_4\,L_4$	20.	336.	16.80	-10.	-168.	0.000	0.	0.000	0.
$U_5\,L_5$	20.	336.	16.80	-78.	-1,310.	-.500	655.	0.000	0.
$U_6\,L_6$	30.	336.	11.20	-212.	-2,374.	-.500	1,187.	0.000	0.
$U_7\,L_7$	20.	336.	16.80	125.	2,100.	0.000	0.	0.000	0.
$U_1\,L_2$	40.	413.	10.33	414.	4,275.	.614	2,625.	0.000	0.
$U_2\,L_3$	30.	413.	13.77	248.	3,414.	.614	2,096.	0.000	0.
$U_3\,L_4$	20.	413.	20.65	83.	1,714.	.614	1,052.	0.000	0.
$L_4\,U_5$	20.	413.	20.65	83.	1,714.	.614	1,052.	0.000	0.
$L_5\,U_6$	30.	413.	13.77	248.	3,414.	.614	2,096.	0.000	0.
$L_6\,U_7$	40.	413.	10.33	414.	4,275.	.614	2,625.	0.000	0.
TOTALS							54,149.		22,166.

Vertical Displacement of $L_4 = \dfrac{54,149\ (1,000)}{30 \times 10^6} = 1.80$ in. $\downarrow$

Horizontal Displacement of $L_8 = \dfrac{22,166\ (1,000)}{30 \times 10^6} = 0.74$ in. $\longrightarrow$

of bar forces in statically indeterminate trusses is demonstrated in Chapter 8.

It should be clear that if the displacements of several, or all, panel points of a truss are desired, the method of virtual work can entail a large number of computations. For such cases, the graphical method of Section 6.12 may be preferable. However, as will be shown in Chapter 8, the analysis of statically indeterminate trusses usually requires the calculation of displacements of only one or two points, and the virtual work method is convenient for use in such analyses.

6.11   Truss Deflections by Angle Changes

The loaded chord of a truss in its displaced position forms a closed traverse with the line representing its unloaded position. Therefore, the vertical displacements of the chord can be found as the moments in an equivalent beam loaded with the angle changes which occur at the panel points.

A triangle consisting of sides a, b, and c, and angles α, β, and γ is shown in

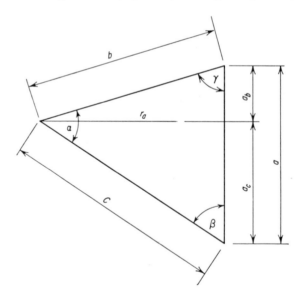

Figure 6-30.   Identification Sketch

Figure 6-30. The dashed line r_a is normal to side a, dividing it into a_b and a_c. The portion a_b is the projection of side b on side a, and a_c is the projection of side c on side a.

If the changes in length, δ, of all three sides are small compared to the original lengths, the change in angle α can be found by dividing the sum of the changes of length projected along side a by the distance r_a. The projected changes in length along a are

$$\text{for } a: \quad \delta_a$$

$$\text{for } b: \quad \delta_b\left(\frac{a_b}{b}\right)$$

$$\text{for } c: \quad \delta_c\left(\frac{a_c}{c}\right)$$

and the change in angle α is then

$$\Delta\alpha = \frac{\delta_a - \delta_b(a_b/b) - \delta_c(a_c/c)}{r_a} \qquad\qquad (6.17)$$

The signs used in Equation (6.17) result in an automatic sign convention for $\Delta\alpha$ if elongations are taken as positive and shortenings as negative. A positive value for $\Delta\alpha$ always indicates an increase in angle, and a negative value always indicates a decrease. Referring to Figure 6-30, it can be seen that if b and c remain constant, the angle α increases when side a increases in length. If a and c are kept constant, angle α decreases when side b gets longer. In a like manner, if a and b remain constant, angle α decreases if side c becomes longer. These relationships account for the signs used in Equation (6.17).

Expressions similar to Equation 6.17 can be determined for change in angle β and change in angle γ. Thus,

$$\Delta\beta = \frac{\delta_b - \delta_c(b_c/c) - \delta_a(b_a/a)}{r_b} \qquad\qquad (6.18)$$

$$\Delta\gamma = \frac{\delta_c - \delta_a(c_a/a) - \delta_b(c_b/b)}{r_c} \qquad\qquad (6.19)$$

in which r_b and r_c are normals drawn to side b and side c, respectively.

In Figure 6-31, displacements of the bottom-chord panel points are found for the truss and changes in bar lengths shown in Figure 6-27. Those changes in length are shown in parentheses along the sides of the individual triangles in Figure 6-31. As in Figure 6-27, relative dimensions of 3, 4, and 5 have been used for the sides of the triangles.

Computations are first made for the angle changes along the bottom chord of each triangle. Since the truss and changes in bar lengths are symmetrical about the centerline, angle change computations are necessary for only one half of the truss. The total angle change at each panel point is obtained by adding algebraically the angle changes in the individual triangles meeting at the point. Displacements are obtained by treating the total angle changes at each panel point as loads and computing the vertical displacements as moments at the panel points.

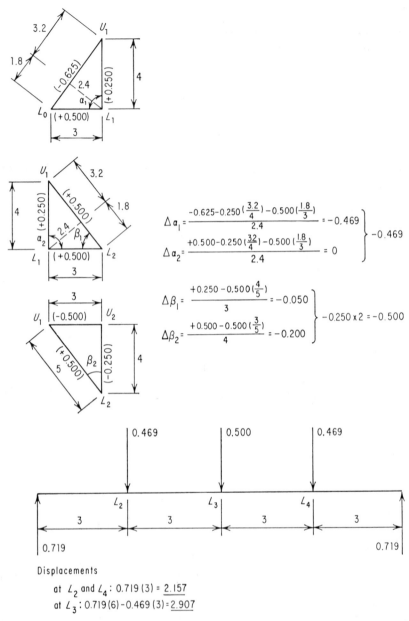

$$\Delta a_1 = \frac{-0.625 - 0.250\left(\frac{3.2}{4}\right) - 0.500\left(\frac{1.8}{3}\right)}{2.4} = -0.469$$

$$\Delta a_2 = \frac{+0.500 - 0.250\left(\frac{3.2}{4}\right) - 0.500\left(\frac{1.8}{3}\right)}{2.4} = 0$$

$$\left.\right\} -0.469$$

$$\Delta \beta_1 = \frac{+0.250 - 0.500\left(\frac{4}{5}\right)}{3} = -0.050$$

$$\Delta \beta_2 = \frac{+0.500 - 0.500\left(\frac{3}{5}\right)}{4} = -0.200$$

$$\left.\right\} -0.250 \times 2 = -0.500$$

Displacements

at L_2 and L_4: 0.719 (3) = <u>2.157</u>

at L_3: 0.719 (6) − 0.469 (3) = <u>2.907</u>

Figure 6-31. Vertical Displacements of Lower Chord of Truss in Fig. 6-27 by Angle Changes

The angle-change method for finding displacements is well suited to the case where the vertical movement of all lower-chord panel points is required. It will be shown in Chapter 8 that such movements are those used to construct influence lines for continuous trusses.

166

6.12   Truss Deflections by Displacement Diagram

A symmetrical truss is shown in its unloaded position by the solid lines in Figure 6-32(a). If a downward load is applied at L_1, all the members will change in length and the panel points of the truss will be displaced from their original positions to new positions shown by the dashed lines. All movements

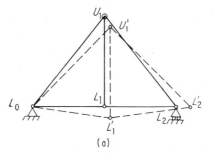

(a)

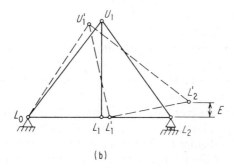

(b)

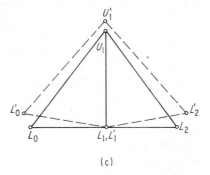

(c)

Figure 6-32.   Truss Displacements

are actually very small compared to the bar lengths but have been grossly exaggerated in the figure for clarity.

Theoretically, the deflected position of the truss could be determined quite easily. Initially, one bar would be assumed fixed in direction and one end of the same bar assumed fixed in position. In Figure 6-32(b) these assumptions are made for bar L_0L_1 and point L_0. Keeping L_0 fixed, lay off the new length L_0L_1', thereby locating point L_1'. Using L_0 and L_1' as pivots, swing arcs equal to the new lengths of L_0U_1 and L_1U_1 to locate U_1'. Finally, swing arcs from L_1' and U_1' to locate L_2'. As L_2' does not lie on a line through L_0L_2, but is a distance E above, it is necessary to rotate the entire constructed figure about point L_0 until the error E is eliminated. This would result in the correct displaced position, as shown in Figure 6-32(a). If the assumed direction L_0L_1 had been the correct one, the error E would be zero and no rotation of the figure would be required.

If both the truss and the changes in length of the bars are symmetrical about some bar, its direction will remain fixed. In Figure 6-32(a) member L_1U_1 remains vertical and, with point L_1 assumed fixed in position, we can locate U_1'. Swinging arcs from U_1' and L_1 for L_0' and L_2', results in the displaced figure shown in Figure 6-32(c). All relative movements are now correct, and the true displaced position of the truss can be obtained by translating the figure, vertically and horizontally until point L_0' corresponds with the physically fixed point L_0.

A graphical application of the procedure outlined in the preceding paragraphs is virtually impossible because the changes in length of the various members are much too small compared with the lengths of the sides. Williot developed a practical graphical construction for displacements by plotting only the changes in length of bars and the arcs. The latter are so short and have such a large radius relative to the changes in length that they are drawn as straight lines perpendicular to the plotted changes in length.

An example of a Williot diagram for a truss is shown in Figure 6-33. This is the same truss, with the same changes in length, shown in Figure 6-27. Because of symmetry of structure and changes in length, bar L_2U_2 remains vertical. The displacement diagram is started from an arbitrary point L_2', and point U_2' is then plotted on a vertical line through L_2' at a distance 0.250 in. from L_2'. Since L_2U_2 decreases in length, point U_2 moves downward relative to L_2.

Having located the new positions of L_2 and U_2, we can now determine the new position of U_1 by plotting the changes in length of U_1L_2 and U_1U_2, and then swinging "arcs" to locate U_1'. The change in length of $U_1L_2(+0.500)$ is plotted upward and to the left from L_2', parallel to bar U_1L_2 of the truss, because U_1 has moved away from L_2. The change in length of $U_1U_2(-0.500)$ is drawn horizontally to the right from U_2 because U_1 has moved to the right relative to U_2. The intersection of normals (arcs) drawn from the ends of these two plotted changes in length locates point U_1'. In a like manner, point L_1' is located from points U_1' and L_2' by plotting the changes in length of U_1L_1 and L_1L_2 in the directions of U_1L_1 and L_1L_2, drawing normals, and then taking their intersection as L_1'. Finally, L_0 is located from points U_1' and L_1' by using the changes in length of U_1L_0 and L_0L_1 and determining the point of intersection of normals. In a similar manner, we could determine the displacements of U_3, L_3, and L_4. The completed displacement diagram would be symmetrical about a line through $U_2'L_2'$. Therefore, in a symmetrical case it is necessary to construct only one half of the displacement diagram.

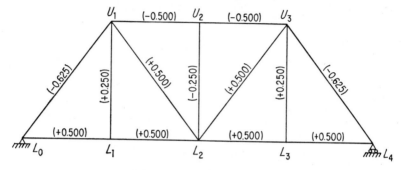

(a) Relative Changes in Bar Lengths

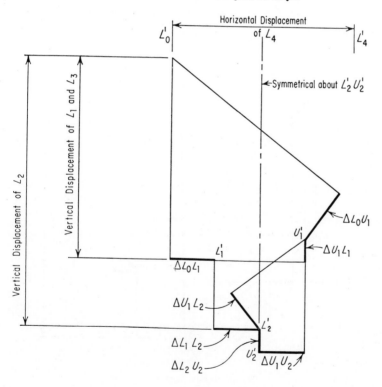

(b) Williot Diagram

Figure 6-33.   Truss Displacements by Williot Diagram

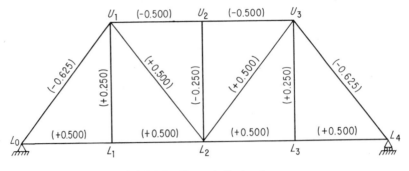

(a) Relative Changes in Bar Lengths

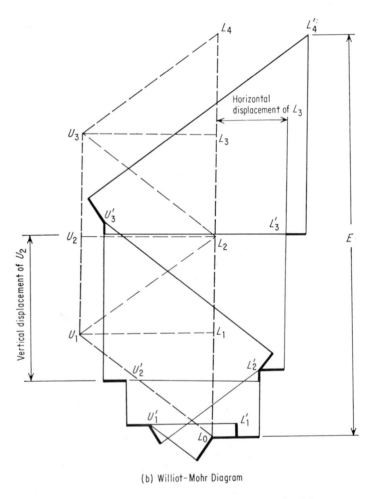

(b) Williot-Mohr Diagram

Figure 6-34. *Truss Displacements by Williot-Mohr Diagram*

If, as a result of lack of symmetry, no member is fixed in direction, it is necessary to assume some member to be so fixed. After the displacement diagram is drawn the panel points at the supports will not be at the correct relative elevations, and the displacements cannot be determined directly as before. Corrections resulting from the rotation of the truss about one of the supports must be added. A method for making this correction was devised by Mohr and the resulting construction is usually referred to as the Williot-Mohr diagram.

The truss and changes in bar lengths in Figure 6-34(a) are identical with those in Figure 6-33(a). In Figure 6-34(b) a displacement diagram, indicated by solid lines, is drawn as in Figure 6-33(b) but with one important difference. Member L_0L_1 was purposely assumed fixed in a horizontal direction and point L_0 fixed in position. The new position of L_1 (labeled L_1') is 0.500 to the right of L_0. The new position of U_1 is determined by laying off from L_0 and L_1' the changes in length of L_0U_1 and U_1L_1, respectively, and erecting normals. In a manner similar to that explained for Figure 6-33(b), the new position of each successive panel point is obtained from the position of two preceding points. When all new points have been located, point L_4' is not at the same elevation as L_0 but is a distance E above it. This error E corresponds to that shown in Figure 6-32(b).

To eliminate the error E in Figure 6-32(b), the entire truss had to be rotated about point L_0 until the vertical position of point L_2' was at the same elevation as point L_0. In this rotation each panel point was displaced an amount proportional to its distance from point L_0. Mohr achieved the same effect in the graphical construction of Williot by drawing the truss to scale, in a 90-degree revolved position, between the two points corresponding to the supports. This construction, shown in dashed lines in Figure 6-34(b), represents the movements of the panel points due to rotation about L_0. Since the true displacement of each point consists of the rotational movement and that obtained with L_0L_1 fixed in direction, it is equal to the scaled distance from the panel point in the Mohr diagram to the corresponding panel point on the revolved truss.

The Williot-Mohr diagram gives all absolute displacements in the truss simultaneously. However, if the truss is unsymmetrical or consists of a large number of members, the scale of the diagram may have to be quite small to limit the drawing to a practical size. This may present drafting problems and accuracy may be impaired.

It should be remembered that all three methods for obtaining truss displacements require knowledge of the change in length of all members. In some cases computations necessary to determine these may be more time consuming than the subsequent determination of required movements. Finally, it is again emphasized that we are dealing with a problem in geometry. The changes in length may be due to load, change in temperature, or any cause whatsoever, and they may be elastic or plastic.

Problems

6.1. Compute the rotation of A, B, and C and the vertical and horizontal displacement of B due to:

(a) a positive angle change of $\frac{1}{1,000}$ rad occurring at point D;

(b) a horizontal movement of 0.01 ft to the right of support C.

6.2. Determine the rotation of the elastic curve at points A, B, and C and the vertical displacement at C and D. The beam has a constant value of EI for its entire length. (Ans.: $\phi_A = 500P/9EI$; $\phi_B = 400P/9EI$; $\phi_C = 200P/EI$; $\delta_C = 4,000P/9EI$; $\delta_D = 2,875P/6EI$.)

6.3. Compute the vertical displacement under the concentrated load. EI is constant for the entire beam length.

6.4. Find the vertical displacement under the 10-kip load. $E = 30 \times 10^3$ ksi. (Ans.: $\delta = 0.62$ in.)

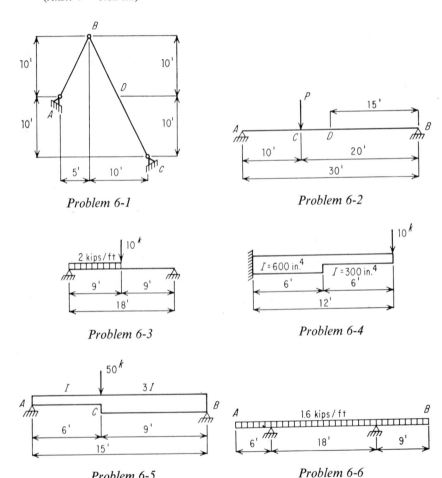

Problem 6-1

Problem 6-2

Problem 6-3

Problem 6-4

Problem 6-5

Problem 6-6

6.5. Determine the vertical displacement of point C in terms of EI.

6.6. Compute the vertical displacement of points A and B.
$E = 30 \times 10^3$ ksi; $I = 290$ in.^{4}. (*Ans.:* $\delta_A = 0.0243$ in. down; $\delta_B = 0.419$ in. down.)

6.7. Evaluate the rotation at B and the vertical displacement at midspan of AB and at midspan of BC in terms of EI.

6.8. Determine the horizontal movement of points B and C and the vertical displacement of point E at the midspan of BC:

(a) using angle changes between A and E;

(b) using angle changes between D and E. (*Ans.:* $\delta_B = 494/EI$ to left.)

6.9. Find the vertical displacement at midspan of AB if the beam shown is of constant section, 16 inches deep, and the *maximum* flexural stress in the beam is 18,000 psi. $E = 10 \times 10^3$ ksi.

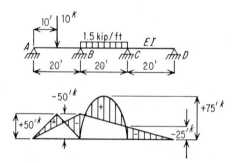

Problem 6-7

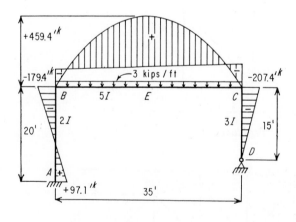

Problem 6-8

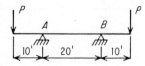

Problem 6-9

6.10. Compute the vertical displacement at midspan by use of the virtual work method. (*Ans.:* $\delta = wL^4/120EI$.)

6.11. Repeat Problem 6.3 using the virtual work method.

6.12. Repeat Problem 6.6 by use of:

(a) virtual work;
(b) Castigliano's theorem.

6.13. Calculate the vertical and horizontal movements of panel point U_2 by the method of virtual work. $E = 30 \times 10^3$ ksi; area of all exterior bars $= 10$ in.²; area of all interior bars $= 5$ in.² (*Ans.:* $\Delta_v = 0.157$ in. down.)

6.14. The truss shown is symmetrical about member U_3L_3. For the changes (in.) in bar lengths shown, determine the displaced positions of:

(a) lower chord panel points by use of angle changes. (*Ans.:* $\Delta L_1 = 1.13$ in.; $\Delta L_2 = 1.55$ in.; $\Delta L_3 = 1.97$ in.);
(b) panel point L_3 by means of virtual work (*x*- and *y*-components);
(c) all panel points by construction of a Williot diagram.

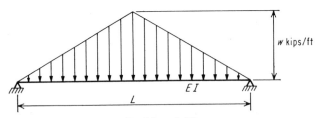

Problem 6-10

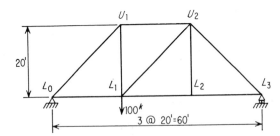

Problem 6-13

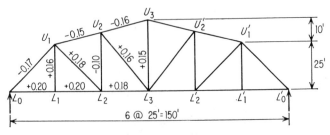

Problem 6-14

Chapter **7**

Statically Indeterminate
Beams and Frames

Approximate methods of analysis of statically indeterminate structures were discussed in Chapter 5. In this chapter and in Chapter 8 precise solutions are obtained for various types of statically indeterminate systems.

All solutions will involve computations of rotations or displacements as described in Chapter 6. It must be kept in mind that forces and geometry are related through quantities such as EI or GJ, and there are often some uncertainties as to the correct values of these products. This is particularly true for reinforced concrete structures. However, only relative values of EI or GJ are involved in the analysis of statically indeterminate structures for effects of load, and uncertainty regarding variations in absolute value of these quantities is not important. On the other hand, in determining effects of temperature, support movements, or change in length resulting from axial force, errors in results will be directly proportional to the errors in EI or GJ. The primary function of analysis is to assist in the development of a satisfactory design. Analytical answers may be acceptable even if not "exact," but judgment and experience are necessary to assess the effect of uncertainties.

7.1 General Methods of Analysis

The analysis of statically indeterminate structures involves satisfying the requirements of equilibrium and geometry. In order to meet both requirements, either of two general approaches may be followed. A statically determinate solution that satisfies the equilibrium requirements may be assumed, and the resulting errors in geometry computed. The geometrical errors are then corrected without disturbing the equilibrium requirements. Conversely, an assumed solution that satisfies the geometrical requirements can be corrected for the resulting errors in static equilibrium.

The first approach is generally called the force, or equilibrium, method, while the second is termed the displacement, or geometrical, method. The

175

name of Maxwell is often associated with the force method and that of Ostenfeld with the displacement method.

7.2   Force (Equilibrium) Method

The force method may be outlined as follows:

1. Assume a solution that satisfies the requirements of statics.
2. Determine the resulting errors in geometry.
3. Apply arbitrary forces and determine the resulting corrections to the geometry.
4. Solve for the correction forces necessary to eliminate the original errors in geometry.
5. Obtain the final forces by adding the correction forces to the corresponding forces of the assumed solution.

The procedure followed in applying the force method is illustrated in Figure 7-1 for a four-span continuous beam of constant cross section. This beam is statically indeterminate in the third degree, and three simultaneous equations must be solved to obtain the values of the reactions. In order to reduce the structure to a statically determinate case, any values can be assumed for any three reactions. In Figure 7-1 the three interior reactions have been assumed equal to zero.

The second step is the computation of the errors in geometry (deflections at B, C, and D). These deflections are functions of the bending moments and can be found by any of the methods of Chapter 6. The scheme used to determine deflections has nothing whatsoever to do with the method of analysis. Values of the deflections, Δ_B, Δ_C, Δ_D, are shown in Figure 7-1(b).

The next step is to determine corrections in the geometry that result from application of arbitrary vertical forces successively at reaction points B, C, and D. In (c) each of these forces has been taken equal to one. The location of each deflection and the force causing it are designated by pairs of subscripts. The first subscript designates the location of the deflection and the second subscript designates the point of application of the force. For example, δ_{BC} represents the deflection at B due to the assumed correction force of one at point C.

Three equations of geometry are written in (d) to satisfy the requirement that the deflection curve for the continuous beam must pass through all support points. One equation is obtained for each of points B, C, and D. Note that the common term L^3/EI has been canceled out.

Since all interior reactions were assumed equal to zero in (b), the correction reactions obtained from the solution of the simultaneous equations are also the final values of the reactions. That is, the reaction at B is equal to +45.5 kips, that at C is +48.4 kips, and that at D is −9.5 kips. The negative sign for reaction at D indicates that it acts opposite to the corresponding unit

force in (c)—that is, downward. The reactions at points A and E are then
obtained by computations of statics. If the unit correction forces were assumed
acting down, the signs of all values δ would be positive and the same values X
would be obtained but with opposite sign to those in Figure 7-1.

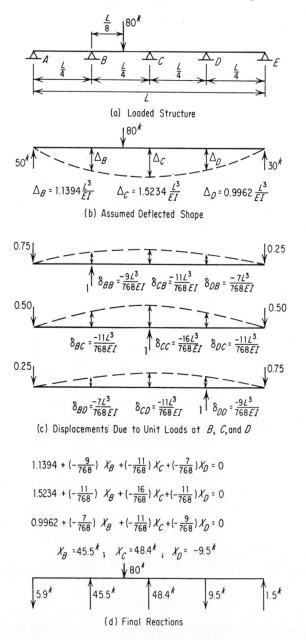

$$1.1394 + \left(-\frac{9}{768}\right) X_B + \left(-\frac{11}{768}\right) X_C + \left(-\frac{7}{768}\right) X_D = 0$$

$$1.5234 + \left(-\frac{11}{768}\right) X_B + \left(-\frac{16}{768}\right) X_C + \left(-\frac{11}{768}\right) X_D = 0$$

$$0.9962 + \left(-\frac{7}{768}\right) X_B + \left(-\frac{11}{768}\right) X_C + \left(-\frac{9}{768}\right) X_D = 0$$

$$X_B = 45.5^k \; ; \quad X_C = 48.4^k \; ; \quad X_D = -9.5^k$$

(d) Final Reactions

Figure 7-1.　Analysis of Continuous Beam by Force Method

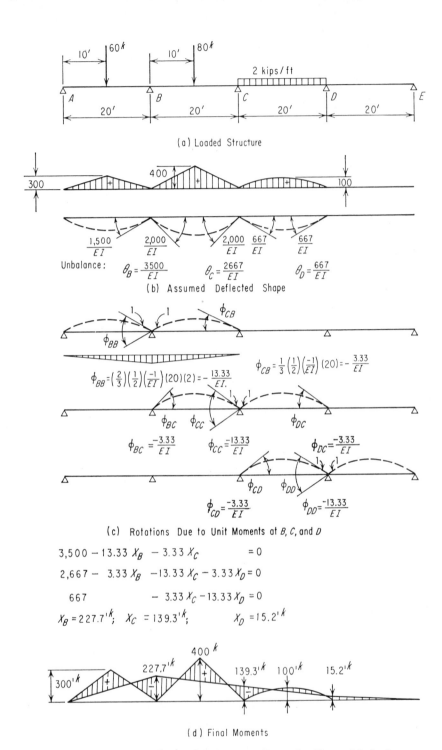

(a) Loaded Structure

(b) Assumed Deflected Shape

(c) Rotations Due to Unit Moments at B, C, and D

$$3,500 - 13.33\,X_B - 3.33\,X_C \qquad\qquad = 0$$

$$2,667 - 3.33\,X_B - 13.33\,X_C - 3.33\,X_D = 0$$

$$667 \qquad\qquad - 3.33\,X_C - 13.33\,X_D = 0$$

$$X_B = 227.7'^k; \quad X_C = 139.3'^k; \qquad X_D = 15.2'^k$$

(d) Final Moments

Figure 7-2. Analysis of Continuous Beam by Force Method

The assumed equilibrium position shown in Figure 7-2(b) is that resulting if the continuous beam is assumed cut at each interior support. In other words, the moment at each support is taken equal to zero. It is emphasized, however, that any set of values could be assumed for the interior moments.

The errors in geometry now consist of rotations at the supports rather than displacements, and the corrections will be moments rather than forces. From the angle changes associated with the moment diagrams in (b), rotations at B, C, and D were computed and are shown in the figure. Rotations are considered positive when caused by positive bending moments in the beam. The error in geometry at each interior support is equal to the algebraic sum of the end rotations of the intersecting members.

In Figure 7-2(c) unit correcting moments are applied to the cut ends and the relative rotation of members meeting at each joint computed. Again, positive rotations accompany positive bending moments and negative rotations accompany negative bending moments.

The equations of geometry are written and the solution given in Figure 7-2(d). The values $X_B = 227.7$ ft-kips, $X_C = 139.3$ ft-kips and $X_D = 15.2$ ft-kips are the correction moments to be added to the assumed moments at B, C, and D. Since all values of X are positive, the correction moments have the same sense as the unit applied moments in (c). The assumed moments were equal to zero; therefore, the final moments are equal to the correction moments. With bending moments at the supports known, the student can now compute the reactions by successively isolating each span.

A solution by the approach followed in Figure 7-2 requires somewhat less work than that for a solution using the procedure in Figure 7-1 because it is generally simpler to compute rotations than deflections.

A two-hinged frame is analyzed in Figure 7-3. The structure shown in (a) is statically indeterminate in the first degree, and the horizontal reaction, H, is the statically indeterminate force. If the value of H is determined, all bending moments and shears can be obtained by simple computations of statics.

The reaction H is assumed equal to zero in Figure 7-3(b). This is equivalent to assuming that one end of the frame is on rollers. The resulting displacement, Δ, is computed as the moment about line AD of all the angle changes in the structure treated as loads normal to the frame. Angle changes occur only along member BC. Of course, if the frame were subjected to horizontal loads on a column, angle changes would also occur along one or both columns.

In Figure 7-3(c), the displacement, δ, due to a unit horizontal load at D is determined. The equation of geometry for determining the horizontal reaction is shown in Figure 7-3(d), and the numerical value, $H = 1.29$ kips, obtained. The moment diagram is drawn by superimposing H times the moments shown in (c) on the assumed moments shown in (b).

If the frame in Figure 7-3 were fixed at its supports, it would be statically indeterminate in the third degree. One possible set of assumptions to use in such a case is that the vertical component of reaction, the horizontal component of reaction, and the moment at one of the supports are each equal to zero. This is equivalent to assuming the structure cantilevered from one support with the other support entirely free. The vertical and horizontal components of movement and the rotation of the free end due to the superimposed loading are computed by any convenient procedure. Then a unit vertical force, a unit horizontal force, and a unit moment are applied successively at the free end.

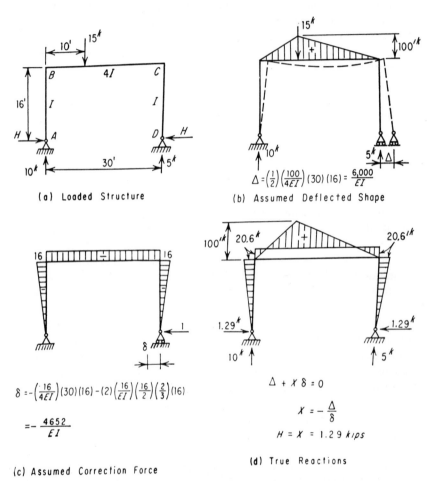

Figure 7-3. Analysis of Rigid Frame by Force Method

For each of these, the resulting vertical and horizontal components of movement and the rotation of the free end are computed. Finally, three equations of geometry are written expressing the requirement that the vertical movement, horizontal movement, and rotation of the support assumed free must each be equal to zero. Solution of these equations yields values for the vertical and horizontal reaction components and the moment at one support. All other shears and moments are then found by statics computations.

Generally speaking, the force method can be used to analyze any continuous beam or frame by solving a set of simultaneous equation of the following form:

$$
\left.\begin{aligned}
\Delta_1 + X_1 f_{11} + X_2 f_{12} + X_3 f_{13} + \cdots + X_n f_{1n} &= 0 \\
\Delta_2 + X_1 f_{21} + X_2 f_{22} + X_3 f_{23} + \cdots + X_n f_{2n} &= 0 \\
\cdot \quad \cdot \quad \cdot \quad \cdot \quad \cdot \quad \cdot \quad \cdot \quad \cdot \quad \cdot \quad \cdot \quad \cdot \quad \cdot \quad \cdot \quad \cdot \quad \cdot \\
\cdot \quad \cdot \quad \cdot \quad \cdot \quad \cdot \quad \cdot \quad \cdot \quad \cdot \quad \cdot \quad \cdot \quad \cdot \quad \cdot \quad \cdot \quad \cdot \quad \cdot \\
\cdot \quad \cdot \quad \cdot \quad \cdot \quad \cdot \quad \cdot \quad \cdot \quad \cdot \quad \cdot \quad \cdot \quad \cdot \quad \cdot \quad \cdot \quad \cdot \quad \cdot \\
\Delta_n + X_1 f_{n1} + X_2 f_{n2} + X_3 f_{n3} + \cdots + X_n f_{nn} &= 0
\end{aligned}\right\}
\qquad \textbf{(7.1)}
$$

The terms Δ represent errors in geometry (displacements or rotations) associated with the assumed solution; the terms f represent flexibility coefficients (displacements due to unit force or rotations due to unit moment); and the terms X represent the desired correction forces or moments.

A support movement can have serious effects on a statically indeterminate structure because the resulting moments and shears may be of the same order of magnitude as those caused by applied loading. In Figures 7-1 and 7-2 the supports of the actual structures were considered unyielding vertically, and in Figure 7-3 the supports were considered unyielding horizontally. These conditions are reflected in each set of geometric equations by the zero terms on the right side of the equality sign.

The determination of the effects of support movement by the force method is accomplished by replacing the zeros in the geometric equations with known or assumed values of displacements. For example, if the loaded beam in Figure 7-1 is subjected to given settlements at the interior supports, the analysis is identical with that in Figure 7-1 except that the values of settlements replace the zeros in the equations. Now, however, the term EI cannot be canceled out of the equations. Answers will be in terms of EI, and the value of this product must be known in order to obtain absolute answers.

If it is desired to determine the effects of settlement independently of any loading condition, Δ_B, Δ_C, and Δ_D in Figure 7-1(b) are set equal to zero and the zeros on the right side of each equation are replaced by the values of the respective support settlements. It is left to the reader to outline a procedure of analysis if either end support A or end support E experiences settlement.

Temperature changes cause stresses in rigid frames. If a uniform temperature change occurs in the frame of Figure 7-3, the value of Δ in Figure 7-3(b) is equal to the product of the span length, the temperature change, and the coefficient of thermal expansion of the material. The remainder of the analysis is identical to that in Figure 7-3 with the value of H, in terms of EI, representing the horizontal component of reaction due to temperature change only. To evaluate H, the value of EI must be known.

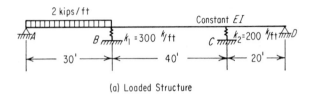

(a) Loaded Structure

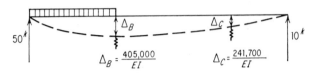

(b) Assumed Deflected Shape

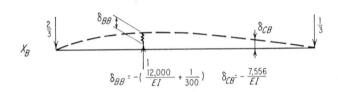

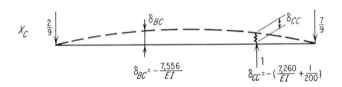

(c) Displacements Due to Unit Loads at B and C

$$\frac{405,000}{EI} + X_B(\frac{-12,000}{EI} - \frac{1}{300}) + X_C(\frac{-7,556}{EI}) = 0$$

$$\frac{241,700}{EI} + X_B(\frac{-7,556}{EI}) + X_C(\frac{-7,260}{EI} - \frac{1}{200}) = 0$$

If $EI = 276,000$ kip-ft^2,

$$12,920\,X_B + 7,556\,X_C = 405,000$$

$$7,556\,X_B + 8,640\,X_C = 241,700$$

2 kips/ft $X_B = 30.68^K$ $X_C = 1.15^K$

29.29^K 30.68^K 1.15^K 1.12^K

(d) True Reactions

Figure 7-4.   Beam on Elastic Supports

7.3   Elastic Supports

Figure 7-4(a) shows a beam with two interior elastic supports represented by springs with given spring constants, k. This beam may be analyzed by the force method in a manner similar to that illustrated in Figure 7-1.

In Figure 7-4(b) the vertical displacements shown at B and C were computed under the assumption that the reactions at B and C are each equal to zero. In Figure 7-4(c) displacements are shown for unit forces of one kip applied at the *bottom* of the springs at B and C, respectively. The first term of δ_{BB} and of δ_{CC} is exactly the same value that would be obtained for unyielding supports. However, since the unit forces are applied at the bottom of the springs, the unit force at B shortens the spring at B by an amount equal to the unit load divided by the spring constant, or $\frac{1}{300}$. This value must be included to obtain the total movement of the support. In a like manner, the unit load at C shortens the spring by $\frac{1}{200}$ and this must be included in δ_{CC}.

The equations of geometry in Figure 7-4(d) express the fact that the bottoms of the springs at B and C cannot move. To obtain numerical results, the absolute value of EI must be used. This has been done in Figure 7-4(d) by assuming the beam to be a standard 21 WF 62 steel section. Solution of the resulting equations for X_B and X_C leads to the reactions shown in Figure 7-4(d). Knowing the value of all reactions, the shear and bending moment at any point can be readily determined.

7.4   Displacement (Geometrical) Method

The displacement method of analysis may be outlined as follows:

1. Assume a solution that satisfies the requirements of geometry.
2. Determine the resulting errors in statics.
3. Apply arbitrary rotations and determine the resulting corrections to the statics.
4. Solve for the correction rotations necessary to eliminate the original errors in statics.
5. Determine the correction moments corresponding to the correction rotations.
6. Obtain the final moments by adding the correction moments to the corresponding moments of the assumed solution.

The loaded beam in Figure 7-5 is the same as that in Figure 7-2. In Figure 7-5(a) the requirements of geometry are that the beam must rest on all supports and the curve of the deflected structure must be smooth, with no break in continuity. The assumed deflected shape is shown in Figure 7-5(b) where the beam is taken as fixed (no rotation) at B, C, and D. The corresponding moments at the assumed fixed ends are included. Such values are readily obtained (Section 7.6). Positive moment has been taken as that which tends to rotate the end of a member clockwise. Thus the error in statics (unbalanced moment) at a support is equal to the algebraic sum of the fixed-end moments at the support. The student should note, however, that the signs of end moments are consistent with the familiar beam convention only in one of the adjacent spans at a support.

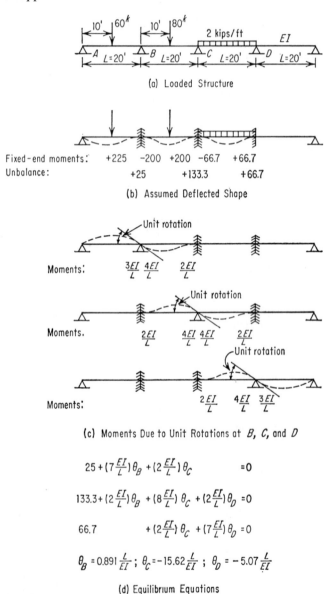

Fixed-end moments: +225   −200   +200   −66.7   +66.7
Unbalance: +25   +133.3   +66.7

(b) Assumed Deflected Shape

Moments: $\dfrac{3EI}{L}\ \dfrac{4EI}{L}$ $\dfrac{2EI}{L}$

Moments. $\dfrac{2EI}{L}$ $\dfrac{4EI}{L}\ \dfrac{4EI}{L}$ $\dfrac{2EI}{L}$

Moments: $\dfrac{2EI}{L}$ $\dfrac{4EI}{L}\ \dfrac{3EI}{L}$

(c) Moments Due to Unit Rotations at B, C, and D

$$25 + (7\tfrac{EI}{L})\theta_B + (2\tfrac{EI}{L})\theta_C = 0$$

$$133.3 + (2\tfrac{EI}{L})\theta_B + (8\tfrac{EI}{L})\theta_C + (2\tfrac{EI}{L})\theta_D = 0$$

$$66.7 \qquad\qquad + (2\tfrac{EI}{L})\theta_C + (7\tfrac{EI}{L})\theta_D = 0$$

$$\theta_B = 0.891\tfrac{L}{EI}\ ;\ \theta_C = -15.62\tfrac{L}{EI}\ ;\ \theta_D = -5.07\tfrac{L}{EI}$$

(d) Equilibrium Equations

Figure 7-5.   *Analysis of Continuous Beam by Displacement Method*

Theoretically, any smooth, continuous deflected shape such as that shown, but with other than zero slope at the interior supports, could be used, but the corresponding moments at the supports are not then readily determined.

In Figure 7-5(c) unit rotations are applied, successively, at B, C, and D, in each case preventing rotation at the other two interior supports. The resulting end moments for each span, as will be demonstrated in Section 7.7, are either $4EI/L$ or $3EI/L$ at the support where unit rotation is applied and $2EI/L$ or zero at the opposite end of the span. The values $4EI/L$ and $2EI/L$ are used for a span fixed at its far end, and $3EI/L$ and zero apply to a span with far end free to rotate.

The three equations of statics are shown in (d). These are solved to obtain the correction rotations, θ, whose values are also included. Since a unit rotation results in a moment of $4EI/L$ or $3EI/L$ at the rotated end and $2EI/L$ or zero at an opposite end, rotations θ will produce moments equal to θ times those values. The determination of a correction moment at m in a span mn can, consequently, be formulated as follows:

(a) Interior span:

$$m_m = \frac{4EI}{L}\theta_m + \frac{2EI}{L}\theta_n \tag{7.2}$$

(b) Exterior span (n is outer support):

$$m_m = \frac{3EI}{L}\theta_m \tag{7.3}$$

If the outer support n were fixed against rotation, Equation (7.3) would become

$$m_m = \frac{4EI}{L}\theta_m \tag{7.3a}$$

and the moment at n would be $(2EI/L)\theta_n$

The correction moment at end B of span BA is, from Equation (7.3),

$$m_{BA} = \frac{3EI}{L}\left(0.891\,\frac{L}{EI}\right) = +2.7 \text{ ft-kips}$$

At end B of span BC, from Equation (7.2),

$$m_{BC} = \frac{4EI}{L}\left(0.891\,\frac{L}{EI}\right) + \frac{2EI}{L}\left(-15.62\,\frac{L}{EI}\right) = -27.7 \text{ ft-kips}$$

similarly, we obtain

$$m_{CB} = -60.7 \text{ ft-kips}; \qquad m_{CD} = -72.6 \text{ ft-kips}$$

$$m_{DC} = -51.5 \text{ ft-kips}; \qquad m_{DE} = -15.2 \text{ ft-kips}$$

The final moments can now be obtained by adding the correction moments to the corresponding moments of the assumed solution, as follows:

$$M_{BA} = +225.0 + 2.7 = +227.7 \text{ ft-kips}$$

$$M_{BC} = -200.0 - 27.7 = -227.7 \text{ ft-kips}$$

$$M_{CB} = +200.0 - 60.7 = +139.3 \text{ ft-kips}$$

$$M_{CD} = -66.7 - 72.6 = -139.3 \text{ ft-kips}$$

$$M_{DC} = +66.7 - 51.5 = +15.2 \text{ ft-kips}$$

$$M_{DE} = 0 - 15.2 = -15.2 \text{ ft-kips}$$

The student should now draw the moment diagram and reinterpret the signs in accordance with the designer's beam convention.

The displacement method can be used to analyze any continuous beam or frame by solving a set of equations of the following form:

$$\left.\begin{array}{l} P_1 + D_1 k_{11} + D_2 k_{12} + D_3 k_{13} + \cdots + D_n k_{1n} = 0 \\ P_2 + D_1 k_{21} + D_2 k_{22} + D_3 k_{23} + \cdots + D_n k_{2n} = 0 \\ \cdots \cdots \cdots \cdots \cdots \cdots \cdots \cdots \cdots \\ \cdots \cdots \cdots \cdots \cdots \cdots \cdots \cdots \cdots \\ \cdots \cdots \cdots \cdots \cdots \cdots \cdots \cdots \cdots \\ P_n + D_1 k_{n1} + D_2 k_{n2} + D_3 k_{n3} + \cdots + D_n k_{nn} = 0 \end{array}\right\} \quad (7.4)$$

The terms P represent errors in statics (moments or forces) associated with the assumed solution; the terms k represent stiffness coefficients, which may be moments due to unit rotation or forces due to unit displacement; and the terms D represent correction rotations or displacements. Application of the displacement method to rigid frames is illustrated in Chapter 9.

Equations of the type of Equations (7.1) and (7.4) have wide applicability in problems of so-called steady state which, in addition to elastic systems, include electric and hydraulic networks. In each case it is necessary to satisfy equilibrium requirements (statics) and interconnection requirements (geometry). Specifically, for electric networks we must satisfy both of Kirchhoff's laws, and for hydraulic networks we must satisfy the requirements of conservation of flow and uniqueness of pressure at all interconnections.

The force and displacement methods of analysis are straightforward and readily understood. The displacement method requires an additional step because the simultaneous equations yield rotations rather than moments. On the other hand, the coefficients for these equations are much more quickly determined than are those in the force method. It should be obvious that for more highly statically indeterminate structures both these methods may be quite time-consuming. If the number of equations exceeds three or four, slide-rule operations are usually not precise enough to lead to an acceptable solution. Recourse must be made to a desk calculator. The time required increases rapidly with increase in the number of simultaneous equations.

Methods for solving simultaneous equations by hand operations are discussed in Chapter 9. If a digital computer is available, the solution of large sets of simultaneous equations generally becomes a routine operation. Matrix formulation is particularly advantageous with a digital computer and is used in Chapters 9, 10, 12, and 13. Several problems of the present chapter are reworked in Chapter 9 by the force and displacement methods, but using matrix formulation.

7.5   Moment Distribution Method

The moment distribution method of Hardy Cross makes possible the analysis of continuous beams and frames through the use of arithmetic only. It places emphasis on physical behavior, is readily applied, and is easily remembered. Moment distribution can be categorized as a displacement method of analysis. However, instead of the rather tedious approach described in Section 7.4, successive converging corrections are made to an assumed set of moments, and results are obtained to any desired precision. Because of the nature of the concept and procedure, the method readily lends itself to the development of design judgment.

The general idea of moment distribution is explained with the use of Figure 7-6. The loaded beam in (a) is actually fixed against rotation at A and supported at B and C. If, as in Figure 7-6(b), the beam is assumed for the present to be fixed at all supports, *fixed-end moments* result at each end of members AB and BC. Arbitrary values have been assigned to these moments in Figure 7-6(b), calling clockwise moment at the end of a member positive.

The fixed-end moments do not satisfy the requirements of statics at B and C because moments on either side of B must be equal and opposite, and no resisting moment can actually be developed at C. There is no unbalance at A because this end is actually fixed. The unbalanced moments at the ends of the members are indicated in (c). Up to this point the procedure is similar to that for the displacement method described in Section 7.4.

To correct the errors in statics (unbalanced moments), we apply correction moments that are equal but opposite to the unbalanced moments. In (d) this has been done separately at B and C. Application of the moment of $+100$ at B induces a moment in both members framing into the support. Since the external moment rotates each member through the same angle at B, the resisting moments in the ends of the members will be proportional to their relative resistances to rotation with their far ends at A and C fixed. These relative resistances to rotation will be hereafter referred to as *relative stiffnesses* and have been arbitrarily taken as 1.0 for BA and 1.5 for BC. As a result, the induced moment at end B of AB is $\frac{1.0}{1.0+1.5}(100) = 40$, and that at end B of BC

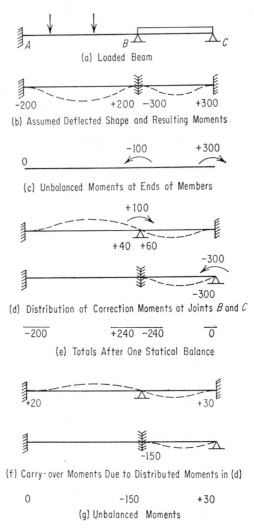

(a) Loaded Beam

−200   +200   −300   +300

(b) Assumed Deflected Shape and Resulting Moments

−100   +300

0

(c) Unbalanced Moments at Ends of Members

+100

+40   +60

−300

−300

(d) Distribution of Correction Moments at Joints B and C

−200   +240   −240   0

(e) Totals After One Statical Balance

+20   +30

−150

(f) Carry-over Moments Due to Distributed Moments in (d)

0   −150   +30

(g) Unbalanced Moments

Figure 7-6. Moment Distribution Method

is $\frac{1.5}{1.0+1.5}$ (100) = 60. Application of the moment of −300 at C results in a moment of −300 at end C of member CB since it is the only member framing into that support. These distributed corrections are a first approximation to the desired correction moments.

If the fixed-end moments in Figure 7-6(b) are added to the distributed moments in (d), the moments in (e) are obtained. These values are a first approximation to the desired final moments. However, when members BA and BC were rotated at B in (d), curvature was induced at ends A and C, which were held fixed. Similarly, when C was rotated, curvature was introduced at B. It follows that when moments of +40 and +60 were distributed at B, moments of the same sign were induced at A and C; and when moment of −300 was distributed at C, a moment of the same sign was induced at B.

188

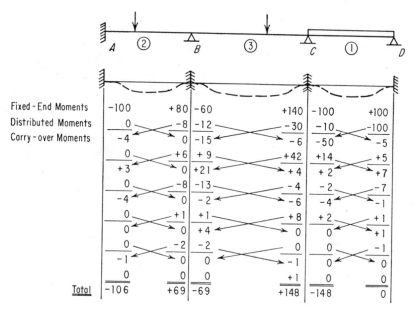

	A	B			C		D
Fixed-End Moments	−100	+80	−60		+140	−100	+100
Distributed Moments	0	−8	−12		−30	−10	−100
Carry-over Moments	−4	0	−15		−6	−50	−5
	0	+6	+9		+42	+14	+5
	+3	0	+21		+4	+2	+7
	0	−8	−13		−4	−2	−7
	−4	0	−2		−6	−4	−1
	0	+1	+1		+8	+2	+1
	0	0	+4		0	0	+1
	0	−2	−2		0	0	−1
	−1	0	0		−1	0	0
	0	0	0		+1	0	0
Total	−106	+69	−69		+148	−148	0

Figure 7-7. Moment Distribution Method

Arbitrary values for these induced moments are shown in Figure 7-6(f). Since they result from moments applied at the opposite end of a member, they are called *carry-over moments*. As will be seen later, a carry-over moment is equal to the product of the applied moment and a *carry-over factor*.

New unbalanced moments, shown in (g), result from the carry-over of moments in (f). The new unbalances are treated exactly as the original unbalanced moments in (c). Each carry-over and distribution results in a new increment of correction moment to be added to the fixed-end moments. The procedure is continued until convergence to final moments is considered adequate.

If desired, a sign convention can be used which is based on the tendency to rotate the joint, rather than the end of the member, clockwise or counter-clockwise. If clockwise joint rotation is defined as positive, all signs are opposite to those in Figure 7-6.

For the present, the application of moment distribution is limited to con-tinuous beams with straight prismatic members and unyielding supports. Yielding supports, rigid frames, multistory frames, and members of variable cross section are treated in Sections 7.10 to 7.13.

Figure 7-7 shows a three-span continuous beam, fixed at one end and simply supported at the other. Relative stiffnesses are shown circled, and the fixed-end moments have been chosen arbitrarily. The determination of stiff-nesses, fixed-end moments, and carry-over factors is considered in Sections 7.6 and 7.7. Clockwise moment at the end of a member is considered positive in this and subsequent problems.

With the fixed-end moments known, the statical unbalance is distributed at each joint. There is never any unbalance at joint A since it is fixed and can accommodate any moment. Therefore, zero moment is distributed at A. At B the unbalanced moment is equal to $(+80) + (-60)$, or $+20$. This unbalance is distributed in proportion to the stiffnesses but with opposite sign,

$$\frac{2}{2+3}(-20) = -8 \text{ to } BA$$

$$\frac{3}{2+3}(-20) = -12 \text{ to } BC$$

At joint C the unbalanced moment is $+40$ and is distributed, with opposite sign,

$$\frac{3}{3+1}(-40) = -30 \text{ to } CB$$

$$\frac{1}{3+1}(-40) = -10 \text{ to } CD$$

As there can be no moment at a simply supported end, the unbalance at joint D is equal to $+100$. To balance this joint, -100 is distributed to member DC. The first cycle has now been completed. At each joint except A, note that the algebraic sum of *all* the moments listed at the joint is equal to zero.

One half of each distributed moment is carried over to the opposite end of the span in Figure 7-7. It will be shown in Section 7.7 that one half is the correct carry-over factor for members of constant section. The direction of all carry-overs is shown by arrows in Figure 7-7. For example, one half of the distributed moment of -12 at end B of member BC is carried over to end C of the same member and is entered as -6. The carry-over from a fixed end, such as A, is always zero. The carry-over moments introduce new unbalances which are distributed as before. This completes the second cycle, and again the algebraic sum of all moments at each joint is equal to zero.

Cycles of carry-over moments and distributions are repeated until the contribution of any cycle is considered negligible. All moments are then totaled. Although it is impossible to generalize, fairly accurate results can often be obtained after two cycles. Four or five cycles usually yield results which are practically exact.

The student should thoroughly understand that although the numerical value of bending moment is identical, as it should be, on either side of each interior joint, this in no way constitutes a proof of the validity of the solution. The unbalanced moment in each case is distributed between adjoining members, but any distribution of that moment will satisfy statics. Only a distribution in proportion to the correct stiffnesses will also satisfy geometry.

All computations in Figure 7-7 were made to the nearest whole number. Any degree of precision is possible, but extreme precision is unjustified in the usual engineering applications.

7.6   Fixed-End Moments

Application of the method of moment distribution requires a knowledge of the fixed-end moments at the supported ends of each span. The correct values of fixed-end moment are those that satisfy the following geometrical requirements:

$$\int d\phi = \int \frac{M\,dx}{EI} = 0 \tag{7.5}$$

$$\int x\,d\phi = \int x\frac{M\,dx}{EI} = 0 \tag{7.6}$$

In which $d\phi = M\,dx/EI$ is the angle change over a differential length dx and M is the bending moment at the same location. In this section only prismatic beams are considered. Members of variable cross section are discussed in Section 7.13.

For a prismatic beam with a single concentrated load, Equations (7.5) and (7.6) are satisfied when the sum of the fixed-end moments is equal to the simple-beam moment at the point of loading, and when, in addition, the end moments are inversely proportional to the distances from the load to the respective ends. This relationship is illustrated in Figure 7-8(a). At end A the fixed-end

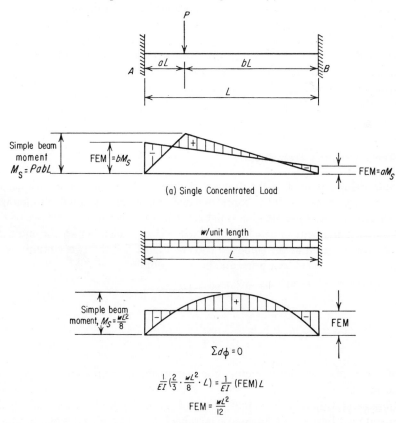

(a) Single Concentrated Load

(b) Uniformly Distributed Load

Figure 7-8.   Fixed-End Moments

192STATICALLY INDETERMINATE BEAMS AND FRAMES[Ch. 7

moment is equal to b times the simple-beam moment at the load point, or ab^2PL. At B the moment is a times the simple-beam moment, or a^2bPL. If there are two or more concentrated loads in a span, the fixed-end moments are obtained as the sums of the values obtained for each load treated separately.

If a prismatic beam is loaded symmetrically, Equation (7.6) is automatically satisfied when Equation (7.5) is satisfied because the closing line superimposed on the simple-beam moment diagram is horizontal. Therefore, it is only necessary to equate the total area under the simple-beam moment diagram to the total area under the closing line. This is illustrated in Figure 7-8(b).

For beams subjected to arbitrarily distributed loadings, fixed-end moments can be obtained by use of substitute concentrated loads. For the special case of a uniformly loaded beam, replacing the total load W by three equal concentrated loads of $W/3$ located at $L/6$ from each end and at the centerline results in a fixed-end moment only about 5 per cent greater than the exact value of $\frac{1}{12}WL$. If the variation in load intensity can be expressed mathematically, precise values of fixed-end moments can be obtained by treating the load on each length dx exactly as the concentrated load in Figure 7-8(a) and integrating the resulting expression.

The beam sign convention must be used in the moment diagrams in Figure 7-8, as indeed in all moment diagrams. For moment distribution computations where the rotation sign convention is used, the fixed-end moment at the end of a member is termed positive or negative in accordance with whether it tends to rotate the end clockwise or counterclockwise.

7.7 Stiffness and Carry-Over Factors

Stiffness, K, as used in the moment distribution method, is defined as the moment necessary to rotate a supported end of a member through a unit angle when the far end of the member is fixed. Carry-over factor, C, is defined as the ratio of the moment induced at the fixed end of a member to the moment producing rotation at the opposite end. In Figure 7-9 the two conditions of geometry are applied to a prismatic beam to obtain

$$K = \frac{4EI}{L}$$

$$C = \frac{1}{2}$$

Stiffnesses and carry-over factors for nonprismatic beams are discussed in Section 7.13.

In general only relative values of stiffness are required for an analysis by moment distribution. For prismatic members, relative stiffnesses can be taken as equal to I/L or some convenient multiple since the quantity $4E$ is constant for all members.

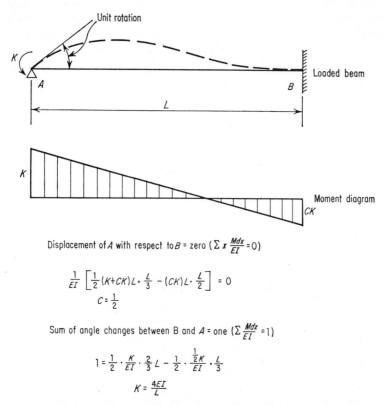

Displacement of A with respect to B = zero $\left(\Sigma \, x \, \frac{Mdx}{EI} = 0\right)$

$$\frac{1}{EI}\left[\frac{1}{2}(K+CK)L \cdot \frac{L}{3} - (CK)L \cdot \frac{L}{2}\right] = 0$$

$$C = \frac{1}{2}$$

Sum of angle changes between B and A = one $\left(\Sigma \, \frac{Mdx}{EI} = 1\right)$

$$1 = \frac{1}{2} \cdot \frac{K}{EI} \cdot \frac{2}{3}L - \frac{1}{2} \cdot \frac{\frac{1}{2}K}{EI} \cdot \frac{L}{3}$$

$$K = \frac{4EI}{L}$$

Figure 7-9.   Stiffness and Carry-Over Factor for Prismatic Beam

7.8   Solution by Moment Distribution

Relative values of moment of inertia are given below the sketch of the beam in Figure 7-10. Divisions of these values by the lengths of the corresponding spans results in a set of relative stiffnesses, I/L. A more convenient set of values, shown circled, is obtained through multiplication by a common factor. Since unbalanced moments at each joint are distributed to the members in proportion to their relative stiffnesses, it is useful to record the distribution ratios at each interior joint. These are shown boxed in Figure 7-10.

Fixed-end moments in each span were computed as indicated in Figure 7-8. There is never an unbalance at A because it is a true fixed support and will resist any induced moment. The initial unbalances are $+250$ at B, -50 at C, and $+100$ at D.

The moment diagram in Figure 7-10 is obtained by superimposing a pattern of linear correction moments on the simple-beam moment diagram. It is necessary to interpret the moments obtained from moment distribution according to whether there is tension or compression on the top or bottom of the beam. The positive sign in the moment diagram indicates tension in the lower fibers. Reactions are also obtained by superposition of the effects of continuity on values for simply supported beams. The shear diagram is then drawn.

In Figure 7-10 the assumption that the simply supported joint D is fixed in each distribution cycle results in slow convergence of the procedure. If

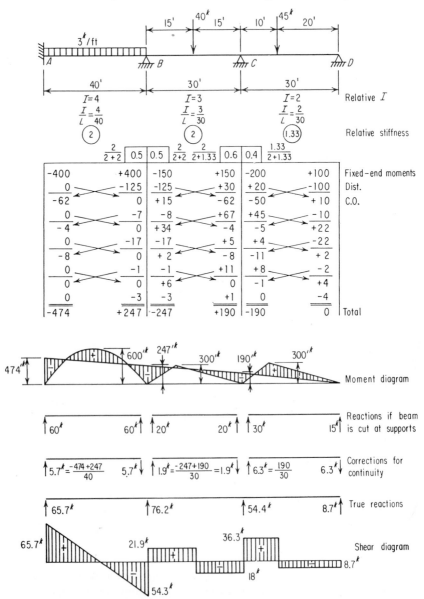

Figure 7-10.   Moment Distribution, End D Assumed Fixed

instead of alternately fixing and releasing D, this end is considered to maintain its true simply supported condition, convergence is hastened. To treat a simply supported end as such, it is necessary first to obtain expressions for fixed-end moment and stiffness when one end of a member is simply supported.

The carry-over concept of moment distribution is used in Figure 7-11 to obtain modified expressions for fixed-end moment and stiffness. In (a) it is determined that for any member the fixed-end moment at end B with end A hinged is

$$M'_B = M_B + C_{AB}M_A \tag{7.7}$$

in which C_{AB} is the carry-over factor from A to B, M_B is the fixed-end moment at B, and M_A is the fixed-end moment at A, *but with opposite sign.* Thus, M'_B is always greater than M_B. If the beam is prismatic, the expression becomes

$$M'_B = M_B + \tfrac{1}{2}M_A \tag{7.7a}$$

The expression for modified stiffness is obtained in Figure 7-11(b) as

$$K'_B = K_B(1 - C_{AB}C_{BA}) \tag{7.8}$$

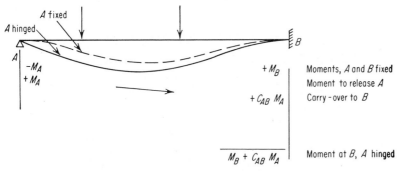

Moments, A and B fixed
Moment to release A
Carry-over to B

Moment at B, A hinged

(a) Fixed-End Moment if Far End is Hinged

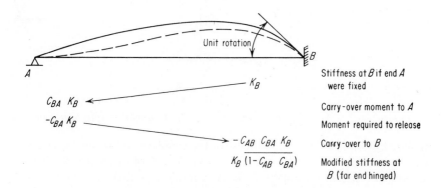

Stiffness at B if end A were fixed

Carry-over moment to A
Moment required to release
Carry-over to B

Modified stiffness at B (far end hinged)

(b) Stiffness if Far End is Hinged (Modified Stiffness)

Figure 7-11. Fixed-End Moment and Stiffness, Far End Simply Supported

in which K_B is the stiffness with the far end fixed, C_{AB} is the carry-over factor from end A to end B, and C_{BA} is the carry-over factor from end B to end A. For prismatic members,

$$K' = \tfrac{3}{4}K = 3\frac{EI}{L} \tag{7.8a}$$

That is, to treat hinged ends of prismatic beams as such, a value of three quarters of the standard stiffness is used.

In Figure 7-12 the problem of Figure 7-10 is reworked, treating the simply supported end D as such. The relative stiffness of CD is modified by using $\tfrac{3}{4}(I/L)$. The fixed-end moment at D is equal to zero, while that at end C becomes, from Equation (7.7a), $-200 + \tfrac{1}{2}(-100)$, or -250. Moment distribution is performed as before but no moments are carried over to the simply supported end D. Also, purely for convenience, instead of carrying over $\tfrac{1}{2}$ the distributed moment from end B to fixed end A of AB after each cycle, $\tfrac{1}{2}$ of the total distributed moment, $(-125, -17, -10, -1)$ at end B has been carried over to A.

A two-span beam, fixed at one end and with an overhang at the other, is

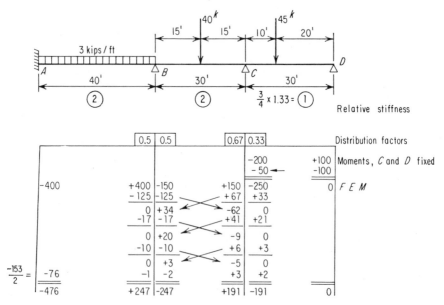

Figure 7-12. Moment Distribution, End D Assumed Simply Supported

analyzed in Figure 7-13. The stiffness of the cantilevered member at end C is zero because no moment is required to rotate end C of member CD when no support or restraint is available at D. As a result, no unbalanced moment at C can be distributed to the cantilever. This is obvious because the moment at the support of the cantilever must remain, by statics, $-6,000$ ft-lb.

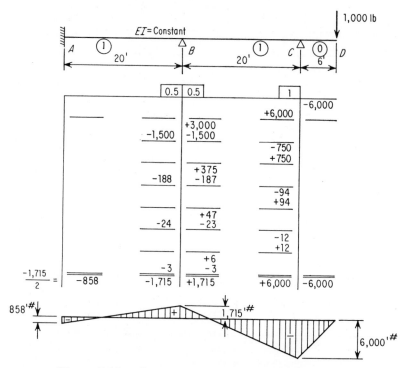

Figure 7-13. Continuous Beam with Overhang

An analysis of the effects of externally applied moments acting at supports of a continuous member is shown in Figure 7-14. The applied moments are labeled negative because they produce counterclockwise rotation at the ends of the spans at B, C, and D. The first distribution divides each external moment, using the same sign, between the members in proportion to their stiffnesses. Then moment distribution proceeds as before. Note that an inflection point occurs at each of the joints subjected to an external moment.

7.9 Maximum Moments and Shears

Maximum moments and shears in a continuous beam subjected to full-span, uniform live load are readily obtained with the aid of moment distribution, Such maxima are particularly important in building design.

The beam in Figure 7-15(a) has a dead load of 1 kip/ft. The live load of 2 kips/ft may cover any combination of spans. The procedure used is to apply live load only to one span at a time. In (b) an analysis is made for live load on AB. Modified stiffnesses have been used for the end members. With the indeterminate moments at the supports computed, the moment diagram is drawn, using the beam sign convention. For live load on span BC the moments are shown in (c). Only the results of moment distribution are included. As a

| | −25 | | −133.3 | | −66.7 | | Constant EI |

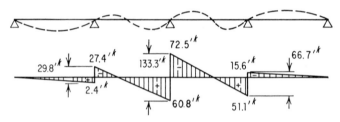

	0.43	0.57		0.50	0.50		0.57	0.43
	−10.7	−14.3		−66.7	−66.6		−38.0	−28.7
		−33.3		−7.2	−19.0		−33.3	
	+14.2	+19.1		+13.1	+13.1		+19.1	+14.2
		+6.5		+9.6	+9.6		+6.5	
	−2.8	−3.7		−9.6	−9.6		−3.7	−2.8
		−4.8		−1.8	−1.8		−4.8	
	+2.1	+2.7		+1.8	+1.8		+2.7	+2.1
		+0.9		+1.4	+1.4		+0.9	
	−0.4	−0.5		−1.4	−1.4		−0.5	−0.4
	+2.4	−27.4		−60.8	−72.5		−51.1	−15.6

Figure 7-14.   Externally Applied Moments

result of symmetry, the moment diagram in (d) is opposite hand to that in (c). The dead-load moment diagram in (e) is obtained by superposition of the live-load moment diagrams in (b), (c), and (d), but multiplying the values thus obtained by $\frac{1}{2}$ to account for dead load equal to one half the live load.

To obtain the curve of maximum moments in Figure 7-16, first the dead-load moment diagram is plotted from a horizontal base line but with positive ordinates plotted downward and negative ordinates upward. The next step is to plot the positive live-load moment ordinates above the base line. At each section only the positive live-load ordinates from Figure 7-15 are plotted, and any negative moments are neglected. For example, at the center of span AB we get $+155(=225 - \frac{141}{2})$ from (b), and $+14(=\frac{28}{2})$ from (d). The corresponding value from (c) is neglected because it is a negative moment. The positive live-load total of 169 ft-kips is plotted above the base line in Figure 7-16. As the dead-load moment at this section is, from Figure 7-15(e), 50 ft-kips $(=112 - \frac{123}{2})$, the maximum possible moment (dead plus live) in the middle of span AB is $169 + 50 = 219$ ft-kips. Finally, maximum negative live-load moments are plotted below the base line, choosing only negative values from the live-load moment diagrams in Figure 7-15 and ignoring the positive values.

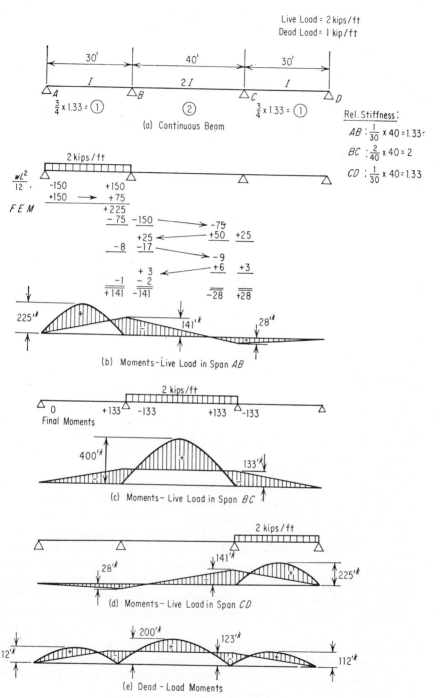

Live Load = 2 kips/ft
Dead Load = 1 kip/ft

30'   40'   30'

I   2I   I

A   B   C   D

$\frac{3}{4} \times 1.33 = ①$ ② $\frac{3}{4} \times 1.33 = ①$

(a) Continuous Beam

Rel. Stiffness:

$AB : \frac{1}{30} \times 40 = 1.33$

$BC : \frac{2}{40} \times 40 = 2$

$CD : \frac{1}{30} \times 40 = 1.33$

2 kips/ft

$\frac{wL^2}{12}$.

-150   +150
+150 → +75
       +225
       - 75   -150 →   -75
              +25 ← +50   +25
       - 8   -17 →   - 9
              + 3 ← + 6   + 3
       -1   - 2
       +141   -141   -28   +28

FEM

225'ᵏ   141'ᵏ   28'ᵏ

(b) Moments–Live Load in Span AB

2 kips/ft

0   +133   -133   +133   -133
Final Moments

400'ᵏ   133'ᵏ

(c) Moments–Live Load in Span BC

2 kips/ft

28'ᵏ   141'ᵏ   225'ᵏ

(d) Moments–Live Load in Span CD

200'ᵏ   123'ᵏ

112'ᵏ   112'ᵏ

(e) Dead–Load Moments

Figure 7-15.   Full-Span Uniform Loads

199

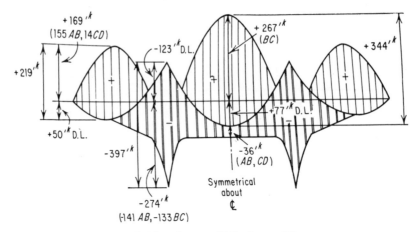

Figure 7-16. Curve of Maximum Moments

Maximum end shears and maximum reactions for the beam and loading of Figure 7-15 are determined in Figure 7-17 by making use of the indeterminate moments obtained in the former figure. As with dead-load moments, the dead-load shears in Figure 7-17(b) are obtained by superposition of live-load values and multiplication by $\frac{1}{2}$, the ratio of dead load to live load.

7.10 Support Settlement

All previous discussion of the method of moment distribution has been restricted to continuous beams in which the joints rotate but do not translate. Moment distribution can, however, be used to determine the effects of joint translation and settlement of supports if fixed-end moments corresponding to such movements are known.

Expressions for moments due to relative translation with no rotation of one end of a member with respect to the other end are developed in Figure 7-18. The relative movement, Δ, of joints A and B is assumed to be so small that the angle BAB' is equal to Δ/L. End B in Figure 7-18(b) is moved to B' and rotated through an angle Δ/L while end A is held fixed. The moment required to rotate the member through this angle is equal to $K_B(\Delta/L)$, where K_B is the stiffness at B. The moment induced at A is equal to $C_{BA}K_B(\Delta/L)$, where C_{BA} is the carry-over factor from B to A. Similar values result in Figure 7-18(c) from rotating end A through an angle Δ/L while holding end B fixed in its displaced position, B'.

Fixed-end moments (FEM) for translation with no rotation in Figure 7-18(a) are obtained by superposition of the results in (b) and (c). Of course. if end A moved downward with respect to B, all signs would be reversed. In general

at A : $\qquad$ $\text{FEM} = (K_A + C_{BA}K_B)\Delta/L$

at B : $\qquad$ $\text{FEM} = (K_B + C_{AB}K_A)\Delta/L$ $\qquad$ (7.9)

200

(a) End Shears – Live Load

(b) End Shears – Dead Load

(c) Maximum End Shears

(d) Maximum Reactions

(e) Minimum Reactions

Figure 7-17. Maximum End Shears and Reactions

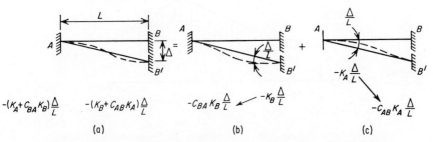

$-(K_A + C_{BA}K_B)\dfrac{\Delta}{L}$ $-(K_B + C_{AB}K_A)\dfrac{\Delta}{L}$ $-C_{BA}K_B\dfrac{\Delta}{L}$ $-K_B\dfrac{\Delta}{L}$ $-K_A\dfrac{\Delta}{L}$ $-C_{AB}K_A\dfrac{\Delta}{L}$

(a) (b) (c)

Figure 7-18. Fixed-End Moments Resulting from Translation

with signs depending upon the direction of the relative movement. If one end of the member is actually free to rotate, the moment at the fixed end will be decreased. For example, if A is hinged, then in Figure 7-18(a) we balance out the moment at A and carry over a moment of $+C_{AB}(K_A + C_{BA}K_B)\Delta/L$ to B. The fixed-end moment at B is then

$$FEM = K_B(1 - C_{AB}C_{BA})\frac{\Delta}{L} \tag{7.9a}$$

For the special case of prismatic members, K at both ends is equal to $4EI/L$ and the carry-over factor is $\frac{1}{2}$. Therefore, Equation (7.9) becomes

$$FEM = 6EI\frac{\Delta}{L^2} \tag{7.10}$$

If one end is hinged, Equation (7.9a) yields

$$FEM = 3EI\frac{\Delta}{L^2} \tag{7.10a}$$

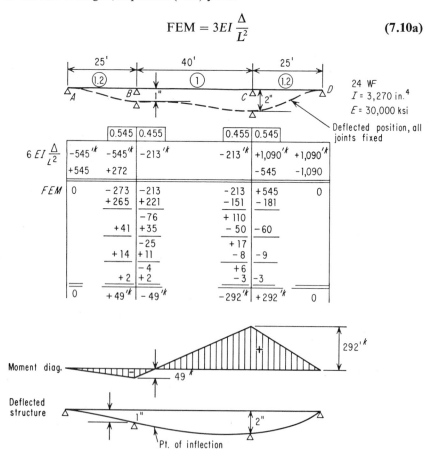

Figure 7-19.   Settlement of Supports

Moments due to support settlement in a 24-in. steel beam are determined by moment distribution in Figure 7-19. The interior supports of the beam are assumed to settle 1 in. and 2 in., respectively. Since, in the subsequent analysis, ends A and D will be considered simply supported, as they actually are, the circled relative stiffnesses for BA and CD are modified values.

The fixed-end moments in span AB, treating end A as fixed for the present, are

$$6EI \frac{\Delta}{L^2} = \frac{6 \times 30,000 \times 3,270 \times 1}{(25 \times 12)^2} = 6,540 \text{ in.-kips} = 545 \text{ ft-kips}$$

Values for spans BC and CD are obtained in the same manner, using $\Delta = 1$ in. for BC and $\Delta = 2$ in. for CD. Before proceeding with the actual moment distribution, however, the fixed-end moments in the end spans are adjusted to account for treating ends A and D as free to rotate. Alternatively, these fixed-end moments could be obtained directly from Equation (7.10a).

Since fixed-ends moments are proportional to $EI\Delta/L^2$, so are the final moments. Also, since the bending stress, σ, is proportional to Md/I where d is the depth of the section,

$$\sigma \propto \frac{Md}{I} \propto E \frac{\Delta}{L} \frac{d}{L} \tag{7.11}$$

Therefore, bending stresses due only to movement of supports are independent of the moment of inertia of the section but are a direct function of the depth of the section. The effects of settlement of supports may be particularly important in relatively deep, short spans.

The bending moments obtained in Figure 7-19 are for settlement only. Moments resulting from loads must be combined with these. To determine values of moments resulting from settlement of supports, it is of course necessary to know the absolute value of EI. As pointed out in Chapter 6, considerable uncertainties may be involved in attempting to set a value for EI for reinforced concrete structures.

11   Rigid Frames

A rectangular rigid frame that is symmetrical and symmetrically loaded can be analyzed by moment distribution exactly as if it were a continuous beam. If the requirements of symmetry are not satisfied, joint translation, commonly termed sidesway, takes place. Results obtained by ordinary moment distribution must be corrected. This can be done approximately, as illustrated in Section 5.3, or precisely by distributing fixed-end moments resulting from joint translation.

The frame in Figure 7-20(a) is symmetrical but supports a load that is not placed symmetrically. Relative stiffnesses are determined in (a) through use of the relative values of I shown in the sketch. Fixed-end moments are determined in (b).

The fixed-end moments are distributed in (c). All values of moments are written at right angles to the member on which they act. For convenience, distributed moments and carry-over moments are written only for the girder. The final moments at the tops of the columns are identical to the girder moments, but opposite in sign. Since all of the moment at the top of each column is a distributed moment, the moment at the base is one half of the moment at the top.

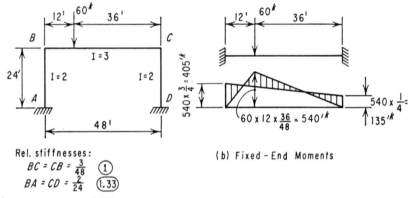

Rel. stiffnesses:
$$BC = CB = \frac{3}{48} \quad ①$$
$$BA = CD = \frac{2}{24} \quad ①.33$$

(a) Loaded Frame and Relative Stiffnesses

(b) Fixed-End Moments

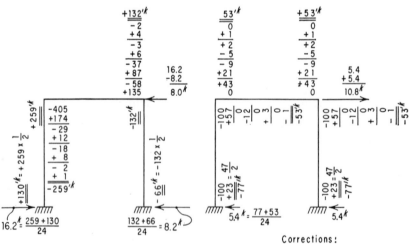

(c) Moment Distribution,
Translation Prevented

Corrections:

at knees: $\dfrac{8.0}{10.8}(-53) = -39'^k$

at bases: $\dfrac{8.0}{10.8}(-77) = -57'^k$

(d) Moment Distribution, Arbitrary Translation

Figure 7-20.   Rigid Frame

When the horizontal components of reaction at A and D are obtained by dividing the sum of the top- and bottom-column moments by the height, it is found that they are not equal. The difference, or 8.0 kips, is the force necessary to prevent sidesway. If this external force is furnished anywhere along BC, the joints will not translate and the moments and reactions in (c) are correct. However, if such a restraint cannot be developed, it is necessary to correct the values given in Figure 7-20(c) for the effect of the error in statics. As the amount of translation is not known, we can assume a value and obtain corresponding fixed-end moments from Equation (7.10). It is more convenient, however, directly to assume fixed-end moments proportional to I/L^2 for each column. The assumption of column moments in this ratio is equivalent to assuming some particular, but unknown, amount of translation. The results from distributing such *consistent* fixed-end moments are adjusted so as to represent the corrections corresponding to the error in statics. Finally, the corrections are added to the original results.

In Figure 7-20(d), consistent fixed-end moments equal to -100 ft-kips have been assumed for translation without rotation. These correspond to a translation of the tops of the columns to the right, with no rotation top or bottom. After moment distribution is performed, the sum of the column shears is computed as 10.8 kips. Since the unbalanced shear force in (c) is 8.0 kips, the true values of moments and shears due to sidesway are found by multiplying the results in (d) by the ratio 8.0/10.8.

The deflected structure, moments, and reactions are shown in Figure 7-21.

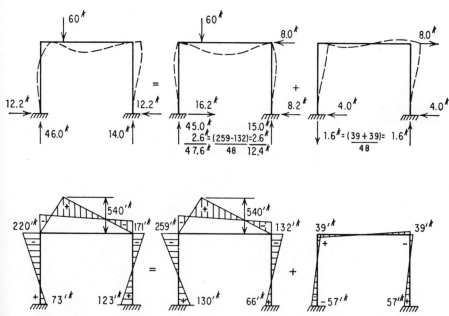

Figure 7-21. Final Reactions and Moments for Rigid Frame of Figure 7-20

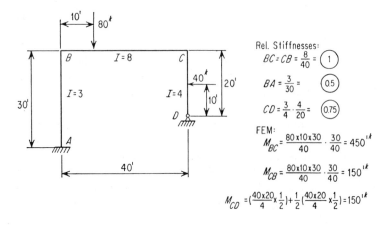

Rel. Stiffnesses:

$BC = CB = \dfrac{8}{40} = $ ①

$BA = \dfrac{3}{30} = $ ⓪⑤

$CD = \dfrac{3}{4} \cdot \dfrac{4}{20} = $ ⓪⑦⑤

FEM:

$M_{BC} = \dfrac{80 \times 10 \times 30}{40} \cdot \dfrac{30}{40} = 450^{'k}$

$M_{CB} = \dfrac{80 \times 10 \times 30}{40} \cdot \dfrac{30}{40} = 150^{'k}$

$M_{CD} = \left(\dfrac{40 \times 20}{4} \times \dfrac{1}{2}\right) + \dfrac{1}{2}\left(\dfrac{40 \times 20}{4} \times \dfrac{1}{2}\right) = 150^{'k}$

(a) Loaded Frame, Stiffnesses, and FEM

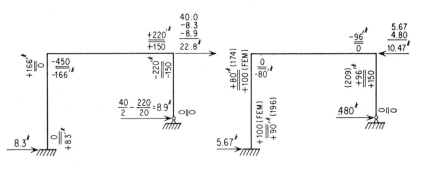

(b) Translation Prevented   (c) Arbitrary Translation

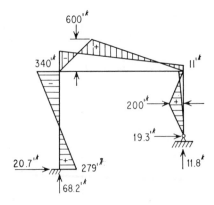

(d) Moment Diagram

Figure 7-22. Unsymmetrical Rigid Frame

Final moments and reactions have been determined by superimposing corrections due to sidesway on the results obtained when no sidesway was permitted. The sign convention used for the moment diagram considers bending moment positive when tension is developed on an inner face of a member. This is an extension of the familiar designer's beam convention for bending moment, and is often referred to as the ring convention.

The corrections due to sidesway are relatively small. In Section 5.3 it was pointed out that great precision in determining the sidesway correction is, in general, unwarranted. Using the recommendation of Section 5.3 that the inflection point in the columns for the sidesway correction be assumed to occur at midheight of the columns, the moments due to sidesway in Figure 7-21 become (8.0)(24)/4, or 48 ft-kips at both the knees and the bases.

If the frame in Figure 7-20 were hinged at the bases, modified stiffnesses could be used for the columns and the same fixed-end moments as in Figure 7-20(b) distributed. Computation of the shears at the bases would again indicate an unbalanced shear. Since the frame is symmetrical, the correction for sidesway would be obtained directly because the correction column shears are each numerically equal to one half the unbalanced shear.

An example of a very unsymmetrical condition is shown in Figure 7-22. Only the fixed-end moments and the results of moment distribution are shown in (b) and (c). A modified stiffness is used for column CD. The fixed-end sidesway moments for BA and CD in (c) must be consistent with Equations (7.10) and (7.10a). Therefore if the fixed-end moments at B and A are assumed as 100, that at C must be $(\frac{3}{6})(\frac{4}{3})(\frac{30}{20})^2(100) = 150$.

The consistent assumed fixed-end moments in (c) lead to a total column shear of 10.47 kips. The true corrections are determined by multiplying the values in (c) by $\frac{22.8}{10.47}$, and the corrected moments in (c) are shown in parentheses. The corrections are added to the values in (b) to get the final results in (d).

In Figure 7-23 the frame of Figure 7-20 is analyzed for a uniform horizontal load of 1 kip/ft acting on the left column. The fixed-end moments of 48 ft-kips were distributed and the unbalanced shear of 10.59 kips computed. Since the results of an arbitrary translation are not dependent on the applied loading, the moments and reactions due to translation are taken from Figure 7.20(d) and shown in Figure 7-23(c). The true sidesway corrections are obtained by multiplying the values in Figure 7-23(c) by $\frac{10.59}{10.8}$. The corrected moments are shown in parentheses. Superposition of these results on those of Figure 7-23(b) gives the values of moments and reactions shown in (d).

All frames considered up to this point have consisted of vertical and horizontal members. In such cases the column fixed-end moments resulting from sidesway are proportional to I/L^2 because Δ is equal at the top of each column. In addition, there are no translational fixed-end moments in the girders.

The solid lines in Figure 7-24(a) show an unsymmetrical frame which has sloping legs. To analyze such a structure by moment distribution, fixed-end

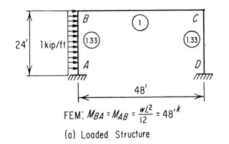

$$\text{FEM: } M_{BA} = M_{AB} = \frac{wL^2}{12} = 48'^k$$

(a) Loaded Structure

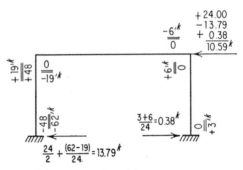

(b) Translation Prevented

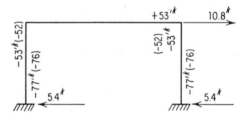

(c) Arbitrary Translation
(From Fig. 7.20(d))

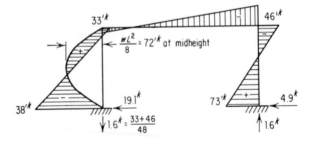

(d) Moment Diagram

Figure 7-23.   Rigid Frame with Uniform Horizontal Load

208

moments due to applied loads are computed and distributed in the ordinary manner. The unbalanced horizontal force is then obtained from the horizontal components of reaction in the legs, including both the contribution of shear and axial force in the legs. As shown by dashed lines in (a), fixed-end moments due to horizontal translation will occur in the girder as well as the legs, and a relationship must be obtained between Δ_{AB}, Δ_{BC}, and Δ_{CD}. Points B and C move in a direction perpendicular to the columns since very short arcs

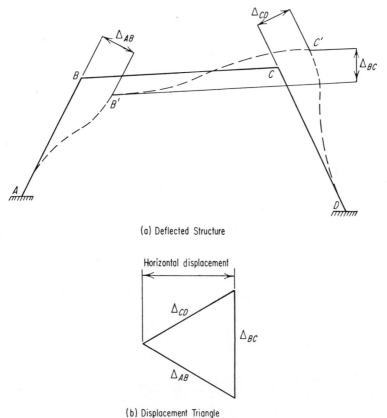

(a) Deflected Structure

(b) Displacement Triangle

Figure 7-24.   Geometry of Translated Frame

may be replaced by perpendiculars. The deformation triangle shown in (b) can be drawn and, for any magnitude and direction of one deformation, the others may be computed or obtained graphically.

As in rectangular frames, bending moments and reactions obtained by distributing fixed-end moments due to translation are adjusted to correct for the unbalanced force obtained on the assumption of no translation. The adjusted moments and reactions are superimposed on the original values to obtain final values.

The frame shown in Figure 7-25(a) is often called a gable bent. The fixed-end moments developed at B and C by the concentrated load are computed in the ordinary manner, and (b) shows the results of distributing these fixed-end

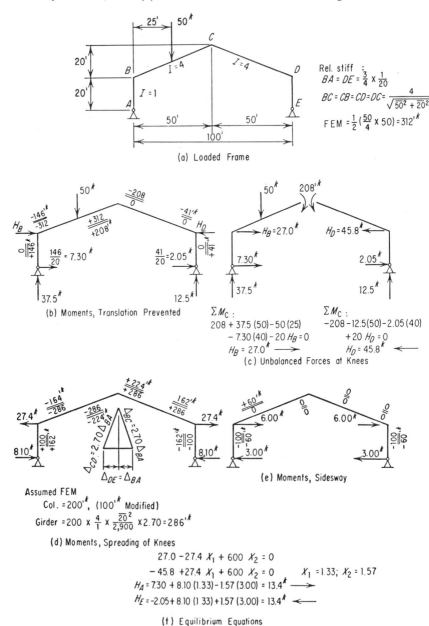

(a) Loaded Frame

Rel. stiff :
$$BA = DE = \frac{3}{4} \times \frac{1}{20}$$

$$BC = CB = CD = DC = \frac{4}{\sqrt{50^2 + 20^2}}$$

$$FEM = \frac{1}{2}\left(\frac{50}{4} \times 50\right) = 312'^k$$

(b) Moments, Translation Prevented

ΣM_C :
$208 + 37.5 \,(50) - 50\,(25)$
$- 7.30\,(40) - 20\,H_B = 0$
$H_B = 27.0^k \longrightarrow$

ΣM_C :
$-208 - 12.5\,(50) - 2.05\,(40)$
$+ 20\,H_D = 0$
$H_D = 45.8^k \longleftarrow$

(c) Unbalanced Forces at Knees

(d) Moments, Spreading of Knees

Assumed FEM
Col. $= 200'^k$, $(100'^k$ Modified$)$
Girder $= 200 \times \frac{4}{1} \times \frac{20^2}{2,900} \times 2.70 = 286'^k$

(e) Moments, Sidesway

$27.0 - 27.4\,X_1 + 6.00\,X_2 = 0$
$- 45.8 + 27.4\,X_1 + 6.00\,X_2 = 0$ $X_1 = 1.33; \; X_2 = 1.57$
$H_A = 7.30 + 8.10\,(1.33) - 1.57\,(3.00) = 13.4^k \longrightarrow$
$H_E = -2.05 + 8.10\,(1.33) + 1.57\,(3.00) = 13.4^k \longleftarrow$

(f) Equilibrium Equations

Figure 7-25. Symmetrical Bent

moments. In this type of structure, translation at joints B and D is *not* equal. This is due to the fact that joints B and D move apart from each other because of the spreading action of the gable, as well as moving laterally due to side-sway. Computations for the unbalanced lateral forces at B and C are shown in Figure 7-25(c). They are determined by summing moments about C for each half of the structure.

Because the movements of joints B and D are not equal, the corrections to the results in Figure 7-25(b) consist of two parts. In (d) assumed but consistent fixed-end moments due to a relative movement of B and D away from each other are distributed and the resulting forces at B and D computed. Note that fixed-end moments occur in BC and CD as well as in the columns. Relative displacements for obtaining the fixed-end moments are determined as ex-plained for Figure 7-24. The results for the conventional sidesway are given in Figure 7-25(e). Fixed-end moments occur only in the columns. Two simultaneous equations are written in (f) expressing the fact that the restrain-ing forces, H_B and H_D, must each be equal to zero. Multiplying the values of moments and reactions in (d) and (e) by X_1 and X_2, respectively, yields correction values which must be added to the corresponding values obtained in (b). This has been done in (f) to obtain final values for H_A and H_E. The student should obtain the final moments and draw the moment diagram and the deflected structure.

.12 Multistory Frames

A three-story rigid frame is shown in Figure 7-26(a). The concentrated lateral loads applied at each story are the type commonly used to represent wind forces. In (b), (c), and (d), the results of introducing arbitrary translations of DE, CF, and BG, respectively, are determined. Any set of *consistent* fixed-end moments can be assumed for a story. Only the fixed-end moments and the results of moment distribution are shown. Moments tending to rotate a *joint* clockwise were taken as positive. Therefore, all moments are of opposite sign to those heretofore used.

Three simultaneous equations are written in Figure 7-26(e) expressing the equilibrium requirement that the sum of all column moments for each story must be equal to the actual shear in the story multiplied by the story height. Thus, in these equations, the sum of the column moments in each story in (b) is multiplied by X_1, the sum in (c) by X_2, and the sum in (d) by X_3. The equations are then solved for X_1, X_2, and X_3. Final moments, shown in (f), are obtained by multiplying values in (b) by X_1, values in (c) by X_2, values in (d) by X_3, and then adding the results algebraically. The moment diagram in (f) is drawn on the tension side of all members.

Referring to Figure 7-26, it is obvious, from the moment distributions and the equations, that the translation of any story affects the final moments in

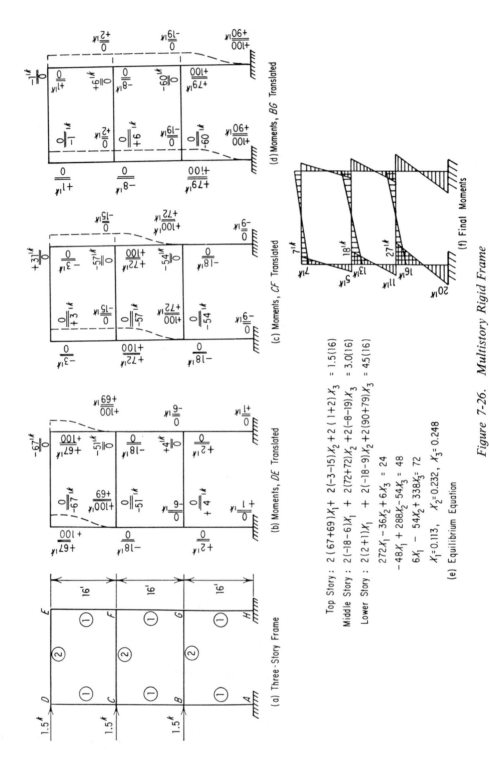

(a) Three-Story Frame

(b) Moments, *DE* Translated

(c) Moments, *CF* Translated

(d) Moments, *BG* Translated

Top Story : $2(67+69)X_1 + 2(-3-15)X_2 + 2(1+2)X_3 = 1.5(16)$

Middle Story : $2(-18-6)X_1 + 2(72+72)X_2 + 2(-8-19)X_3 = 3.0(16)$

Lower Story : $2(2+1)X_1 + 2(-18-9)X_2 + 2(90+79)X_3 = 4.5(16)$

$272X_1 - 36X_2 + 6X_3 = 24$

$-48X_1 + 288X_2 - 54X_3 = 48$

$6X_1 - 54X_2 + 338X_3 = 72$

$X_1 = 0.113, \quad X_2 = 0.232, \quad X_3 = 0.248$

(e) Equilibrium Equation

(f) Final Moments

Figure 7-26. Multistory Rigid Frame

that story to a much greater extent than the moments in any other story. In addition, the moments induced in columns other than those of the adjacent stories are practically negligible. This relative insensitivity forms the basis for the approximate method of analysis which follows.

In Figure 7-27 the frame of Figure 7-26 is analyzed by a shear adjustment procedure in which all assumed fixed-end moments in the columns are introduced at one time and distributed. The fixed-end moments are exactly the same

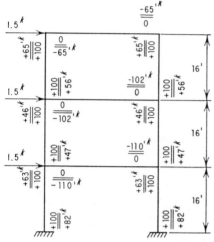

(a) Moments from Arbitrary Displacements

$$\text{Shear} = \frac{65 + 65 + 56 + 56}{16} = 15.12^k$$

$$\text{Shear} = \frac{46 + 46 + 47 + 47}{16} = 11.62^k$$

$$\text{Shear} = \frac{63 + 63 + 82 + 82}{16} = 18.12^k$$

(b) Shears from Arbitrary Displacements

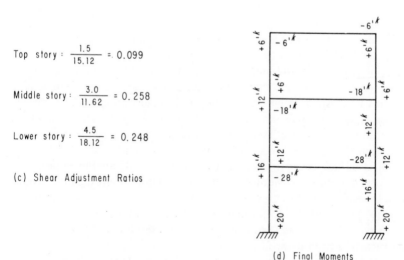

$$\text{Top story}: \quad \frac{1.5}{15.12} = 0.099$$

$$\text{Middle story}: \quad \frac{3.0}{11.62} = 0.258$$

$$\text{Lower story}: \quad \frac{4.5}{18.12} = 0.248$$

(c) Shear Adjustment Ratios

(d) Final Moments

Figure 7-27.   Moments in Multistory Frame by Shear Adjustment

as those introduced, one story at a time, in Fig. 7-26. In the general case, with columns of different size or length in successive stories, the fixed-end moments usually used are taken as proportional to I/L^2 of each column. The shear in each story, equal to the sum of the column moments divided by the story height, is computed in Figure 7-27(b). An adjustment factor for each story, equal to the applied shear divided by the shear values in (b), is computed in (c).

To obtain the final column moments, column moments in the top story in (a) are multiplied by 0.999, those in the middle story by 0.258, and those in the bottom story by 0.248. Final girder moments are equal but opposite in sign to the sum of the column moments at a joint. For a frame more than one bay wide, at an interior joint the *sum* of the girder moments is equal and opposite to the sum of the column moments. Divide this sum between the girders in the same ratio as the girder moments obtained in distributing the original fixed-end moments.

The final moments in Figure 7-27 are virtually identical with those in Figure 7-26. For wider or more irregular frames the comparison is not so good but, except in quite irregular frames, the approximate results are generally fairly accurate. Inaccurate results can be expected when the shear ratios in stories other than the top story differ widely. In such a case it may be necessary to increase or decrease fixed-end moments in corresponding stories in order to obtain more consistent shear ratios and, hence, more accurate results.

7.13   Members with Variable Section

In the usual building frame the beams, girders, and columns are prismatic or very nearly so. In continuous girder bridges the girders are often deeper near the supports than at midspan. Both columns and girders in rigid frames are generally much deeper near their intersection than at other points. Such members are often referred to as haunched.

The application of the moment distribution method to a continuous beam or frame composed of haunched members is exactly the same as that for similar structures with prismatic members. However, the values of fixed-end moments, stiffnesses, and carry-over factors differ from those for prismatic members. Since some of the carry-over factors may be rather large, the convergence may be somewhat slower than for members of constant section.

The effect of haunching on fixed-end moments is illustrated in Figure 7-28. For uniform loading on a symmetrical member, in (a), the closing line through the simple-beam moment curve remains horizontal and is located somewhere between $(\frac{1}{12})wL^2$ and $(\frac{1}{8})wL^2$ no matter how much the member is haunched. In the unsymmetrical case shown in (b), the closing line is tilted as well as shifted vertically from its position for constant I. In any case the closing line is that which satisfies the requirements of geometry. That is, the sum of all angle changes must be equal to zero, and there must be no displacement of one end of the member relative to the other end. If both the haunching and the loading are symmetrical, as in (a), the second requirement is automatically satisfied when the sum of the angle changes is equal to zero.

A good approximation for fixed-end moments in a symmetrical case can be

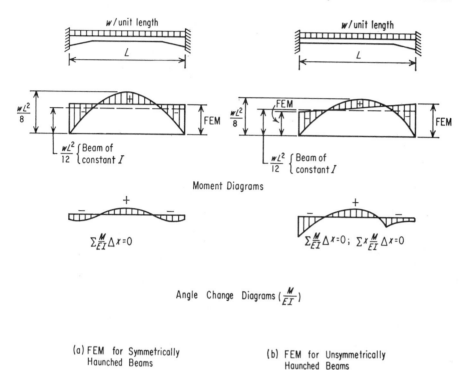

Moment Diagrams

Angle Change Diagrams $(\frac{M}{EI})$

(a) FEM for Symmetrically   (b) FEM for Unsymmetrically
      Haunched Beams   Haunched Beams

Figure 7-28.   Fixed-End Moments for Haunched Beams

made by shifting the closing line up or down until the areas of the angle-change diagram balance. This is much more difficult to do in the unsymmetrical case.

The member in Figure 7-29 is symmetrically loaded. However, since the member itself is unsymmetrical, fixed-end moments, M_A and M_B, must be computed by satisfying the two geometric requirements, viz.:

$$\sum \frac{M}{EI} \Delta x = 0$$

$$\sum x \frac{M}{EI} \Delta x = 0$$

The moment of inertia of the member varies as the cube of the depth and is equal to 1 ft^4 at A and 8 ft^4 at B. For analysis, the member has been divided into five segments and the values of moment, M, and moment of inertia, I, used are those at the midlength of each segment. Greater precision could be obtained if the member were divided into a greater number of segments. The expressions for M tabulated in Figure 7-29 are obtained by adding, at

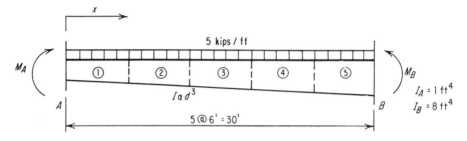

Segment	x	Δx	I	Moment, M	$M\Delta x/I$	$xM\Delta x/I$
①	3	6	1.33	$0.9M_A + 0.1M_B + 202$	$4.06M_A + 0.45M_B + 911$	$12.18M_A + 1.35M_B + 2{,}730$
②	9	6	2.20	$0.7M_A + 0.3M_B + 472$	$1.91M_A + 0.82M_B + 1{,}290$	$17.19M_A + 7.38M_B + 11{,}610$
③	15	6	3.38	$0.5M_A + 0.5M_B + 562$	$0.89M_A + 0.89M_B + 998$	$13.35M_A + 13.35M_B + 14{,}970$
④	21	6	4.91	$0.3M_A + 0.7M_B + 472$	$0.37M_A + 0.86M_B + 576$	$7.77M_A + 18.06M_B + 12{,}100$
⑤	27	6	6.86	$0.1M_A + 0.9M_B + 202$	$0.09M_A + 0.79M_B + 177$	$2.43M_A + 21.33M_B + 4{,}780$
				Σ	$7.32M_A + 3.81M_B + 3{,}952$	$52.92M_A + 61.47M_B + 46{,}190$

$$\Sigma \frac{M}{I}\Delta x = 0: \quad 7.32\,M_A + 3.81\,M_B + 3{,}952 = 0$$

$$\Sigma x\frac{M}{I}\Delta x = 0: \quad 52.92\,M_A + 61.47\,M_B + 46{,}190 = 0$$

$$M_A = -270'^k; \quad M_B = -519'^k$$

Figure 7-29.   Calculation of Fixed-End Moments

each segment, the moment resulting from M_A and M_B to the simple-beam moment. Thus at midlength of segment 1 the simple-beam moment is

$$75(3) - 5(3)(\tfrac{3}{2}) = 202 \text{ ft-kips}$$

and the effects of M_A and M_B, which vary linearly, are $0.9M_A$ and $0.1\,M_B$, respectively. The expression for M at each segment is multiplied by $\Delta x/I$ and tabulated in the adjacent column. This expression is multiplied by x and tabulated in the last column. All of the expressions in each of the latter two columns are summed and set equal to zero, and the resulting equations solved simultaneously for M_A and M_B. The negative signs in the results indicate that M_A and M_B act in the opposite sense to that shown on the sketch.

In Figure 7-30 an unsymmetrical, nonprismatic member is rotated through a unit angle at A with the opposite end B prevented from rotating. The moment K_A is then the stiffness at end A. The geometrical requirements are the following:

$$\sum \frac{M}{EI} \Delta x = 1$$

$$\sum x \frac{M}{EI} \Delta x = 0$$

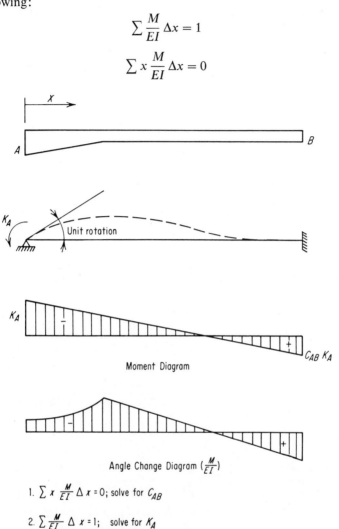

1. $\sum x \frac{M}{EI} \Delta x = 0$; solve for C_{AB}

2. $\sum \frac{M}{EI} \Delta x = 1$;   solve for K_A

Figure 7-30.   Stiffness and Carry-Over, Haunched Beam

where x is measured from the rotated end. The carry-over factor C_{AB} can be evaluated directly by satisfying the second requirement. The stiffness can then be obtained from the first geometric condition. Similarly, end B can be rotated through a unit angle to obtain K_B and C_{BA}. For a member symmetrical about midspan, $K_B = K_A$, and $C_{BA} = C_{AB}$.

Only rough approximations for stiffness and carry-over factor can be obtained by balancing the angle changes in Figure 7-30. Precise results are obtained in a manner similar to that used to obtain fixed-end moments in

Figure 7-29. This is done in Figure 7-31 for the same member shown in Figure 7-29.

In Figure 7-31 we determine K_A and C_{AB} by applying a unit rotation at end A. In a similar manner, we can determine K_B and C_{BA} by applying a unit rotation at end B. All coefficients in the tabulations for M, $M(\Delta x)/I$, and

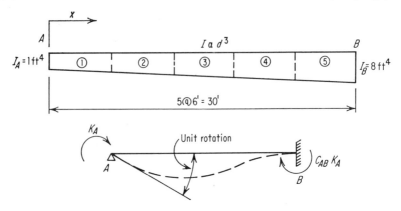

Segment	x	Δx	I	Moment, M	$M\Delta x/I$	$xM\Delta x/I$
①	3	6	1.33	$0.9K_A - 0.1\,C_{AB}K_A$	$4.06K_A - 0.45C_{AB}K_A$	$12.18K_A - 1.35C_{AB}K_A$
②	9	6	2.20	$0.7K_A - 0.3\,C_{AB}K_A$	$1.91K_A - 0.82C_{AB}K_A$	$17.19K_A - 7.38C_{AB}K_A$
③	15	6	3.38	$0.5K_A - 0.5\,C_{AB}K_A$	$0.89K_A - 0.89C_{AB}K_A$	$13.35K_A - 13.35C_{AB}K_A$
④	21	6	4.91	$0.3K_A - 0.7\,C_{AB}K_A$	$0.37K_A - 0.86C_{AB}K_A$	$7.77K_A - 18.06C_{AB}K_A$
⑤	27	6	6.86	$0.1K_A - 0.9\,C_{AB}K_A$	$0.09K_A - 0.79C_{AB}K_A$	$2.43K_A - 21.33C_{AB}K_A$
				$\sum$	$7.32K_A - 3.81C_{AB}K_A$	$52.92K_A - 61.47C_{AB}K_A$

$$\sum x\,\frac{m}{EI}\,\Delta x = 0 \qquad\qquad \sum \frac{m}{EI}\,\Delta x = 1$$

$$52.92K_A - 61.47C_{AB}K_A = 0 \qquad\qquad 7.32\,K_A - 3.81(0.861)\,K_A = E$$

$$C_{AB} = 0.861 \qquad\qquad\qquad K_A = 0.248E$$

Figure 7-31.   Calculation of Stiffness and Carry-Over Factor

$xM(\Delta x)/I$ are identical to those in Figure 7-29. Notice, however, that all signs preceding the $C_{AB}K_A$ terms are negative because, as shown in the sketch, $C_{AB}K_A$ has been assumed opposite in sense to M_B in Figure 7-29. The values $C_{AB} = 0.861$ and $K_A = 0.248E$ are obtained directly from the equations of geometry. In a similar manner, measuring x from B, we can obtain $C_{BA} = 0.317$ and $K_B = 0.671E$.

The expression for K_A can be obtained in general form, in terms of length, L, and I_A, as follows:

$$K_A = (0.248E)\left(\frac{I_A}{L}\right)\left(\frac{30}{1}\right) = 7.44\,\frac{EI_A}{L}$$

This expression holds for any member, regardless of length, provided the variation in moment of inertia is directly proportional to that in Figure 7-31.

Fixed-end moments resulting from translation can be obtained from Equations (7.9) and (7.9a). Modified fixed-end moments and modified stiffnesses can be obtained from Equations (7.7) and (7.8).

A continuous beam, having the member of Figure 7-29 in its central span, is analyzed in Figure 7-32. The actual stiffness for members BA and CD,

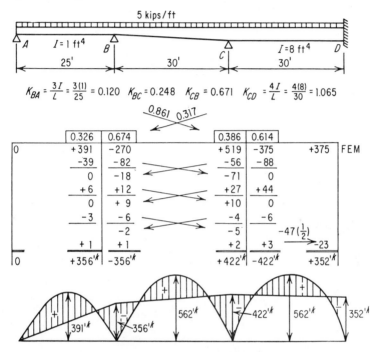

Figure 7-32. *Continuous Beam with Nonprismatic Member*

computed from $3EI/L$ and $4EI/L$, respectively, must now be used. The application of the moment distribution procedure is exactly the same as for a continuous beam having only prismatic members.

7.14   Slope-Deflection Method

The force and displacement methods and the moment distribution procedure discussed in this chapter, and the column analogy method presented in Chapter 10 are favored by the authors for the analysis of most statically indeterminate beams and frames. The slope-deflection method, however, has also been used fairly extensively in the United States. This method involves the solution of sets of simultaneous algebraic equations to determine the rotations and displacements of all joints in a structure.

In Figure 7-33 the basic slope-deflection relationships for the deflected member in (a), all of which have been explained in connection with the method of moment distribution, are shown in (b), (c), (d), and (e). A clockwise moment acting on the end of a member is considered positive. A clockwise end rotation is positive, and a relative displacement which tends to cause a clockwise rotation of the *member* is positive. As a result, a clockwise end rotation is accompanied by a clockwise moment but a *positive* relative displacement induces *negative* end moments.

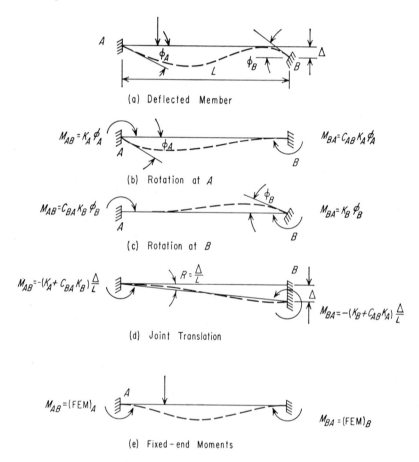

(a) Deflected Member

(b) Rotation at A

(c) Rotation at B

(d) Joint Translation

(e) Fixed-end Moments

Figure 7-33. Slope-Deflection Relationships

From Figure 7-33, and using R for the angle Δ/L, the total moments at A and B are the following:

$$M_{AB} = K_A\phi_A + C_{BA}K_B\phi_B - (K_A + C_{BA}K_B)R + (\text{FEM})_A \qquad (7.12)$$
$$M_{BA} = K_B\phi_B + C_{AB}K_A\phi_A - (K_B + C_{AB}K_A)R + (\text{FEM})_B$$

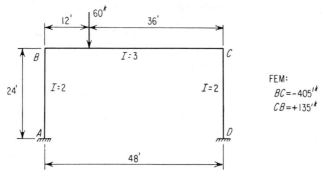

Figure 7-34.   Rigid Frame

FEM:
$BC = -405'^k$
$CB = +135'^k$

If the member is prismatic, these equations reduce to the following:

$$M_{AB} = \frac{2EI}{L}(2\phi_A + \phi_B - 3R) + (FEM)_A$$

$$M_{BA} = \frac{2EI}{L}(2\phi_B + \phi_A - 3R) + (FEM)_B$$ **(7.12a)**

Generally, the modulus of elasticity, E, can be omitted from these equations.

The slope-deflection method is illustrated in connection with Figure 7-34. The loaded frame is the same analyzed by moment distribution in Figure 7-20. The first step is to express the moments at both ends of all members in terms of end slopes, relative end displacements, and fixed-end moments in accordance with Equations (7.12a), as follows:

$$M_{AB} = \frac{2(2)}{24}(0 + \phi_B - 3R) = \frac{1}{6}\phi_B - \frac{R}{2}$$

$$M_{BA} = \frac{2(2)}{24}(2\phi_B + 0 - 3R) = \frac{1}{3}\phi_B - \frac{R}{2}$$

$$M_{BC} = \frac{2(3)}{48}(2\phi_B + \phi_C) - 405 = \frac{1}{4}\phi_B + \frac{1}{8}\phi_C - 405$$

$$M_{CB} = \frac{2(3)}{48}(2\phi_C + \phi_B) + 135 = \frac{1}{8}\phi_B + \frac{1}{4}\phi_C + 135$$

$$M_{CD} = \frac{2(2)}{24}(2\phi_C + 0 - 3R) = \frac{1}{3}\phi_C - \frac{R}{2}$$

$$M_{DC} = \frac{2(2)}{24}(0 + \phi_C - 3R) = \frac{1}{6}\phi_C - \frac{R}{2}$$

Observe that no relative displacement of the ends of the girder is possible. Therefore, R for BC is zero, and AB and CD have identical values of R. Also, since ends A and D are fixed, $\phi_A = \phi_D = 0$.

221

The algebraic sum of the end moments of all members framing into a joint must be equal to zero; therefore, $M_{BA} + M_{BC} = 0$, and $M_{CB} + M_{CD} = 0$. As there is no horizontal load applied to the frame, the horizontal reactions at A and D must be equal and opposite. Then, since the columns are of equal length, $M_{AB} + M_{BA} + M_{CD} + M_{DC} = 0$. Substituting into these three equations of equilibrium, and collecting terms, we obtain

$$\frac{7}{12}\phi_B + \frac{1}{8}\phi_C - \frac{R}{2} = 405$$

$$\frac{1}{8}\phi_B + \frac{7}{12}\phi_C - \frac{R}{2} = -135$$

$$\frac{1}{2}\phi_B + \frac{1}{2}\phi_C - 2R = 0$$

Solution of the three simultaneous equations gives

$$\phi_B = +884; \qquad \phi_C = -295; \qquad R = +147$$

Substitution of these values in the equations relating them to end moments yields the following:

$$M_{AB} = +74 \text{ ft-kips}$$
$$M_{BA} = +221 \text{ ft-kips}; \qquad M_{BC} = -221 \text{ ft-kips}$$
$$M_{CD} = -172 \text{ ft-kips}; \qquad M_{CB} = +172 \text{ ft-kips}$$
$$M_{DC} = -123 \text{ ft-kips}$$

If the frame had hinged bases, five simultaneous equations would result unless modified stiffnesses were used for the columns. For frames in general, the number of simultaneous equations is equal to the number of joints plus the number of stories. For continuous beams, R is equal to zero or, in the case of support settlement, equal to a known amount.

7.15   Influence Lines

It was shown in Chapter 3 that influence lines for moment, shear, and reaction for statically determinate structures consist of straight-line segments. As a result, only one computed ordinate and the known shape are sufficient to define such influence lines exactly.

In Figure 7-35 the Müller-Breslau concept is used to obtain the shape of influence lines for a continuous beam. All influence lines consist of curves. In each case a distortion based on the Müller-Breslau concept is known. However, contrary to the statically determinate case, several ordinates must be computed to obtain influence lines with any degree of precision. Use of the Müller-Breslau concept indicates, however, which spans should be loaded to obtain maximum effects.

One way of obtaining precise influence lines for continuous structures is

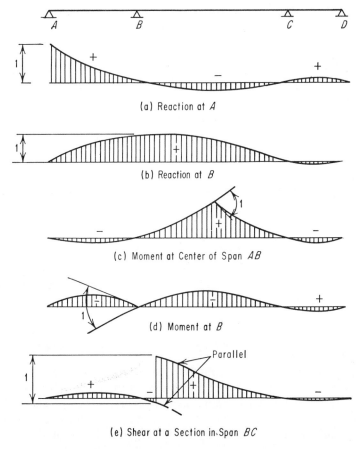

(a) Reaction at A

(b) Reaction at B

(c) Moment at Center of Span AB

(d) Moment at B

(e) Shear at a Section in Span BC

Figure 7-35. Influence Lines by Müller-Breslau Concept

to determine individual ordinates for various positions of a unit load. These ordinates may be obtained from results of analyses of the structure by means of moment distribution or any other method. Use of matrix formulation (Chapter 9) is particularly useful.

In Figure 7-36, influence lines of a two-span continuous beam are obtained by correcting influence lines for a statically determinate beam for the effects of continuity. In (a), (b), and (c), the determinate influence line is that for a simply supported beam AC. The correction pattern is some multiple of the influence line for the indeterminate reaction at B. The ordinate of the correction curve at B is determined from the fact that the influence ordinate at B in the actual continuous beam must equal zero. Thus, $i = i_s$. The only uncertainty is the exact shape of the correction curve. However, this shape is the same as the deflection curve of a simply supported beam AC subjected to a concentrated load at B. As a result, ordinates for the correction curve can be obtained by ratio from the deflections resulting from a concentrated load at B. These ordinates are then superimposed on the simple-beam influence line to obtain final ordinates.

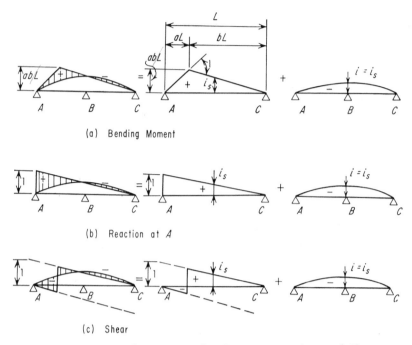

(a) Bending Moment

(b) Reaction at A

(c) Shear

Figure 7-36.   Influence Lines by Correcting an Assumed Shape

Precise ordinates are obtained for two influence lines of a three-span continuous beam in Figure 7-37. Since this structure is statically indeterminate in the second degree, relative ordinates to two deflection curves must be known in order to obtain the corrections to an assumed influence line. The relative ordinates in (b) were obtained by computing the shapes of the deflection curves for a simply supported beam AD subjected first to a concentrated vertical load at B and then to a concentrated vertical load at C. Any set of relative ordinates can be used.

In (c) and (d) the statically determinate influence lines obtained by considering supports B and C removed are each corrected by adding multiples of values of the predetermined correction shapes in (b) such that the final ordinates at B and C are each equal to zero. This requires the solution of two simultaneous equations to obtain the multipliers of each correction pattern for each desired influence line. In (c) the ordinates to the assumed influence line are $+20.0$ and $+10.0$ at B and C, respectively. Corresponding ordinates in (b) are adjusted so that

at B: $1.000X_B + 0.875X_C + 20.0 = 0$

at C: $0.875X_B + 1.000X_C + 10.0 = 0$

Solution yields

$$X_B = -48$$

$$X_C = +32$$

224

All ordinates in (b) resulting from force at B are multiplied by -48, and those resulting from force at C are multiplied by $+32$ to obtain the corrections shown in (c). The corrections are added to the assumed (static) ordinates to obtain the final values shown in the sketch. Signs are automatic throughout.

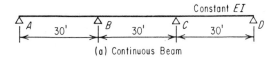

(a) Continuous Beam

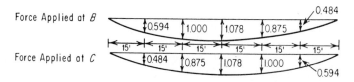

(b) Relative Deflection Curves of Simple Span AD

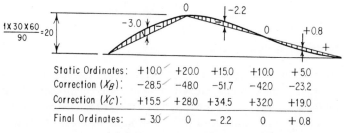

Static Ordinates:	+10.0	+20.0	+15.0	+10.0	+5.0
Correction (X_B):	−28.5	−48.0	−51.7	−42.0	−23.2
Correction (X_C):	+15.5	+28.0	+34.5	+32.0	+19.0
Final Ordinates:	− 3.0	0	− 2.2	0	+ 0.8

(c) Influence Line for Moment at Support B

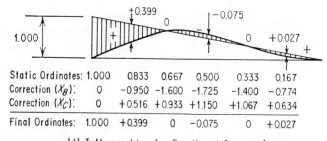

Static Ordinates:	1.000	0.833	0.667	0.500	0.333	0.167
Correction (X_B):	0	−0.950	−1.600	−1.725	−1.400	−0.774
Correction (X_C):	0	+0.516	+0.933	+1.150	+1.067	+0.634
Final Ordinates:	1.000	+0.399	0	−0.075	0	+0.027

(d) Influence Line for Reaction at Support A

Figure 7-37. Influence Lines by Correcting an Assumed Shape

Similarly, the influence line in (d) is obtained by solving the following equations:

at B: $\qquad\qquad .000X_B + 0.875X_C + 0.667 = 0$

at C: $\qquad\qquad 0.875X_B + 1.000X_C + 0.333 = 0$

to obtain

$$X_B = -1.600$$

$$X_C = +1.067$$

The beam in Figure 7-37 is statically indeterminate in the second degree. Therefore, when any two influence lines have been obtained all other influence lines desired can then be determined by computations of statics only.

The determination of simple-beam deflections is quite tedious unless the beam has a constant section throughout its length. A procedure for obtaining influence line ordinates using an angle distribution approach is considerably easier to apply in such cases.[1]

Influence lines for two-hinged rigid frames not subject to sidesway may be obtained as in Figure 7-37. If sidesway is permitted, precise influence ordinates are probably best obtained by computation of individual ordinates due to a unit load moved along the structure or by the angle distribution procedure mentioned above.

7.16 Three-Dimensional Frameworks

Out-of-plane members in general and continuous curved members loaded normal to their plane can be included in an analysis by moment distribution[1] providing the appropriate stiffnesses and carry-over factors can be determined. For the special case of an out-of-plane prismatic member subjected to pure torque, stiffness is GJ/L and the carry-over factor is 1. In the preceding expression, G is the modulus of elasticity in shear and J is a torsion factor such that GJ is the torque necessary to twist the member through a unit angle per unit length. Distribution at a joint is made to *all* members framing into the joint, in proportion to their relative stiffnesses.

When a digital computer is available, the displacement method, using matrix formulation (Chapter 9), is advantageous for the analysis of large three-dimensional frameworks.

Problems

7.1. Compute all reactions for the constant section beam by application of the force method of analysis. For the solution satisfying statics, assume that the reactions at B and C are each equal to 20 kips upward. Draw the final moment diagram. (*Ans.*: $R_B = R_C = 22$ kips.)

[1] James Michalos, *Theory of Structural Analysis and Design* (New York: Ronald, 1958).

7.2. Removing the applied load of 1 kip/ft from the beam of Problem 1, determine all reactions if support B settles vertically 0.5 in. $E = 30 \times 10^3$ ksi; $I = 200$ in.⁴

7.3. Repeat Problem 7.1 by the force method using the statically determinate assumption that the structure is cut (simply supported) at supports B and C.

7.4. If the loaded beam in Problem 7.1 is supported at A, B, C, and D by elastic supports having equal spring constants of 50 kips/ft, compute all reactions and draw the final moment diagram. $E = 30 \times 10^3$ ksi; $I = 200$ in.⁴ (*Ans.:* $R_B = R_C = 20.6^k$.)

7.5. Analyze the frame by use of the force method of analysis.
(*Note:* This frame is analyzed by use of moment distribution in Figure 7-25.)

7.6. Evaluate the moments at all supports by use of moment distribution using the relative values of I shown. Compute final reactions and draw the moment diagram:
(a) assuming support A to be fixed in computing stiffness and fixed-end moments;
(b) assuming the beam to be simply supported at A throughout the analysis.

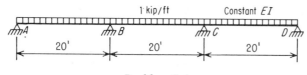

Problem 7-1

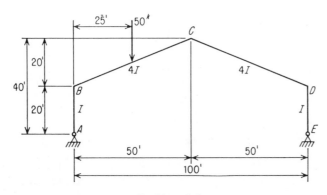

Problem 7-5

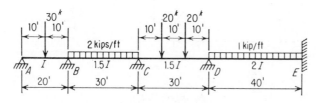

Problem 7-6

7.7.   Determine the values of moment at B, C, and D of the beam of Problem 7.6 by the displacement method of analysis illustrated in Figure 7-5.

7.8.   Draw the curve of maximum moments for the structure for a full-span uniform live load of 2 kips/ft and dead load of 1 kip/ft. Show values at center of spans AB and BC and at the supports. Compute all moments necessary for plotting the curve by use of moment distribution. (*Ans.:* At A, $-12'^k$; at midspan AB, $+95'^k$, $-15'^k$; at B, $-147'^k$; at midspan BC, $+105'^k$.)

7.9.   Compute the values of moments at all joints and draw the moment diagram if support E settles 1 in. $E = 30 \times 10^3$ ksi; $I = 2{,}096$ in.^{4} for the girder; $I = 310$ in.^{4} for the columns. (*Note:* Fixed-end moments occur only in spans AB and BC.)

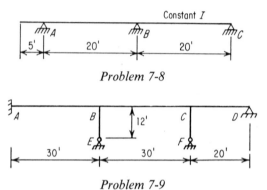

Constant I

Problem 7-8

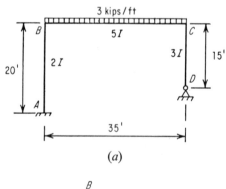

Problem 7-9

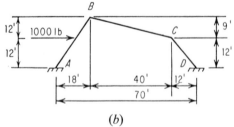

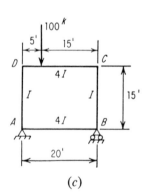

(a)

(b)

(c)

Problem 7-11

7.10. Determine the values of all reactions and draw the moment diagram for the frame in Figure 7-20(a) if there are hinged supports at A and D.

7.11. Analyze the frame by means of moment distribution. Compute all reactions and draw the moment diagram for the following:

(a) unsymmetrical frame (see Problem 6-8);

(b) frame with inclined legs $I_{AB} = 600$ in.[4], $I_{BC} = 1,230$ in.[4], $I_{CD} = 120\sqrt{2}$ in.[4]   (*Ans.: $H_A = 733$ lb; $H_D = 267$ lb.*);

(c) closed frame.

7.12. Compute the moments at all joints in the three-story frame:

(a) by introducing fixed-end moments in each story separately, performing moment distribution, evaluating shears, and solving three simultaneous equations;

(b) by shear adjustment.

The circled values in the figure are relative stiffnesses.   (*Ans.: $M_A = 16.2$ ft-kips; $M_B = 39.6$ ft-kips.*)

7.13. Analyze the multispan frame and draw the moment diagram.

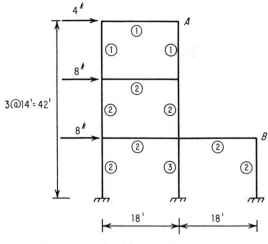

Problem 7-12

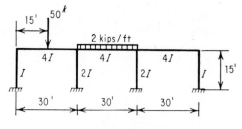

Problem 7-13

7.14. The moment of inertia of the member varies as the cube of the depth. Dividing the variable section member into eight segments as shown and calling the moment of inertia of the 2'-0" deep section I, compute:

(a) fixed-end moments at A and B;

(b) stiffness K_{AB} and carry-over factor C_{AB};

(c) stiffness K_{BA} and carry-over factor C_{BA}.

(*Note:* This member is analyzed by use of the column analogy method in Figure 10-11.)

7.15. Analyze by use of the slope-deflection method:

(a) Problem 7.6;

(b) Problem 7.11(a);

(c) Problem 7.11(c).

7.16. Using the data in Figure 7-37(b), draw the following influence lines for the beam in Figure 7-37(a):

(a) moment at center of span BC;

(b) shear at center of span AB;

(c) reaction at B.

For each influence line indicate final ordinates at all supports and at the center of each span.

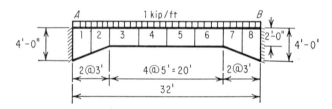

Problem 7-14

Chapter 8

Statically Indeterminate Trusses

The analysis of various types of statically indeterminate trusses by the force method is considered in this chapter. A displacement method for truss analysis is presented in Chapter 9. Influence lines for statically indeterminate trusses are obtained, as for beams, by combining statically determinate influence lines with corrections for continuity.

8.1 Force Method

Three methods of computing displacements in trusses were presented in Chapter 6: virtual work, angle changes, and the displacement diagram. Since only a small number of displacements must be computed in order to analyze most statically indeterminate trusses, the method of virtual work is used in most of the examples in this chapter. However, it must be remembered that the method of analysis does not depend upon the manner in which displacements are computed.

The continuous truss shown in Figure 8-1(a) is statically indeterminate in the second degree. It can be analyzed by the force method by correcting the errors in geometry resulting from assuming values for two reactions. In Figure 8-1(b) the two interior reactions are each taken equal to zero. Based on this assumption, the bar forces are computed and the vertical displacements at B and C determined. These are the errors in geometry shown in Figure 8-1(c). Since these displacements should be zero, correction forces must be introduced at B and C. In Figure 8-1(d), a unit force is applied at B and C, respectively. The resulting displacements at B and C, δ_{BB}, δ_{CB}, δ_{BC}, and δ_{CC}, are indicated in (d). The two equations of geometry written in (e) state mathematically that the actual displacements at B and C must be equal to zero.

The terms X_B and X_C are the forces necessary to adjust the correction displacements in (d) so that the errors in geometry in (c) are eliminated. Therefore X_B and X_C are corrections that must be added to the assumed reaction values at B and C, which have been assumed as equal to zero. Bar forces are obtained as the sum of those of the statically determinate assumption plus X_B times the forces resulting from the unit reaction at B plus X_C times the forces resulting from the unit reaction at C. For the general case of a truss statically indeterminate in the nth degree, n equations of geometry are obtained, and a set of n simultaneous equations of the form of Equations (7.1) must be solved.

The truss in Figure 8-1 also can be analyzed by cutting the upper chord at

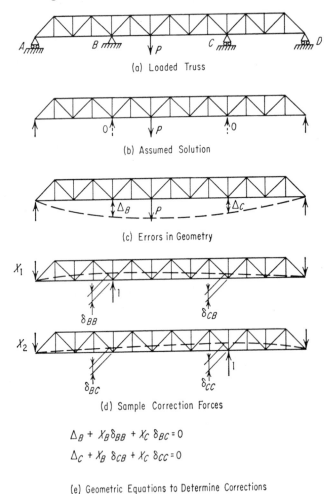

(a) Loaded Truss

(b) Assumed Solution

(c) Errors in Geometry

(d) Sample Correction Forces

$$\Delta_B + X_B \delta_{BB} + X_C \delta_{BC} = 0$$

$$\Delta_C + X_B \delta_{CB} + X_C \delta_{CC} = 0$$

(e) Geometric Equations to Determine Corrections

Figure 8-1.   Analysis of Continuous Truss by Force Method

the interior supports. The resulting three simple spans are statically determinate, and all bar forces can be computed. Errors in geometry would be the relative movements of the cut ends of the upper chord at B and C. Corrections at B and C would be obtained by applying unit correction forces successively to each pair of cut ends and determining the relative movements at these ends. The resulting geometrical equations would be identical in form with those in Figure 8-1(e). The terms X_B and X_C now represent the forces necessary to bring the cut ends of the top chord at B and C together.

8.2   Continuous Trusses

In Figure 8-2 and Table 8-1 the force method of analysis is applied to a loaded three-span continuous truss on unyielding supports. Relative areas, A, and lengths, L, of the bars are listed in columns 2 and 3 of the table, and relative values of L/A are listed in column 4. Actual areas are not necessary

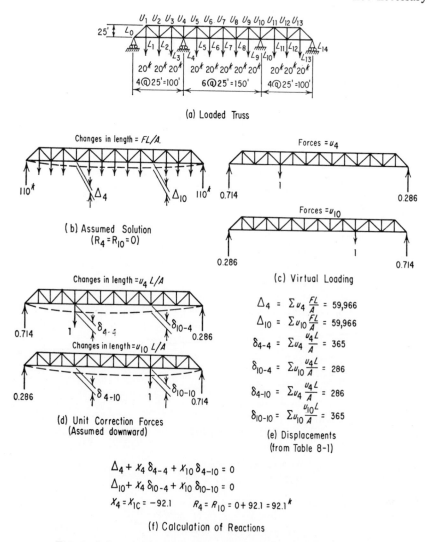

$$\Delta_4 + X_4 \, \delta_{4-4} + X_{10} \, \delta_{4-10} = 0$$
$$\Delta_{10} + X_4 \, \delta_{10-4} + X_{10} \, \delta_{10-10} = 0$$
$$X_4 = X_{1C} = -92.1 \qquad R_4 = R_{10} = 0 + 92.1 = 92.1^k$$

(f) Calculation of Reactions

Figure 8-2.   Analysis of Three-Span Continuous Truss

TABLE 8-1 Simple Truss Displacements

	1	2	3	4	5	6	7	8	9	10	11	12	13
Member		A (rel.)	L (ft.)	L/A	F	FL/A	u_4	u_{10}	$u_4 FL/A$	$u_{10}FL/A$	$u_4^2 L/A$	$u_4 u_{10}L/A$	$u_{10}^2 L/A$
$L_0 L_1$		5.	25.00	5.000	110.00	550.00	.714	.286	393.	157.	3.	1.	0.
$L_1 L_2$		5.	25.00	5.000	110.00	550.00	.714	.286	393.	157.	3.	1.	0.
$L_2 L_3$		5.	25.00	5.000	270.00	1,350.00	2.143	.857	2,893.	1,157.	23.	9.	4.
$L_3 L_4$		5.	25.00	5.000	270.00	1,350.00	2.143	.857	2,893.	1,157.	23.	9.	4.
$L_4 L_5$		5.	25.00	5.000	370.00	1,850.00	2.572	1.428	4,758.	2,642.	33.	18.	10.
$L_5 L_6$		5.	25.00	5.000	370.00	1,850.00	2.572	1.428	4,758.	2,642.	33.	18.	10.
$L_6 L_7$		5.	25.00	5.000	410.00	2,050.00	2.000	2.000	4,100.	4,100.	20.	20.	20.
$L_7 L_8$		5.	25.00	5.000	410.00	2,050.00	2.000	2.000	4,100.	4,100.	20.	20.	20.
$L_8 L_9$		5.	25.00	5.000	370.00	1,850.00	1.428	2.572	2,642.	4,758.	10.	19.	33.
$L_9 L_{10}$		5.	25.00	5.000	370.00	1,850.00	1.428	2.572	2,642.	4,758.	10.	19.	33.
$L_{10} L_{11}$		5.	25.00	5.000	270.00	1,350.00	.857	2.143	1,157.	2,893.	4.	9.	23.
$L_{11} L_{12}$		5.	25.00	5.000	270.00	1,350.00	.857	2.143	1,157.	2,893.	4.	9.	23.
$L_{12} L_{13}$		5.	25.00	5.000	110.00	550.00	.286	.714	157.	393.	0.	1.	3.
$L_{13} L_{14}$		5.	25.00	5.000	110.00	550.00	.286	.714	157.	393.	0.	1.	3.
$U_1 U_2$		5.	25.00	5.000	-200.00	-1,000.00	-1.429	-.571	1,429.	571.	10.	4.	2.
$U_2 U_3$		5.	25.00	5.000	-200.00	-1,000.00	-1.429	-.571	1,429.	571.	10.	4.	2.
$U_3 U_4$		8.	25.00	3.125	-320.00	-1,000.00	-2.857	-1.143	2,857.	1,143.	26.	10.	4.
$U_4 U_5$		8.	25.00	3.125	-320.00	-1,000.00	-2.857	-1.143	2,857.	1,143.	26.	10.	4.
$U_5 U_6$		8.	25.00	3.125	-400.00	-1,250.00	-2.286	-1.714	2,858.	2,143.	16.	12.	9.
$U_6 U_7$		8.	25.00	3.125	-400.00	-1,250.00	-2.286	-1.714	2,858.	2,143.	16.	12.	9.
$U_7 U_8$		8.	25.00	3.125	-400.00	-1,250.00	-1.714	-2.286	2,143.	2,858.	9.	12.	16,
$U_8 U_9$		8.	25.00	3.125	-400.00	-1,250.00	-1.714	-2.286	2,143.	2,858.	9.	12.	16.
$U_9 U_{10}$		8.	25.00	3.125	-320.00	-1,000.00	-1.143	-2.857	1,143.	2,857.	4.	10.	26.
$U_{10}U_{11}$		8.	25.00	3.125	-320.00	-1,000.00	-1.143	-2.857	1,143.	2,857.	4.	10.	26.
$U_{11}U_{12}$		5.	25.00	5.000	-200.00	-1,000.00	-.571	-1.429	571.	1,429.	2.	4.	10.
$U_{12}U_{13}$		5.	25.00	5.000	-200.00	-1,000.00	-.571	-1.429	571.	1,429.	2.	4.	10.
$L_0 U_1$		5.	35.35	7.070	-155.55	-1,099.74	-1.010	-.404	1,111.	444.	7.	3.	1.
$U_1 L_2$		3.	35.35	11.783	127.26	1,499.55	1.010	.404	1,515.	606.	12.	5.	2.
$L_2 U_3$		3.	35.35	11.783	-98.98	-1,166.31	-1.010	-.404	1,178.	471.	12.	5.	2.
$U_3 L_4$		8.	35.35	4.419	70.70	312.41	1.010	.404	316.	126.	5.	2.	0.
$L_4 U_5$		8.	35.35	4.419	-70.70	-312.41	.404	-.404	-126.	126.	0.	0.	0.
$U_5 L_6$		8.	35.35	4.419	42.42	187.44	-.404	.404	-76.	76.	0.	0.	0.
$L_6 U_7$		8.	35.35	4.419	-14.14	-62.48	.404	-.404	-25.	25.	0.	0.	0.
$U_7 L_8$		8.	35.35	4.419	-14.14	-62.48	-.404	.404	25.	-25.	0.	0.	0.
$L_8 U_9$		8.	35.35	4.419	42.42	187.44	.404	-.404	76.	-76.	0.	0.	0.
$U_9 L_{10}$		8.	35.35	4.419	-70.70	-312.41	-.404	.404	126.	-126.	0.	0.	0.
$L_{10}U_{11}$		8.	35.35	4.419	70.70	312.41	.404	1.010	126.	316.	0.	2.	5.
$U_{11}L_{12}$		3.	35.35	11.783	-98.98	-1,166.31	-.404	-1.010	471.	1,178.	2.	5.	12.
$L_{12}U_{13}$		3.	35.35	11.783	127.26	1,499.55	.404	1.010	606.	1,515.	2.	5.	12.
$U_{13}L_{14}$		5.	35.35	7.070	-155.55	-1,099.74	-.404	-1.010	444.	1,111.	1.	3.	7.
TOTALS									59,966.	59,966.	365.	286.	365.

234

because only relative displacements are required in the following analysis. The vertical bars of the truss have been omitted from Table 8-1 because, as explained later, they do not contribute to the displacements used in the analysis.

In Figure 8-2(b) it is assumed that the reactions at L_4 and L_{10} are each equal to zero. On the basis of this assumption, bar forces, F, are determined and relative changes in length, FL/A, are computed. The displacements Δ_4 and Δ_{10} are the errors in geometry corresponding to the assumed solution. They are obtained by the method of virtual work, using the two virtual loadings shown in (c). The expressions for determining Δ_4 and Δ_{10} are included in (e) together with their values (relative) obtained in Table 8-1. The reason why the vertical bars can be omitted from the tabulation now becomes clear. The bar force, F, or the virtual force, u, is zero for each of these members.

Unit correction forces are applied first at L_4 and then at L_{10} in Figure 8-2(d). For convenience, these forces have been applied downward. The resulting bar forces are then identical to the virtual forces in (c), and the relative changes in length of the bars are $u_4 L/A$ and $u_{10} L/A$. Displacements due to the unit forces are also computed by the method of virtual work. Expressions for these displacements are given in Figure 8-2(e), and their values obtained in Table 8-1. In general the displacement at point m due to a unit load at n is

$$\delta_{mn} = \sum u_m \frac{u_n L}{AE} \tag{8.1}$$

The problem considered in Figure 8-2 involves a symmetrical loading on a symmetrical structure and, as a result, $\Delta_4 = \Delta_{10}$. In addition, $\delta_{4-4} = \delta_{10-10}$, which depends only on the symmetry of the structure. Because of these equalities, columns 10 and 13 could be eliminated from Table 8-1. They have been included to illustrate the procedure for the more general condition where no symmetry is involved.

The equations of geometry are written in Figure 8-2(f) and are solved to determine the correction forces. The negative sign indicates that the corrections must be applied in a direction opposite to that assumed. Therefore, the reactions R_4 and R_{10} both act upward.

All other reactions and bar forces can now be computed by statics. The force in any bar is

$$\text{Force} = F + X_4 u_4 + X_{10} u_{10} \tag{8.2}$$

That is, the force is equal to that for the assumed solution, plus the product of each correction force and the corresponding virtual force in the bar. For example, the force in bar $L_0 L_1$ is

$$110.00 + (-92.1)(0.714) + (-92.1)(0.286) = 17.90 \text{ kips}$$

The positive value indicates tension.

True values of displacements, rather than relative values, must be used in the case of support settlement in a continuous truss. To determine only the effects of support settlements at L_4 and L_{10} in the truss of Figure 8.2, Δ_4 and Δ_{10} are omitted from the equations in Figure 8-2(f) and the zeros are replaced by the known or anticipated settlements. Since the values of the correction displacements, δ, are absolute, E must be included and the true areas and lengths must be used, all in consistent units. For example, if the relative areas listed in Table 8-1 are taken as the actual areas in square inches, all totals in Table 8-1 must be multiplied by $12/E$ because the values of L are in ft units. If $E = 30 \times 10^3$ ksi, then for $\Delta_4 = 1$ in. downward and $\Delta_{10} = \frac{1}{2}$ in. downward, the equations of Figure 8-2(f) become

$$X_4\left(365 \times \frac{12}{30 \times 10^3}\right) + X_{10}\left(286 \times \frac{12}{30 \times 10^3}\right) = 1.0$$

$$X_4\left(286 \times \frac{12}{30 \times 10^3}\right) + X_{10}\left(365 \times \frac{12}{30 \times 10^3}\right) = 0.5$$

and the interior reactions X_4 and X_{10} are equal to $+10.79$ kips and -5.03 kips, respectively. A positive sign indicates a reaction in the positive direction of displacement (downward) and a negative sign an upward reaction.

If the interior reactions are furnished by elastic supports, the procedure of analysis is similar to that for the continuous beam in Figure 7-4. True values of displacements must be used and the change in length of the supports due to the correction forces must be included in the equations of geometry.

8.3 Trussed Arches

The two-hinged arch truss shown in Figure 8-3 is statically indeterminate in the first degree. The horizontal reactions in (b) are each assumed equal to zero and the bar forces and changes in length due to the applied load are those of a simple truss. The general procedure of analysis is outlined in Figure 8-3, and the required values of displacements, Δ and δ, are obtained in Table 8-2. Relative areas of 2.5 were assumed for the lower chord and 1 for all other members.

Since both the structure and loading are symmetrical, it is necessary to compute the contributions of only one half of the truss to the required displacements. In Table 8-2 the sum of the values of uFL/A and u^2L/A for all members to the left of U_3L_3 are doubled, and the values for U_3L_3 are added to these subtotals. The negative value for X in Figure 8-3(e) indicates that the true correction force, and hence H, acts in a direction opposite to that chosen for the sample unit correction force in (d).

In Figure 8-3 the particular assumed value of H equal to zero was chosen for convenience only. As previously discussed, any arbitrary value can be used. Furthermore, any other statically possible solution can be assumed. For

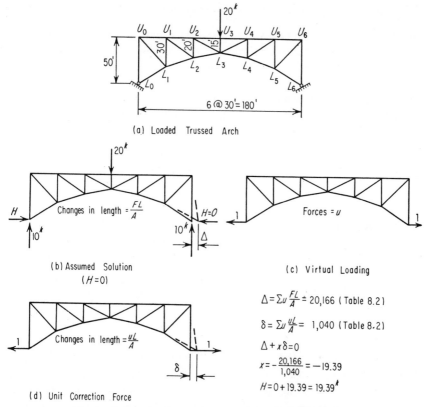

(a) Loaded Trussed Arch

(b) Assumed Solution
(H=0)

(c) Virtual Loading

$$\Delta = \Sigma u \frac{FL}{A} \doteq 20,166 \; (\text{Table } 8.2)$$

$$\delta = \Sigma u \frac{uL}{A} \doteq 1,040 \; (\text{Table } 8.2)$$

$$\Delta + x\delta = 0$$

$$x = -\frac{20,166}{1,040} = -19.39$$

$$H = 0 + 19.39 = 19.39^k$$

(d) Unit Correction Force

Figure 8-3. Analysis of a Two-Hinged Trussed Arch

TABLE 8-2 Determination of Displacements for Trussed Arch (Figure 8-3)

Member	A (rel.)	L (ft.)	L/A	F	FL/A	u	u FL /A	u²L/A
$L_0 L_1$	2.5	36.06	14.42	0.00	0.00	1.202	0.	21.
$L_1 L_2$	2.5	31.62	12.65	10.54	133.31	1.757	234.	39.
$L_2 L_3$	2.5	30.41	12.16	30.40	369.79	2.534	937.	78.
$U_0 U_1$	1.0	30.00	30.00	-10.00	-300.00	-.667	200.	13.
$U_1 U_2$	1.0	30.00	30.00	-30.00	-900.00	-1.500	1,350.	68.
$U_2 U_3$	1.0	30.00	30.00	-60.00	-1,800.00	-2.333	4,199.	163.
$L_0 U_0$	1.0	50.00	50.00	-10.00	-500.00	-.667	334.	22.
$L_1 U_1$	1.0	30.00	30.00	-13.33	-399.99	-.555	222.	9.
$L_2 U_2$	1.0	20.00	20.00	-15.00	-300.00	-.417	125.	3.
$U_0 L_1$	1.0	42.42	42.42	14.14	599.82	.943	566.	38.
$U_1 L_2$	1.0	36.06	36.06	24.06	867.60	1.000	868.	36.
$U_2 L_3$	1.0	33.54	33.54	33.54	1,124.93	.932	1,048.	29.
Subtotals							10,083.	520.
x 2							20,166.	1,040.
$U_3 L_3$	1.0	15.00	15.00	-20.00	-300.00	0.	0.	0.
TOTALS							20,166.	1,040.

237

example, a chord member could be assumed cut, and the resulting three-hinged arch would be statically determinate. The term Δ would then represent the relative displacement of the cut bar ends. Unit correction forces and the virtual loading would be applied to the cut ends.

When foundation conditions are such that the abutments cannot resist horizontal thrust, a trussed arch can be supported in the same manner as a simple truss and a tie introduced between the two ends of the structure in order to resist the horizontal reaction components. The analysis is identical with that indicated in Figure 8-3, with the exception that the effect of the tie must be included. An assumed solution obtained by cutting the tie does not change the value of Δ in Figure 8-3(b). However, the unit correction forces are applied to the cut ends of the tie, and the resulting change in length of the tie must be included in the determination of δ.

If the arch truss of Figure 8-3(a) had a tie whose relative area was equal to 1.5,

$$\frac{L}{A} = \frac{180}{1.5} = 120 \, ; \qquad F = 0 \, ; \qquad \frac{FL}{A} = 0$$

$$u = 1 \, ; \qquad \frac{uFL}{A} = 0 \, ; \qquad \frac{u^2L}{A} = 120$$

The value of 120 for u^2L/A would be added to the total of 1,040.00 in Table 8-2 to obtain a new value of δ equal to 1,160.00. The value of H then becomes $\frac{20,166}{1,160} = 17.38$ kips, which is smaller than the value shown in Figure 8-3 for the arch truss without a tie. This is due to the fact that the tie in the actual structure elongates, thereby permitting a relative horizontal movement of the ends of the structure.

A trussed two-hinged arch is affected by changes in temperature since it is not permitted to move horizontally at its supports, as does an ordinary truss, or to change position freely because of an interior hinge, as does a three-hinged arch. Assume that a temperature change of $+75°F$ is undergone by the trussed arch in Figure 8-3. If the coefficient of thermal expansion is 0.0000065, the change in span is

$$\Delta = 0.0000065(75)(180)(12) = 1.05 \text{ in.}$$

The remainder of the analysis is as in Figure 8-3 except that it is necessary to modify the values in Table 8-2 so as to include the value of E as well as the lengths of the bars in inches and the true bar areas in square inches. The tied arch would develop no temperature stresses providing the tie was subjected to the same temperature change. If the temperature change is not identical, Δ is computed as the *difference* in free elongation of arch and tie.

The identical procedure is used to determine the effects of known assumed relative horizontal displacement between the two supports. A small relative vertical movement, however, has no effect on the reactions or bar forces.

The continuous arch truss in Figure 8-4 is statically indeterminate in the third degree. An assumed solution can be obtained by cutting the tie between B and C and assuming vertical reaction values, generally taken as zero, at B and C. Three equations of geometry can be written in which Δ_1, Δ_2, and Δ_3 represent, respectively, the vertical displacements at B and C, and the hori-

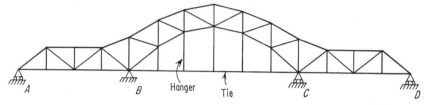

Figure 8-4.   Continuous Trussed Arch

zontal displacement of the cut ends of the tie, all due to the actual load on the assumed structure. The term δ_{31} would represent the horizontal displacement of the cut ends of the tie due to a unit vertical force applied at B, and so forth.

8.4   Method of Least Work

Suppose the reactions at the supports L_4 and L_{10} in Figure 8-2(a) are called X_4 and X_{10}, respectively. (These are equivalent to a set of assumed reactions in the force method.) All bar forces, F, in the truss can now be expressed in terms of the loads and X_4 and X_{10}.

From Castigliano's second theorem, the first partial derivative of the total strain energy of the system, $U = \frac{1}{2}\sum F^2 L/AE$, with respect to X_4 is equal to the deflection of the actual truss at L_4. Similarly, the partial derivative of U with respect to X_{10} is the deflection at L_{10}. But the deflections are zero for a truss on unyielding supports. Therefore,

$$\frac{\partial U}{\partial X_4} = 0$$

$$\frac{\partial U}{\partial X_{10}} = 0$$

(8.3)

These equations are the mathematical expression of the theorem of least work. They state that the correct values of the statically indeterminate quantities are those which make the strain energy a minimum. Only then are the requirements of geometry, as well as statics, satisfied.

The student should apply this method to the truss in Figure 8-2(a). He will discover that Equations (8.3) become identical to the equations of the force method.

If desired, the original "guesses" can be $(X_4 + C_4)$ and $(X_{10} + C_{10})$, where C_4 and C_{10} are constants. These are picked so as to make X_4 and X_{10}

small corrections, thus reducing the effect on the statically indeterminate quantities of errors or lack of precision in the analysis.

8.5   Internally Indeterminate Trusses

The truss in Figure 8-5(a) is statically indeterminate in the second degree because each interior panel has one bar in excess of those required for stability. *Any* bar in each of these panels can be regarded as redundant. In some instances, however, trusses of this type are designed in such a way that the

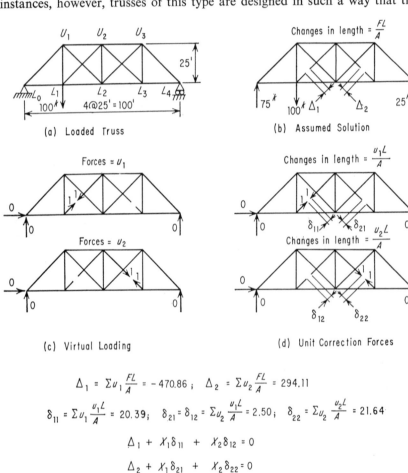

$$\Delta_1 = \Sigma u_1 \frac{FL}{A} = -470.86\,; \quad \Delta_2 = \Sigma u_2 \frac{FL}{A} = 294.11$$

$$\delta_{11} = \Sigma u_1 \frac{u_1 L}{A} = 20.39\,; \quad \delta_{21} = \delta_{12} = \Sigma u_2 \frac{u_1 L}{A} = 2.50\,; \quad \delta_{22} = \Sigma u_2 \frac{u_2 L}{A} = 21.64$$

$$\Delta_1 + X_1 \delta_{11} + X_2 \delta_{12} = 0$$

$$\Delta_2 + X_1 \delta_{21} + X_2 \delta_{22} = 0$$

$$X_1 = +25.13 \text{ kips (tension)}\,; \quad X_2 = -16.50 \text{ kips (compression)}$$

(e)   Calculation of Indeterminate Bar Forces

Figure 8-5.   Internally Indeterminate Truss

diagonals are capable of developing tension only. For such trusses all members are required for stability and the truss is statically determinate.

Again we use the force method of analysis. The truss in Figure 8-5(a) has been made statically determinate in (b) by assuming a diagonal in each of the interior panels to be cut. It is emphasized, however, that any two bars could be cut providing the structure remained stable. The analysis proceeds with the aid of Table 8-3. The virtual loadings necessary to determine the values of the relative movements of the ends of the cut bars are shown in (c). Note that the virtual loading of equal and opposite forces on the ends of a cut bar induces no reactions at the supports L_0 and L_4, and only the six members of the panel are stressed.

The negative value of Δ_1, shown in (e), indicates that the movement of the cut ends is opposite to the direction of the virtual loading used in (c) to obtain Δ_1. The positive value of Δ_2 indicates that the movement is in the same direction as the corresponding virtual loading. These signs are retained and the sample unit corrections in (d) applied in the same directions as the virtual loads in (c). Signs are then automatic, and a positive sign for a correction force, X, will indicate that it acts in the same direction as its corresponding unit force in (d). Furthermore, if all unit forces in (c) and (d) are taken as tensions, a positive sign for X indicates tension.

The statically indeterminate bar forces are 25.13 kips tension in U_2L_1 and 16.50 kips compression in U_2L_3. All other bar forces can be obtained conveniently as indicated by Equation (8.2).

In the internally indeterminate truss an axial force applied to a redundant member induces stress in all other members of the panel. A force applied to a bar in a statically determinate panel has no effect on the other bars, since the triangles involved are free to change shape.

T A B L E 8-3 Determination of Displacements for Truss (Figure 8-5)

Member	A (in².)	L (ft.)	L/A	F	FL/A	u_1	u_2	$u_1 FL/A$	$u_2 FL/A$	$u_1^2 L/A$	$u_1 u_2 L/A$	$u_2^2 L/A$
$U_1 U_2$	10.	25.00	2.500	-50.00	-125.00	-.707	0.000	88.38	0.00	1.25	0.00	0.00
$U_2 U_3$	10.	25.00	2.500	-50.00	-125.00	0.000	-.707	0.00	88.38	0.00	0.00	1.25
$L_1 L_2$	10.	25.00	2.500	75.00	187.50	-.707	0.000	-132.56	0.00	1.25	0.00	0.00
$L_2 L_3$	10.	25.00	2.500	25.00	62.50	0.000	-.707	0.00	-44.19	0.00	0.00	1.25
$U_1 L_1$	10.	25.00	2.500	100.00	250.00	-.707	0.000	-176.75	0.00	1.25	0.00	0.00
$U_2 L_2$	5.	25.00	5.000	0.00	0.00	-.707	-.707	0.00	0.00	2.50	2.50	2.50
$U_3 L_3$	5.	25.00	5.000	0.00	0.00	0.000	-.707	0.00	0.00	0.00	0.00	2.50
$U_1 L_2$	5.	35.35	7.070	-35.35	-249.92	1.000	0.000	-249.92	0.00	7.07	0.00	0.00
$L_2 U_3$	5.	35.35	7.070	35.35	249.92	0.000	1.000	0.00	249.92	0.00	0.00	7.07
$L_1 U_2$	5.	35.35	7.070	0.00	0.00	1.000	0.000	0.00	0.00	7.07	0.00	0.00
$U_2 L_3$	5.	35.35	7.070	0.00	0.00	0.000	1.000	0.00	0.00	0.00	0.00	7.07
TOTALS								-470.86	294.11	20.39	2.50	21.64

The redundant member L_1U_2 of the truss in Figure 8-6(a) is assumed to have been fabricated 0.1 in. too long and forced into place during erection. The error in geometry, Δ, is equal to 0.1 in. In Table 8-4 the relative displacement, δ, is 24.14. The absolute value of δ is found in Figure 8-6 by multiplying 24.14 by 12 (to convert length to inch units) and by dividing by $E = 30,000$ ksi. With the force in bar U_2L_1 known, all other bar forces can be obtained by multiplying -10.36 by the corresponding "u" values from Table 8-4.

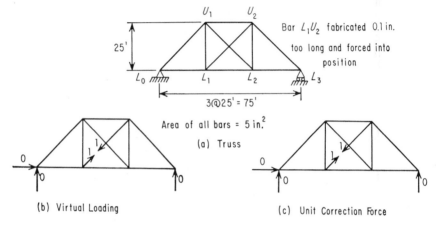

$$\Delta + X\delta = 0$$
$$0.1 + \frac{24.14 \times 12}{30 \times 10^3}X = 0$$
$$X = -10.36 \text{ kips}$$

Force in $L_1U_2 = 10.36$ kips compression

Figure 8-6.   Effects of Errors in Fabrication

TABLE 8-4 Displacement Determination for Truss (Figure 8-6)

Member	L, ft	A, in.^{2}	u	u^2L/A
L_1L_2	25.00	5	-0.707	2.50
U_1U_2	25.00	5	-0.707	2.50
U_1L_1	25.00	5	-0.707	2.50
U_2L_2	25.00	5	-0.707	2.50
U_1L_2	35.35	5	1.000	7.07
L_1U_2	35.35	5	1.000	7.07
TOTAL				24.14

8.6   Influence Lines for Continuous Trusses

Influence lines for continuous trusses are obtained in the same manner as influence lines for continuous beams (see Section 7.15). Assumed statically determinate influence lines are corrected for the effects of continuity by superposition of a correction pattern. Application of the procedure to a continuous truss statically indeterminate in the first degree is illustrated in Figure 8-7. As with continuous beams, it is convenient to draw the statically determinate influence lines by assuming the center reaction to be zero. Influence lines for force in two bars of the assumed statically determinate truss are shown in (c) and (e). Such influence lines were discussed in Section 3.9.

The shape of the correction curve for continuity is the same as the shape of the influence line for the center reaction. Using Müller-Breslau's principle, this required shape may be obtained as the deflected load line (lower chord) due to a known vertical force applied at L_3. Deflections can be determined by applying the method of angle changes (Section 6.11), or virtual work (Section 6.10), or by drawing a displacement diagram (Section 6.12). The ordinates in (b) are those resulting from a unit force applied at L_3, and were obtained by drawing the displacement diagram in Figure 8-8, using data shown in Table 8-5. The resulting deflected shape consists of straight-line segments between panel points. The influence line for reaction at L_3 in the continuous truss can be obtained from (b) by dividing all ordinates by the value of the center ordinate, 315.

It is known that any bar force is zero if a load acts at the center support of the continuous truss. Therefore the final influence ordinate at L_3 must be zero. This fixes the value of the multiplier to be applied to the relative displacements of the lower chord in (b) in order to obtain the correction pattern in each case. The multiplier to be applied to the ordinates in (b) before combining them with those in (c) is determined from

$$-1.333 + 315X = 0$$

from which

$$X = \frac{1.333}{315}$$

The ordinate in (d) at L_2, for example, can now be obtained as

$$-1.777 + (\tfrac{1.333}{315})234 = -1.777 + 0.990 = -0.787$$

The multiplier to be applied to the ordinates in (b) before combining them with those in (e) is determined from

$$0.833 + 315X = 0$$

from which

$$X = -\frac{0.833}{315}$$

The ordinate in (f) at L_2, for example, can now be obtained as

$$+1.111 + (-\tfrac{0.833}{315})234 = 1.111 - 0.619 = 0.492$$

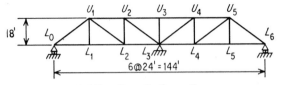

(a) Two-Span Continuous Truss

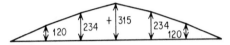

(b) Relative Displacements of Lower Chord Due to Vertical Force Applied at L_3 (Simple Span L_0-L_6)

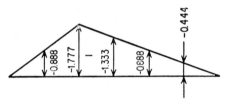

(c) Influence line for Force in $U_1 U_2$, Simple Span

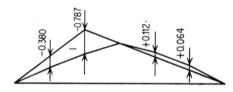

(d) Influence Line for Force in $U_1 U_2$, Continuous Truss

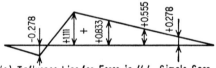

(e) Influence Line for Force in $U_1 L_2$, Simple Span

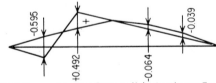

(f) Influence Line for Force in $U_1 L_2$, Continuous Truss

Figure 8-7. *Influence Lines for a Two-Span Continuous Truss by Superposition of a Correction on Values for a Simple Span*

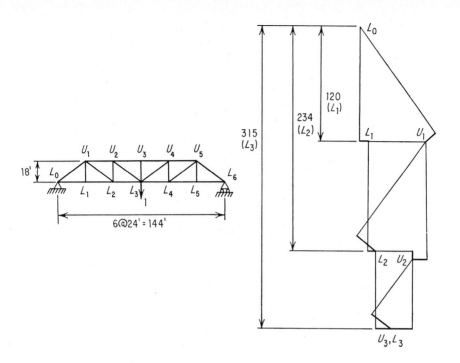

Figure 8-8. Relative Displacements of Lower Chord

TABLE 8-5 Relative Changes in Lengths of Bars for Truss (Figure 8-8)

Member	A	F	L	FL/A
$L_0 L_1$	10	0.667	24	1.60
$L_1 L_2$	10	0.667	24	1.60
$L_2 L_3$	10	1.333	24	3.20
$L_0 U_1$	10	-0.833	30	-2.50
$U_1 U_2$	10	-1.333	24	-3.20
$U_2 U_3$	10	-2.000	24	-4.80
$U_1 L_1$	5	0	18	0
$U_2 L_2$	5	-0.500	18	-1.80
$U_3 L_3$	5	0	18	0
$U_1 L_2$	5	0.833	30	5.00
$U_2 L_3$	5	0.833	30	5.00

Since the final influence ordinates at all supports must equal zero, useful approximate influence lines may be obtained by superimposing sketched curves on simple-span influence lines. The more important large ordinates can usually be obtained with tolerable accuracy by such a sketch approach. Approximate influence lines obtained by sketching the correction pattern can be of some importance in preliminary design.

A three-span continuous truss is shown in Figure 8-9(a). Any influence line for bar force can be obtained by superimposing the effect of reactions at B and C on the influence line for bar force in the truss considered supported at A and D only. In Figure 8-9(b) and (c) relative lower-chord displacements due to a vertical force applied at B and due to a vertical force applied at C are shown. They were obtained by use of the angle-change procedure. Ordinates to the influence line for force in member U_5U_7 of the truss with simple span AD are given in Figure 8-9(d). The ordinates in (b) and (c) must be adjusted so that when they are added to those in (d) the final values at B and C are equal to zero. Thus,

$$-2.286 + 4.20X_1 + 3.26X_2 = 0$$

$$-1.714 + 3.26X_1 + 4.20X_2 = 0$$

from which,

$$X_1 = +0.5724; \qquad X_2 = -0.0362$$

where X_1 is the multiplier for the ordinates in (b) and X_2 is the multiplier for the ordinates in (c). The correction ordinates in (e) are a result of combining ordinates in (b) multiplied by X_1 with ordinates in (c) multiplied by X_2. For example, the correction ordinate at panel point L_2 is

$$0.5724(2.45) - 0.0362(1.76) = 1.339$$

and the final influence ordinate at point L_2 is

$$-1.143 + 1.339 = 0.196$$

as shown in (f).

Influence lines for other bar forces are obtained in the same way by superimposing on the statically determinate line, corrections due to the effect of the reactions at B and C. For each bar a pair of equations must be solved for particular values of X_1 and X_2.

The influence line for reaction at B is shown in Figure 8-9(g). In this case the final ordinate at B must be equal to unity and that at C equal to zero. The influence line ordinates are obtained by a linear combination of the lower-chord displacements given in (b) and (c). The controlling equations for the multipliers for (b) and (c) are

$$4.20X_1 + 3.26X_2 = 1$$

$$3.26X_1 + 4.20X_2 = 0$$

from which

$$X_1 = +0.599; \qquad X_2 = -0.465$$

The final ordinates are obtained as the sum of two parts. For example, the ordinate at point L_2 is

$$0.599(2.45) - 0.465(1.76) = 0.649$$

For design, preliminary influence lines can be obtained by assuming relative areas for the bars. With these influence lines and the known loading, bar areas

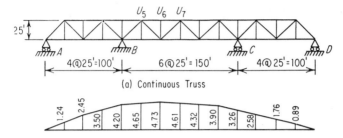

(a) Continuous Truss

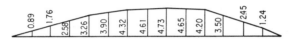

(b) Relative Displacements of Lower Chord Due to Vertical Force Applied at B

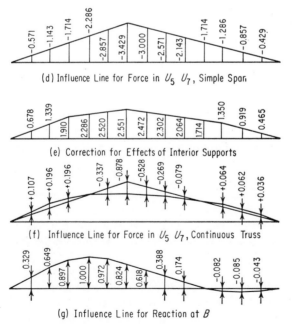

(c) Relative Displacements of Lower Chord Due to Vertical Force Applied at C

(d) Influence Line for Force in $U_5 U_7$, Simple Span

(e) Correction for Effects of Interior Supports

(f) Influence Line for Force in $U_5 U_7$, Continuous Truss

(g) Influence Line for Reaction at B

Figure 8-9.   Influence Lines for Three-Span Continuous Truss

can be picked and then new influence lines obtained. This procedure is repeated, generally once or twice, until two successive sets of areas correspond.
Alternatively, influence lines for the indeterminate reactions can be obtained
by treating the continuous truss as a continuous beam. With these preliminary
influence lines for reactions, the influence lines for bar forces can be obtained
and a set of preliminary bar areas picked. The remainder of this procedure is
identical to that previously outlined.

8.7   Influence Lines for Trussed Arch

The trussed arch shown in Figure 8-10(a) is statically indeterminate in the
first degree. Therefore, if a true influence line for horizontal reaction component, H, is known, all influence line ordinates for bar stress can be found by use
of statics.

Based on the Müller-Breslau principle, the influence line for H may be
determined as the deflected loaded (upper) chord resulting from a unit
horizontal displacement at the support. Since the value of horizontal reaction
necessary to cause the unit movement is not known, the deflected position of
the loaded chord resulting from an *assumed* horizontal reaction will be computed and then adjusted for a unit displacement. If δ is the vertical movement
of a panel point on the loaded chord due to the arbitrary horizontal force at
the support and Δ is the accompanying horizontal displacement at the support,
then at the panel point the influence ordinate for H is

$$i = \frac{\delta}{\Delta} \qquad (8.4)$$

The displacements δ and Δ can be determined by use of the displacement
diagram, the method of angle changes, or by virtual work. If the method of
virtual work is used, Equation (8.4) may be written as

$$i = \frac{\sum u_V(u_H L/A)}{\sum u_H^2(L/A)} \qquad (8.5)$$

where u_V represents the bar forces due to a unit vertical load applied at a
panel point on the loaded chord, and u_H represents the bar forces due to a unit
horizontal load applied at a support. To obtain an influence ordinate at any
other panel point, new values of u_V must be computed in Equation (8.5), but
the denominator has the same value for all panel points.

The values of the displacements represented by the numerator and denominator of Equation (8.5) are obtained in Table 8-6 for the arch in Figure
8-10(a). This structure is identical to that in Figure 8-3. As a result, u_{V3} and

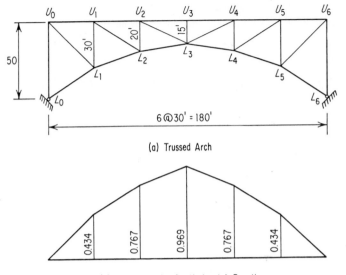

(a) Trussed Arch

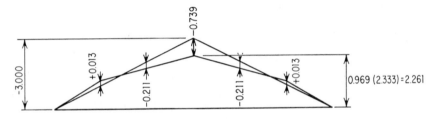

(b) Influence Line for Horizontal Reaction

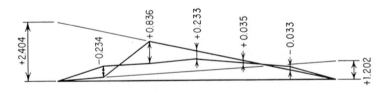

(c) Influence Line for Force in $U_2 U_4$

(d) Influence Line for Force in $U_1 L_2$

Figure 8-10. Influence Lines for Two-Hinged Trussed Arch

u_H in Table 8-6 are respectively equal to $F/20$ and u in Table 8-2. Using Equation (8.5), the influence ordinates at panel points 1, 2, and 3 are

$$i_1 = \frac{451}{1,040} = 0.434$$

$$i_2 = \frac{798}{1,040} = 0.767$$

$$i_3 = \frac{1,008}{1,040} = 0.969$$

The influence line for horizontal reaction is shown in Figure 8-10(b).

249

TABLE 8-6
Displacements for Determining Influence Values for H

Member	L/A	u_{V1}	u_{V2}	u_{V3}	u_H	$u_{V1}u_H L/A$	$u_{V2}u_H L/A$	$u_{V3}u_H L/A$	$u_H^2 L/A$
$L_0 L_1$	14.424	0.000	0.000	0.000	1.202	0.	0.	0.	21.
$L_1 L_2$	12.648	.878	.702	.527	1.757	20.	16.	12.	39.
$L_2 L_3$	12.164	1.013	2.026	1.520	2.534	31.	62.	47.	78.
$L_3 L_4$	12.164	.507	1.013	1.520	2.534	16.	31.	47.	78.
$L_6 L_5$	12.648	.176	.351	.527	1.757	4.	8.	12.	39.
$L_5 L_6$	14.424	0.000	0.000	0.000	1.202	0.	0.	0.	21.
$U_0 U_1$	30.000	-.833	-.667	-.500	-.667	17.	13.	10.	13.
$U_1 U_2$	30.000	-1.000	-2.000	-1.500	-1.500	45.	90.	68.	68.
$U_2 U_3$	30.000	-1.000	-2.000	-3.000	-2.333	70.	140.	210.	163.
$U_3 U_4$	30.000	-1.000	-2.000	-3.000	-2.333	70.	140.	210.	163.
$U_4 U_5$	30.000	-.500	-1.000	-1.500	-1.500	23.	45.	68.	68.
$U_5 U_6$	30.000	-.167	-.333	-.500	-.667	3.	7.	10.	13.
$L_0 U_0$	50.000	-.833	-.667	-.500	-.667	28.	22.	17.	22.
$L_1 U_1$	30.000	-1.111	-.889	-.667	-.555	18.	15.	11.	9.
$L_2 U_2$	20.000	0.000	-1.000	-.750	-.417	0.	8.	6.	3.
$L_3 U_3$	15.000	0.000	0.000	-1.000	0.000	0.	0.	0.	0.
$L_4 U_4$	20.000	-.250	-.500	-.750	-.417	2.	4.	6.	3.
$L_5 U_5$	30.000	-.222	-.445	-.667	-.555	4.	7.	11.	9.
$L_6 U_6$	50.000	-.167	-.333	-.500	-.667	6.	11.	17.	22.
$U_0 L_1$	42.420	1.178	.942	.707	.943	47.	38.	28.	38.
$U_1 L_2$	36.060	.200	1.603	1.203	1.000	7.	58.	43.	36.
$U_2 L_3$	33.540	0.000	0.000	1.677	.932	0.	0.	52.	29.
$U_4 L_3$	33.540	.559	1.118	1.677	.932	17.	35.	52.	29.
$U_5 L_4$	36.060	.401	.802	1.203	1.000	14.	29.	43.	36.
$U_6 L_5$	42.420	.236	.471	.707	.943	9.	19.	28.	38.
TOTALS						451.	798.	1008.	1040.

Influence lines for force in members U_2U_4 and U_1L_2 are shown in Figure 8-10(c) and (d). Each was obtained by superimposing the effect of the horizontal reaction component on influence lines obtained by assuming the truss to be simply supported. The effect of the horizontal thrust is conveniently computed by multiplying the ordinates in (b) by minus one times the u_H force, from Table 8-6, for the bar considered. For example, the correction ordinate at midspan for the influence line for force in U_2U_4, illustrated in Figure 8-10(c), is equal to $0.969(2.333) = 2.261$, where 0.969 is the influence ordinate for horizontal thrust and 2.333 is minus one times the u_H force for member U_2U_4.

For design purposes, a preliminary influence line for horizontal reaction may be obtained by assuming relative areas for the arch members. On the basis of these relative areas, preliminary influence lines for bar forces are obtained in the manner outlined in Figure 8-10 and Table 8-6. With these influence lines, new areas are computed. Using these areas, a second set of influence lines is obtained, and new areas computed. This procedure is repeated until there is good agreement between successive areas. A second approach involves the use of an assumed influence line for H for obtaining a first set of areas.[1]

Problems

8.1. Compute values of reactions and force in each member of the truss for the following cases:

    (a) areas of all members are equal   (*Ans.*: $L_0U_1 = +33.1^k$; $L_0L_1 = +16.6^k$);

    (b) areas of all external members $= 10$ in.[2], areas of all interior members $= 5$ in.[2]

8.2. Determine the values of all reactions and bar forces if the center support of the truss in Problem 8.1(b) settles vertically 0.5 in. Do not include the effects of the two 50-kip concentrated loads. $E = 30 \times 10^3$ ksi.

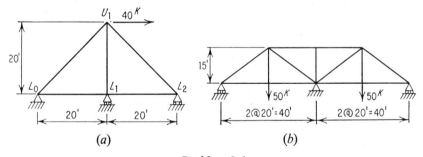

(a)   (b)

Problem 8-1

[1] James Michalos, *Theory of Structural Analysis and Design* (New York: Ronald, 1958).

8.3. Evaluate the horizontal reaction and all bar forces for the trussed arch. Relative areas of members: two for top chord, one for all other members.

8.4. Calculate the values for all bar forces in the following internally indeterminate trusses:

  (a) area of all members $= 10$ in.^{2}
  (b) area of members U_0L_1 and $L_0U_1 = 5$ in.^{2}
      all others $= 10$ in.^{2} (*Ans.: $L_0U_1 = +53^k$.*)
  (c) area of all members $= 10$ in.^{2} (*Ans.: $L_0U_1 = U_1L_2 = -39.2^k$.*)

8.5. Determine the force in bar U_3L_1 if it is fabricated 0.25 in. too short and is forced into place during erection. Areas of all bars are equal. (*Ans.: 1.458×10^{-4} AE.*)

8.6. Construct the following influence lines for the truss shown in Figure 8-9(a):
  (a) reaction at A;
  (b) force in the endpost at A;
  (c) force in the diagonal B–U_5.

8.7 Construct the following influence lines for the two-hinged trussed arch shown in Figure 8-10(a):
  (a) force in U_1L_1;
  (b) force in L_1L_2.

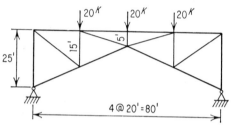

Problem 8-3

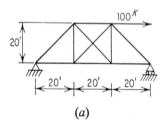

(a)

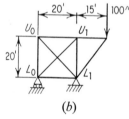

(b)

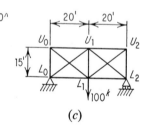

(c)

Problem 8-4

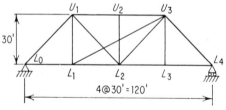

Problem 8-5

Chapter 9

Matrix Methods

In this chapter matrix algebra is used in the analysis of continuous beams, rigid frames, and trusses. Strictly speaking, so-called matrix methods are not methods for analyzing structures but are, rather, mathematical procedures that may reduce the computational time required to complete an analysis by conventional classical methods. It has been shown, in Sections 7.2 and 7.4, that both the force and displacement methods of analysis lead to simultaneous equations. Any method of analysis that involves linear algebraic equations may be put into matrix notation, and matrix operations may be used to obtain solutions. Stiffness and flexibility matrices, which are properties of a structure, are developed and their physical significance explained.

Since standard digital computer programs are readily available for inversion and multiplication of matrices, forms of solution involving matrix operations should be considered for complicated structural problems that lead to large sets of simultaneous equations. Matrix methods are particularly advantageous if a structure must be analyzed for the effects of several loading patterns.

9.1 Properties of Matrices

A few basic concepts of matrix algebra are introduced for those unfamiliar with the subject. The treatment is adequate for understanding the use of matrix methods in this book.

A matrix is a rectangular array of numbers. In a set of linear algebraic equations such as

$$a_{11}x_1 + a_{12}x_2 + a_{13}x_3 = c_1$$

$$a_{21}x_1 + a_{22}x_2 + a_{23}x_3 = c_2 \qquad (9.1)$$

$$a_{31}x_1 + a_{32}x_2 + a_{33}x_3 = c_3$$

253

the coefficients on the left-hand side of the equations constitute the matrix

$$A = \begin{bmatrix} a_{11} & a_{12} & a_{13} \\ a_{21} & a_{22} & a_{23} \\ a_{31} & a_{32} & a_{33} \end{bmatrix} \tag{9.2}$$

This is called a 3×3 matrix because it has three rows and three columns. A matrix with m rows and n columns is designated as an $m \times n$ matrix. Two $m \times n$ matrices are equal only if all corresponding elements are equal. A matrix with an equal number of rows and columns is called a square matrix.

The reader will note that if the array of elements in Equation (9.2) is enclosed by two vertical bars, it represents the familiar determinant of the coefficients of the system of Equations (9.1).

$$D = \begin{vmatrix} a_{11} & a_{12} & a_{13} \\ a_{21} & a_{22} & a_{23} \\ a_{31} & a_{32} & a_{33} \end{vmatrix} \tag{9.3}$$

The value of the determinant is most readily obtained by means of cofactors (signed minors) as will be seen later. The determinant (9.3) is also referred to as the determinant of the matrix (9.2).

Equations (9.1) may be written in matrix notation as

$$\begin{bmatrix} a_{11} & a_{12} & a_{13} \\ a_{21} & a_{22} & a_{23} \\ a_{31} & a_{32} & a_{33} \end{bmatrix} \begin{bmatrix} x_1 \\ x_2 \\ x_3 \end{bmatrix} = \begin{bmatrix} c_1 \\ c_2 \\ c_3 \end{bmatrix} \tag{9.4}$$

in which the arrays of x's and c's are 3×1 matrices. Such single-column arrays are called column vectors or column matrices, and can be represented by $\{x_i\}$ and $\{c_i\}$, respectively. In "short-hand" matrix notation, Equations (9.1) can be written

$$A\{x_i\} = \{c_i\} \tag{9.5}$$

We can write instead,

$$AX = C \tag{9.5a}$$

in which X represents the column vector of the unknowns and C represents the column vector of the constant terms.

A matrix A can be multiplied by a constant k. This results in a new matrix, all of whose elements are k times those of matrix A. We can multiply a matrix A by a matrix B only if the number of columns, n, of A is equal to the number of rows of B. The product matrix E will have the same number of rows, m, as A and the same number of columns, p, as B—that is,

$$A_{mn}B_{np} = E_{mp} \tag{9.6}$$

The element in row i and column j of the product matrix E is obtained by multiplying row i of **A** by column j of **B**. The procedure is illustrated by the following example:

$$\begin{bmatrix} 2 & 1 \\ 3 & 5 \\ 4 & 6 \end{bmatrix} \begin{bmatrix} 6 & 2 & 3 \\ 1 & 4 & 5 \end{bmatrix} = \begin{bmatrix} 13 & 8 & 11 \\ 23 & 26 & 34 \\ 30 & 32 & 42 \end{bmatrix}$$

The number 13 is obtained from $(2)(6) + (1)(1)$, and the number 26 is obtained from $(3)(2) + (5)(4)$.

The matrix product **AB** is *not* equal to the product **BA**. Thus,

$$\begin{bmatrix} 6 & 2 & 3 \\ 1 & 4 & 5 \end{bmatrix} \begin{bmatrix} 2 & 1 \\ 3 & 5 \\ 4 & 6 \end{bmatrix} = \begin{bmatrix} 30 & 34 \\ 34 & 51 \end{bmatrix}$$

Each term in the latter product matrix is obtained as the sum of three products. For example, 51 is obtained from $(1)(1) + (4)(5) + (5)(6)$.

Since a column vector is an $m \times 1$ matrix, the product of a rectangular matrix and a column vector, as shown in Equation (9.4), is equal to another column vector.

Two $m \times n$ matrices can be added to obtain a new $m \times n$ matrix. Thus

$$\mathbf{A}_{mn} + \mathbf{B}_{mn} = \mathbf{S}_{mn} \tag{9.7}$$

in which each element of **S** is obtained by adding the corresponding elements of **A** and **B**.

For the rest of this section and in Section 9.2 we confine ourselves to the practically important square matrix. A special form of the square matrix is one in which all elements except those of the main diagonal are equal to zero. If, in addition, all the elements of the main diagonal are equal to 1, such a matrix

$$\mathbf{I} = \begin{bmatrix} 1 & 0 & 0 \\ 0 & 1 & 0 \\ 0 & 0 & 1 \end{bmatrix} \tag{9.8}$$

is called the identity, or unit, matrix, and $\mathbf{AI} = \mathbf{IA} = \mathbf{A}$.

The inverse of a square matrix **A**, designated $\mathbf{A}^{-1}$, is another square matrix, which when multiplied by **A** yields a matrix product equal to the unit matrix—that is,

$$\mathbf{AA}^{-1} = \mathbf{I} \tag{9.9}$$

Matrix inversion is considered in detail in the following section.

The transpose of a matrix **A**, designated $\mathbf{A}^T$, is obtained by using the rows of **A** as columns in $\mathbf{A}^T$. The transpose of the matrix (9.2) is

$$\mathbf{A}^T = \begin{bmatrix} a_{11} & a_{21} & a_{31} \\ a_{12} & a_{22} & a_{32} \\ a_{13} & a_{23} & a_{33} \end{bmatrix} \tag{9.10}$$

If transposition of a matrix does not change the value of any of its elements, it is termed a symmetric matrix.

9.2　Matrix Inversion

Matrix inversion is of particular importance in engineering calculations, and many methods are available for performing the inversion. Two methods, which are particularly useful for inversion when slide rule or desk calculator is used, are considered in this section. The first method, which utilizes cofactors of the matrix, is recommended for inverting 2 × 2 or 3 × 3 matrices. The second method, called pivotal condensation, is suggested for 4 × 4, or larger, matrices. Standard programs are available for matrix inversion by digital computer. The availability of such computers makes possible the inversion of extremely large matrices.

The cofactor of any element of a matrix is obtained by evaluating the determinant (or minor) of the matrix that results from elimination of the row and column of the element, and then multiplying it by $+1$ or -1, depending on the position of the element. If the sum of the column and row numbers of the element is an even number, the value of the determinant is multiplied by $+1$; if odd, it is multiplied by -1. For example, the element a_{11} of matrix (9.2) is in column 1, row 1, and its cofactor is equal to $+(a_{22}a_{33} - a_{23}a_{32})$. The cofactor of a_{23} is equal to $-(a_{11}a_{32} - a_{12}a_{31})$.

Once the cofactors have all been obtained, the inverse of matrix $\mathbf{A}$ can be obtained by dividing the transpose of its cofactors by the determinant, $|\mathbf{A}|$, of the matrix. The transpose of the cofactors of a matrix $\mathbf{A}$ is called the Adjoint of $\mathbf{A}$, and

$$\mathbf{A}^{-1} = \frac{\text{Adjoint of } \mathbf{A}}{|\mathbf{A}|} \tag{9.11}$$

Suppose it is desired to invert the matrix

$$\mathbf{A} = \begin{bmatrix} 2 & 3 & 4 \\ 1 & 2 & 1 \\ 3 & -2 & 2 \end{bmatrix}$$

First we compute the cofactors, and obtain

$$\begin{bmatrix} 6 & 1 & -8 \\ -14 & -8 & 13 \\ -5 & 2 & 1 \end{bmatrix}$$

These values are computed as previously explained. For example, the cofactor of the element 1 in the first column and second row of the matrix is equal to $-[(3)(2) - (4)(-2)] = -14$, as shown. The transpose of the cofactors is

$$\text{Adjoint of } \mathbf{A} = \begin{bmatrix} 6 & -14 & -5 \\ 1 & -8 & 2 \\ -8 & 13 & 1 \end{bmatrix}$$

The determinant of matrix $\mathbf{A}$ can be found by summing the products of *any* row or column of elements and their corresponding cofactors. For example, if we use the first row of elements (2, 3, 4) and the corresponding cofactors (6, 1, −8), we obtain

$$|\mathbf{A}| = 2(6) + 3(1) + 4(-8) = -17$$

Then, from Equation (9.11),

$$\mathbf{A}^{-1} = \frac{\begin{bmatrix} 6 & -14 & -5 \\ 1 & -8 & 2 \\ -8 & 13 & 1 \end{bmatrix}}{-17} = \begin{bmatrix} -\frac{6}{17} & \frac{14}{17} & \frac{5}{17} \\ -\frac{1}{17} & \frac{8}{17} & -\frac{2}{17} \\ \frac{8}{17} & -\frac{13}{17} & -\frac{1}{17} \end{bmatrix}$$

The inversion is checked by determining that it satisfies Equation (9.9).

This method of inversion is unwieldy for matrices larger than 3 × 3. In addition, since the only check is to multiply the inverse by the original matrix, computational errors may be difficult to locate. The method of pivotal condensation is recommended for inverting such matrices. For illustrative purposes, it is used in the following to invert a 3 × 3 matrix.

The tabulations in Figure 9-1 illustrate the inversion of

$$\mathbf{F} = \begin{bmatrix} 9 & 11 & 7 \\ 11 & 16 & 11 \\ 7 & 11 & 9 \end{bmatrix}$$

by the method of pivotal condensation. The elements of the matrix are entered in locations $a(1)$ through $c(3)$ of tabulation I. The unit matrix is entered below the original matrix, and −1 times the unit matrix is entered in columns d, e, and f of lines (1), (2), and (3). The unit digit is entered in location $g(6)$, and zero is entered in all other locations above line (7). The values entered in line (7) are the totals of the respective columns.

If a 2 × 2 matrix were to be inverted, the matrix would appear in locations $a(1)$ through $b(2)$. Rows 3 and 6 and columns c and f would be eliminated, and the unit digit in location $g(6)$ would be placed in $g(5)$.

To start the inversion procedure, a pivot element is chosen from the original matrix. In this example the number 9 in location $a(1)$ is chosen. Row (1) is then termed the pivot row, and column a is the pivot column. Each entry in lines (2) through (6) of tabulation II of Figure 9-1 is obtained by multiplying the pivot by the corresponding term in tabulation I, and subtracting from this product the product of the corresponding values in the pivot row and pivot column. To illustrate, the entry in location $b(2)$ of tabulation II is obtained as $(9)(16) - (11)(11) = 23$, and the entry in $c(3)$ is $(9)(9) - (7)(7) = 32$. Values in row (7) are computed in the same way. Thus the entry in $b(7)$ is $(9)(39) - (11)(28) = 43$. A check on the procedure can now be made by adding all values above row (7) to obtain 43 again.

The array of tabulation II is reduced to tabulation III by use of the 23 in position $b(2)$ as a pivot. Finally, tabulation IV results from a similar reduction of tabulation III using 252 as a pivot. Values $d(4)$ through $f(6)$ in tabulation IV constitute the inverse of the original matrix multiplied by the product of all pivots, $(9)(23)(252) = 52{,}164$. Division by this number, which is listed in $g(6)$, yields the inverse shown in tabulation V.

	a	b	c	d	e	f	g	b	c	d	e	f	g
(1)	9	11	7	-1	0	0	0						
(2)	11	16	11	0	-1	0	0	23	22	11	-9	0	0
(3)	7	11	9	0	0	-1	0	22	32	7	0	-9	0
(4)	1	0	0	0	0	0	0	-11	-7	1	0	0	0
(5)	0	1	0	0	0	0	0	9	0	0	0	0	0
(6)	0	0	1	0	0	0	1	0	9	0	0	0	9
(7)	28	39	28	-1	-1	-1	1	43√	56√	19√	-9√	-9√	9√

     I   II

	c	d	e	f	g	d	e	f	g	d	e	f
(3)	252	-81	198	-207	0							
(4)	81	144	-99	0	0	42849	-40986	16767		0.82143	-0.78571	0.32143
(5)	-198	-99	81	0	0	-40986	59616	-40986		-0.78571	1.14286	-0.78571
(6)	207	0	0	0	207	16767	-40986	42849	52164	0.32143	-0.78571	0.82143
(7)	342√	-36	180√	-207√	207√	18630√	-22356√	18630√	52164√			

    III   IV   V

Figure 9-1. Matrix Inversion by Pivotal Condensation

The theory behind the choice of pivots is beyond the scope of this text. In general, use of the largest of possible pivots yields the best accuracy. Obviously, a pivot value of zero cannot be used. At any stage of the inversion procedure all values of any column or row may be divided by a constant without affecting the final results. Since the pivotal condensation procedure involves the evaluation of the differences of relatively large numbers, it is usually not adaptable to slide rule computations.

The product of the original matrix and its inverse should equal the unit matrix. Thus

$$\begin{bmatrix} 9 & 11 & 7 \\ 11 & 16 & 11 \\ 7 & 11 & 9 \end{bmatrix} \begin{bmatrix} 0.82143 & -0.78571 & 0.32143 \\ -0.78571 & 1.14286 & -0.78571 \\ 0.32143 & -0.78571 & 0.82143 \end{bmatrix}$$

$$= \begin{bmatrix} +1.00007 & +0.00010 & +0.00007 \\ +0.00010 & +1.00011 & +0.00010 \\ +0.00007 & +0.00010 & +1.00007 \end{bmatrix}$$

The deviation of this matrix product from the unit matrix is small. Repetition of the pivotal condensation procedure, but now using minus one times the residuals of the matrix product in locations $d(1)$ through $f(3)$, results in corrections to the inverse. Theoretically, this correction procedure can be repeated a number of times to obtain any degree of accuracy.

Standard programs are available for matrix inversion by digital computer. It is not uncommon to invert 100×100 or larger matrices in this manner.

9.3 Eigenvalues

The solution of certain problems in structural dynamics and buckling involves the determination of a column vector $\mathbf{X}$ and a constant λ, such that

$$\mathbf{AX} = \lambda \mathbf{X} \qquad (9.12)$$

in which $\mathbf{A}$ is a square matrix. That is, the matrix transforms the vector $\mathbf{X}$ into a multiple of itself. Such a vector is called an eigenvector of $\mathbf{A}$, and λ is termed an eigenvalue of $\mathbf{A}$. Equation (9.12) can be rewritten in the following form:

$$(\mathbf{A} - \lambda \mathbf{I})\mathbf{X} = 0 \qquad (9.13)$$

which represents n homogeneous linear equations. In order for nontrivial solutions to exist, we must have

$$\det(\mathbf{A} - \lambda \mathbf{I}) = 0 \qquad (9.14)$$

Suppose we wish to determine the eigenvalues of the matrix

$$\mathbf{A} = \begin{bmatrix} 9 & 11 & 7 \\ 11 & 16 & 11 \\ 7 & 11 & 9 \end{bmatrix}$$

From Equation (9.14), we write

$$\begin{vmatrix} 9 - \lambda & 11 & 7 \\ 11 & 16 - \lambda & 11 \\ 7 & 11 & 9 - \lambda \end{vmatrix} = 0$$

and, evaluating this determinant by cofactors, we proceed as follows:

$$(9 - \lambda)\begin{vmatrix} 16 - \lambda & 11 \\ 11 & 9 - \lambda \end{vmatrix} - 11\begin{vmatrix} 11 & 11 \\ 7 & 9 - \lambda \end{vmatrix} + 7\begin{vmatrix} 11 & 16 - \lambda \\ 7 & 11 \end{vmatrix} = 0$$

$$-\lambda^3 + 34\lambda^2 - 78\lambda + 28 = 0$$

$$\lambda_1 = 31.56; \qquad \lambda_2 = 2.000; \qquad \lambda_3 = 0.444$$

The number of eigenvalues is equal to the number of rows or columns in the square matrix.

As shown, the determination of eigenvalues involves straightforward computations. The evaluation of the corresponding eigenvectors is considered in Section 13.5. In most problems in structural dynamics or buckling only the so-called first, or largest, eigenvalue and its corresponding eigenvector are of physical significance. An iteration procedure may be used to determine these particular values, as explained in what follows.

A value of the eigenvector is assumed, and substituted into the left-hand side of Equation (9.12). This yields a value λ and a new vector. If this new vector is equal to the assumed vector, it is an eigenvector and λ is an eigenvalue. If the new vector is not equal to the assumed vector, it is used as a new assumed solution. This procedure is repeated until Equation (9.12) is satisfied. The rate of convergence of the iterations may be slow unless a good choice is made for the initially assumed eigenvector. However, in physical problems it is often possible to make such a choice. The following is an example of the matrix iteration procedure, using the same matrix as before. The values under X_1 represent the first assumption of the eigenvector.

$$\begin{bmatrix} 9 & 11 & 7 \\ 11 & 16 & 11 \\ 7 & 11 & 9 \end{bmatrix} \begin{bmatrix} 1.000 \\ 1.410 \\ 1.000 \end{bmatrix} = \begin{bmatrix} 31.51 \\ 44.56 \\ 31.51 \end{bmatrix} = 31.51 \begin{bmatrix} 1.000 \\ 1.414 \\ 1.000 \end{bmatrix}$$

X_1 ... X_2

$$\begin{bmatrix} 9 & 11 & 7 \\ 11 & 16 & 11 \\ 7 & 11 & 9 \end{bmatrix} \begin{bmatrix} 1.000 \\ 1.414 \\ 1.000 \end{bmatrix} = \begin{bmatrix} 31.550 \\ 44.624 \\ 31.550 \end{bmatrix} = 31.55 \begin{bmatrix} 1.000 \\ 1.414 \\ 1.000 \end{bmatrix}$$

X_2 ... X_3

The assumption of the initial eigenvector X_1 is based on certain physical considerations to be explained in Section 13.5. Multiplication of matrix $\mathbf{A}$ and the assumed vector X_1 yields 31.51 times the vector X_2. Since X_2 is not equal to X_1, X_2 and A are multiplied to give 31.55 times X_3. Since $X_3 = X_2$, X_2 is an eigenvector and 31.55 is the largest eigenvalue.

9.4 Solution of Linear Algebraic Equations

Three methods for the solution of sets of linear algebraic equations are discussed in this article. These are the use of the matrix inverse, a pivotal condensation method, and the Gauss-Seidel iteration scheme. The student is undoubtedly familiar with the method of direct elimination, and with Cramer's method (use of determinants).

The inverse of the matrix corresponding to the coefficients of the unknowns of a set of linear equations can be used to determine the values of the unknowns for any set of values of the constant terms appearing in the equations. It was shown in Equation (9.5a) that a set of equations can be written in matrix notation as $\mathbf{AX} = \mathbf{C}$. Therefore

$$\mathbf{X} = \mathbf{A}^{-1}\mathbf{C} \tag{9.15}$$

and the matrix inverse consists of the coefficients of the general solution of the set of simultaneous equations.

Consider the following set of equations:

$$2x_1 + 3x_3 + 4x_3 = 20$$
$$x_1 + 2x_2 + x_3 = 8$$
$$3x_1 - 2x_2 + 2x_3 = 5$$

In matrix formulation

$$\begin{bmatrix} 2 & 3 & 4 \\ 1 & 2 & 1 \\ 3 & -2 & 2 \end{bmatrix} \begin{bmatrix} x_1 \\ x_2 \\ x_3 \end{bmatrix} = \begin{bmatrix} 20 \\ 8 \\ 5 \end{bmatrix}$$

The matrix of the unknowns is the same one that was inverted in Section 9.2 to obtain

$$\mathbf{A}^{-1} = -\frac{1}{17} \begin{bmatrix} 6 & -14 & -5 \\ 1 & -8 & 2 \\ -8 & 13 & 1 \end{bmatrix}$$

Therefore, from Equation (9.15), we obtain

$$\begin{bmatrix} x_1 \\ x_2 \\ x_3 \end{bmatrix} = -\frac{1}{17} \begin{bmatrix} 6 & -14 & -5 \\ 1 & -8 & 2 \\ -8 & 13 & 1 \end{bmatrix} \begin{bmatrix} 20 \\ 8 \\ 5 \end{bmatrix} = \begin{bmatrix} 1 \\ 2 \\ 3 \end{bmatrix}$$

It can be seen that if another column vector of constant terms were involved in the original simultaneous equations, the corresponding values of unknowns would be obtained by multiplying this new vector with the inverse of the matrix of unknowns.

A second procedure for solving a set of linear algebraic equations is a special case of the pivotal condensation method presented in Section 9.2 for matrix inversion.

Consider the following set of equations:

$$9x_1 + 11x_2 + 7x_3 = 10$$
$$11x_1 + 16x_2 + 11x_3 = 10$$
$$7x_1 + 11x_2 + 9x_3 = 2$$

In matrix formulation we have

$$\begin{bmatrix} 9 & 11 & 7 \\ 11 & 16 & 11 \\ 7 & 11 & 9 \end{bmatrix} \begin{bmatrix} x_1 \\ x_2 \\ x_3 \end{bmatrix} = \begin{bmatrix} 10 \\ 10 \\ 2 \end{bmatrix}$$

This is the matrix that was inverted in Figure 9-1. The tabular form in Figure 9-2 is essentially the same as that for matrix inversion shown in Figure 9-1. The 3×3 matrix is entered in locations $a(1)$ through $c(3)$. Minus one times the

	a	b	c	d	b	c	d	c	d	d
(1)	9	11	7	-10						
(2)	11	16	11	-10	23	22	20			
(3)	7	11	9	-2	22	32	52	252	756	
(4)	1	0	0	0	-11	-7	10	81	450	52164
(5)	0	1	0	0	9	0	0	-198	-180	104328
(6)	0	0	1	0	0	9	0	207	0	-156492
(7)	0	0	0	1	0	0	9	0	207	52164
(8)	28	39	28	-21	43	56	91	342	1233	

$$X_1 = \frac{52,164}{52,164} = 1; \qquad X_2 = \frac{104,328}{52,164} = 2; \qquad X_3 = -\frac{156,492}{52,164} = -3$$

Figure 9-2. Solution of Simultaneous Equations by Pivotal Condensation

		X_1	X_2	X_3	C
(1)	X_1		0.132	-0.022	0.088
(2)	X_2	0.167		0.187	0.167
(3)	X_3	-0.018	0.159		0.213
(4)		0.088	0	0	0.088
(5)		0.015	0.182	0	0.167
(6)		-0.002	0.029	0.240	0.213
(7)		0.107	0.024	-0.005	0.088
(8)		0.018	0.230	0.045	0.167
(9)		-0.002	0.037	0.248	0.213
(10)		0.113	0.030	-0.005	0.088
(11)		0.019	0.232	0.046	0.167
(12)		-0.002	0.037	0.248	0.213
(13)		0.114	0.031	-0.005	0.088
(14)		0.019	0.232	0.046	0.167

$$X_1 = 0.114; \qquad X_2 = 0.232; \qquad X_3 = 0.248$$

Figure 9-3. Solution of Diagonal Equations

column vector is entered in $d(1)$ through $d(3)$. The values in rows 4 to 6 are the same as in Figure 9-1. Row 7 is used to sum the pivot products, and row 8 is the checking row. The matrix is reduced by three successive pivotal condensations, as explained in Section 9.2, with the solution of the equations multiplied by the product of the pivots finally appearing in $d(4)$ to $d(6)$. Division by the pivot product yields the solution $x_1 = 1$, $x_2 = 2$, $x_3 = -3$. One advantage of this scheme is the systematic check in row 8 after each set of operations.

The determination of the behavior of several types of physical systems involves the solution of so-called diagonal sets of simultaneous algebraic equations. In each such equation the absolute value of the coefficient of a different unknown is greater than the sum of the absolute values of the remaining coefficients. The equations in Figure 7-26 are of this type. Diagonal systems can be solved conveniently by an iteration procedure known as the Gauss-Seidel method. Although the example that follows is for a system of three simultaneous equations, the Gauss-Seidel method is of greater advantage for larger sets of diagonal equations.

The equations of Figure 7-26 are

$$272x_1 - 36x_2 + 6x_3 = 24$$

$$-48x_1 + 288x_2 - 54x_3 = 48$$

$$6x_1 - 54x_2 + 338x_3 = 72$$

or

$$x_1 = \quad 0.132x_2 - 0.022x_3 + 0.088$$

$$x_2 = \quad 0.167x_1 + 0.187x_3 + 0.167$$

$$x_3 = -0.018x_1 + 0.159x_2 + 0.213$$

These coefficients are shown in Figure 9-3. The procedure is started by assuming values for x_2 and x_3. Assuming initial values of $x_2 = x_3 = 0$,

$$x_1 = 0 + 0 + 0.088 = 0.088$$

Then using

$$x_1 = 0.088 \quad \text{and} \quad x_3 = 0$$

we obtain

$$x_2 = 0.015 + 0 + 0.167 = 0.182$$

Now, using

$$x_1 = 0.088 \quad \text{and} \quad x_2 = 0.182$$

we obtain

$$x_3 = -0.002 + 0.029 + 0.213 = 0.240$$

The above steps are shown in rows (4), (5), and (6) of Figure 9-3. Since the computed values of x_2 and x_3 do not agree with the assumed values of zero, the procedure is repeated, using as new initial values the computed values $x_1 = 0.088$, $x_2 = 0.182$, and $x_3 = 0.240$. Rows (7), (8), and (9) of Figure 9-3 indicate the computations and the new values of x_1, x_2, and x_3. The iteration procedure is repeated until the computed values of all unknowns are equal to the preceding values. We finally obtain

$$x_1 = 0.114 ; \qquad x_2 = 0.232 ; \qquad x_3 = 0.248$$

The Gauss-Seidel method will converge to the correct values even if arithmetic mistakes are made, since such errors result in new assumed values for the unknowns.

9.5   Stiffness and Flexibility Matrices: General

In Chapters 7 and 8, two general methods of analysis involving the solution of sets of equations were discussed—the force method and the displacement method. In the force method we assumed a solution satisfying statics, and the coefficients of the unknowns in the resulting equations represented displacements (or rotations) resulting from unit forces (or unit moments).

We can write Equations (7.1) in the matrix form of Equation (9.5a) as follows:

$$\mathbf{FX} = \boldsymbol{\Delta} \tag{a}$$

in which $\mathbf{F}$ is the flexibility matrix, $\mathbf{X}$ is the column vector of the correction forces or moments, and $\boldsymbol{\Delta}$ is the column vector of the errors in geometry (displacements or rotations), *but with opposite sign*, due to the assumed solution. The signs are changed because $\boldsymbol{\Delta}$ is now on the other side of the equation—that is, it represents the corrections that must be made to the geometry. If desired, a minus sign can be inserted in the right-hand side of Equation (a) and $\boldsymbol{\Delta}$ kept as the errors in geometry with their original signs. The equations can be solved, as explained in Section 9.4, by inverting the flexibility matrix to obtain

$$\mathbf{X} = \mathbf{F}^{-1}\boldsymbol{\Delta} \tag{9.16}$$

In the displacement method of analysis we assumed a solution satisfying geometry. The coefficients of the unknowns in the equations represented moments (or forces) resulting from unit rotations (or unit displacements).

We can write Equations (7.4) in matrix form as follows:

$$\mathbf{KD} = \mathbf{P} \tag{b}$$

in which $\mathbf{K}$ is the stiffness matrix, $\mathbf{D}$ is the column vector of the correction rotations or displacements, and $\mathbf{P}$ is the column vector of the errors in statics (moments or forces), *but with opposite sign*, due to the assumed solution. The equations can be solved by inverting the stiffness matrix to obtain

$$\mathbf{D} = \mathbf{K}^{-1}\mathbf{P} \tag{9.17}$$

In Section 9.6 it will be seen that the inverse of the flexibility matrix in Equation (a) is a matrix whose elements are stiffness coefficients, but *not* those used in the displacement method of analysis. Similarly, it will be seen that the inverse of the stiffness matrix in Equation (b) is a matrix whose elements are flexibility coefficients, but *not* those used in the force method of analysis.

9.6 Stiffness and Flexibility Matrices: Flexural Systems

Figure 9-4 shows a four-span continuous beam of constant section. A stiffness matrix for use with the displacement method can be easily written. Clockwise rotation and moment of a member at a joint are taken as positive. A modified moment stiffness, $3EI/L$, is used for members BA and DE since ends A and E are simply supported. If A or E were fixed against rotation, $4EI/L$ would be used.

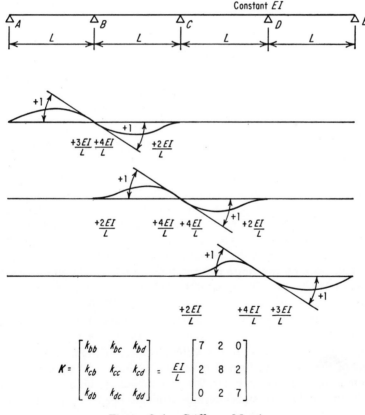

$$K = \begin{bmatrix} k_{bb} & k_{bc} & k_{bd} \\ k_{cb} & k_{cc} & k_{cd} \\ k_{db} & k_{dc} & k_{dd} \end{bmatrix} = \frac{EI}{L} \begin{bmatrix} 7 & 2 & 0 \\ 2 & 8 & 2 \\ 0 & 2 & 7 \end{bmatrix}$$

Figure 9-4. Stiffness Matrix

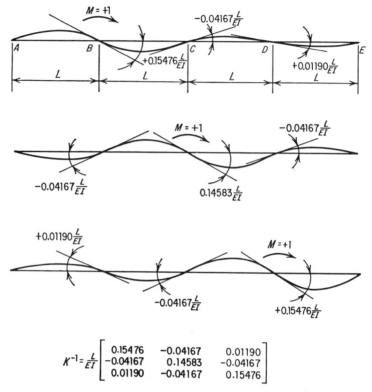

$$K^{-1} = \frac{L}{EI} \begin{bmatrix} 0.15476 & -0.04167 & 0.01190 \\ -0.04167 & 0.14583 & -0.04167 \\ 0.01190 & -0.04167 & 0.15476 \end{bmatrix}$$

Figure 9-5. *Corresponding Flexibility Matrix Obtained by Inverting the Stiffness Matrix of Figure 9-4.*

To obtain the stiffness matrix **K**, all interior supports are assumed fixed, and a clockwise unit rotation is applied at supports B, C, and D, respectively. As a result of the rotation at B, moments equal to $+3EI/L$ and $+4EI/L$ are induced at B. The sum of these moments is k_{bb}, the first element of the stiffness matrix. A moment equal to $2EI/L$ is induced at C. This is k_{cb}, the second element in the first column of the stiffness matrix. Since no moment is induced at D, k_{db} is equal to zero. A unit rotation at C, holding B and D fixed, results in the stiffness coefficients shown in the second column of the stiffness matrix. Column three is obtained by applying a unit rotation at D. In this example the stiffness matrix is a 3 × 3 array. The order of the stiffness matrix for continuous beams is always equal to the number of interior supports if true conditions as to the type of support are used for the two exterior supports. It is left to the student to prove that such matrices are always of the symmetric type.

Notice that the elements in the stiffness matrix of Figure 9-4 are the coefficients of the equations formulated in connection with Figure 7-5. The type of stiffness matrix shown in Figure 9-4, and implied in Figure 7-5, is commonly used in the analysis of statically indeterminate beams by the displacement method.

266

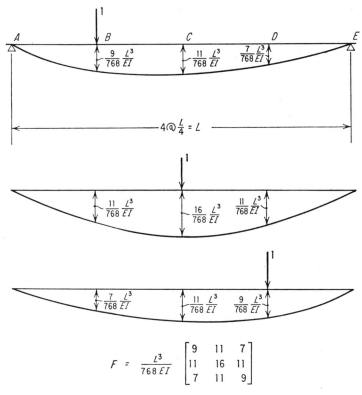

$$F = \frac{L^3}{768\,EI}\begin{bmatrix} 9 & 11 & 7 \\ 11 & 16 & 11 \\ 7 & 11 & 9 \end{bmatrix}$$

Figure 9-6. Flexibility Matrix

If the stiffness matrix in Figure 9-4 is inverted, the corresponding flexibility matrix is

$$\mathbf{K}^{-1} = \frac{L}{EI}\begin{bmatrix} 0.15476 & -0.04167 & 0.01190 \\ -0.04167 & 0.14583 & -0.04167 \\ 0.01190 & -0.04167 & 0.15476 \end{bmatrix}$$

The physical significance of this matrix is shown in Figure 9-5. It can be seen that the elements of this flexibility matrix are equal to the rotations of the beam at the various supports due to unit moments applied successively at each support, *with no artificial restraint or freedom at any other support.* For example, the flexibility coefficients of the second row represent the rotations at B, C, and D, respectively, due to a unit moment at C.

Direct calculation of the flexibility coefficients in Figure 9-5 would require the determination of the behavior of the continuous beam when successive unit moments are applied. By moment distribution or any other method of analysis of indeterminate structures, moments along the structure could be obtained, and rotations then determined at B, C, and D. Obviously, it is more convenient to determine the coefficients of the flexibility matrix by inversion of the readily obtainable stiffness matrix rather than by direct calculation.

Figure 9-6 shows a flexibility matrix whose elements represent the vertical

267

movements of points B, C, and D due to unit loads acting, respectively, at B, C, and D in a beam simply supported at A and E. Note that L in this example has been taken as the total length of the structure. The elements of this matrix were obtained in Chapter 7 for use as the coefficients of the equations in Figure 7-1. Note, however, that the signs are all opposite because the unit forces in Figure 9-6 are acting downward rather than upward.

Inversion of the matrix in Figure 9-6 yields the corresponding stiffness matrix in Figure 9-7. The elements of the latter matrix are equal to the vertical reactions induced at the interior supports by unit vertical movements applied successively at each support, *with no artificial restraint or freedom at any other support.*

The flexibility matrix of Figure 9-6, multiplied by 768 EI/L^3, was inverted as an example in Figure 9-1. The results obtained there must be multiplied by 768 to obtain the elements of the matrix in Figure 9-7.

Another flexibility matrix is determined in Figure 9-8. The beam is assumed cut at the interior supports, and unit moments are applied to the ends of the members. The resulting relative rotations of adjacent members constitute the

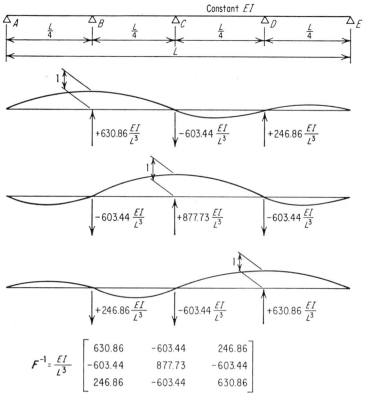

$$F^{-1} = \frac{EI}{L^3} \begin{bmatrix} 630.86 & -603.44 & 246.86 \\ -603.44 & 877.73 & -603.44 \\ 246.86 & -603.44 & 630.86 \end{bmatrix}$$

Figure 9-7. Corresponding Stiffness Matrix Obtained by Inverting the Flexibility Matrix of Figure 9-6.

elements of the flexibility matrix. If multiplied by $L = 20$, these are the co-efficients of the equations in Figure 7-2 but with opposite signs. Either set of signs is acceptable, providing the results of the analysis are interpreted correctly.

Inversion of the flexibility matrix of Figure 9-8 yields the corresponding

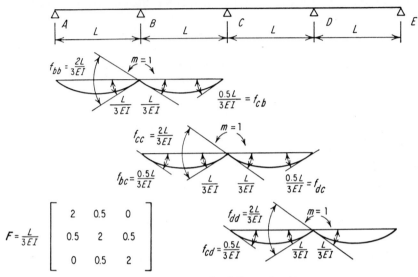

$$F = \frac{L}{3EI} \begin{bmatrix} 2 & 0.5 & 0 \\ 0.5 & 2 & 0.5 \\ 0 & 0.5 & 2 \end{bmatrix}$$

Figure 9-8.   Flexibility Matrix

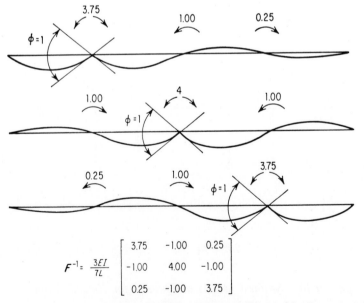

$$F^{-1} = \frac{3EI}{7L} \begin{bmatrix} 3.75 & -1.00 & 0.25 \\ -1.00 & 4.00 & -1.00 \\ 0.25 & -1.00 & 3.75 \end{bmatrix}$$

Figure 9-9.   Corresponding Stiffness Matrix Obtained by Inverting the Flexibility Matrix of Figure 9-8.

stiffness matrix shown in Figure 9-9. The coefficients of this matrix represent the moments induced at the supports by unit rotations applied at successive joints, *with no artificial restraint or freedom at any other support*. These coefficients are shown on the sketches of the deflected structure, but they must all be multiplied by $3EI/7L$.

A stiffness matrix such as that in Figure 9-4 is used in connection with the displacement method of analysis. When it is inverted, a corresponding flexibility matrix (Figure 9-5) is obtained, the elements of which represent flexibility in the actual structure, with no artificial restraint or freedom. This illustrates physically why individual values of the unknowns, D, can be obtained directly, as illustrated in Section 9.8.

A flexibility matrix such as that in Figure 9-6 or Figure 9-8 is used in connection with the force method of analysis. When it is inverted, the result is a corresponding stiffness matrix (Figure 9-7 or Figure 9-9), the elements of which represent stiffness in the actual structure, with no artificial restraint or

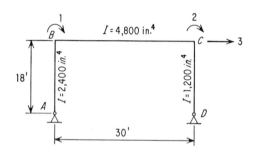

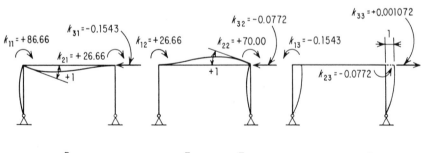

$$K = E \begin{bmatrix} 86.66 & 26.66 & -0.1543 \\ 26.66 & 70.00 & -0.0772 \\ -0.1543 & -0.0772 & 0.001072 \end{bmatrix} ; \quad K^{-1} = \frac{1}{E} \begin{bmatrix} 0.01647 & -0.00397 & 2.085 \\ -0.00397 & 0.01647 & 0.6145 \\ 2.085 & 0.6145 & 1277 \end{bmatrix}$$

Figure 9-10. Stiffness Matrix and Inverse for Hinged Frame

freedom. Thus, values of the unknowns, X, can now be obtained directly, as illustrated in Section 9.8.

Figures 9-10 and 9-11 are used to illustrate the procedure for determining the stiffness matrix for a rigid frame. The frame in Figure 9-10 is hinged at the base of its columns whereas that in Figure 9-11 is fixed.

In both Figure 9-10 and Figure 9-11 it is possible for joints B and C to move sideways (an equal amount) as well as rotate. For convenience, these three degrees of freedom are shown, in their positive sense, as 1, 2, and 3. The stiffness matrix will be

$$\mathbf{K} = \begin{bmatrix} k_{11} & k_{12} & k_{13} \\ k_{21} & k_{22} & k_{23} \\ k_{31} & k_{32} & k_{33} \end{bmatrix}$$

in which all coefficients represent a moment or force due to a unit rotation without displacement, or a moment or force due to a unit displacement without rotation. In Figure 9-10, with clockwise moment and force acting to the right taken as positive,

$$k_{11} = \frac{3E(2,400)}{18(12)} + \frac{4E(4,800)}{30(12)} = 33.33E + 53.33E = 86.66E$$

$$k_{21} = \frac{2E(4,800)}{30(12)} = 26.66E$$

$$k_{31} = -\frac{3E(2,400)}{(18 \times 12)^2} = -0.1543E$$

$$k_{22} = \frac{4E(4,800)}{30(12)} + \frac{3E(1,200)}{18(12)} = 53.33E + 16.66E = 70.00E$$

$$k_{32} = -\frac{3E(1,200)}{(18 \times 12)^2} = -0.0772E$$

$$k_{33} = \frac{3E(2,400)}{(18 \times 12)^3} + \frac{3E(1,200)}{(18 \times 12)^3} = 0.000715E + 0.000357E = 0.001072E$$

$$k_{12} = k_{21}$$

$$k_{13} = k_{31}$$

$$k_{23} = k_{32}$$

The inverse of the stiffness matrix is also shown in Figure 9-10. The elements of this matrix represent rotations or lateral displacements due to the application of unit moment or unit lateral force with no artificial restraint or freedom.

The stiffness coefficients in Figure 9-11 are obtained exactly as for Figure

9-10, except that cognizance is taken of the fact that the columns are fixed at their bases. Thus

$$k_{11} = \frac{4E(1,200)}{16(12)} + \frac{4E(7,200)}{50(12)} = 25E + 48E = 73E$$

$$k_{21} = \frac{2E(7,200)}{50(12)} = 24E$$

$$k_{31} = -\frac{6E(1,200)}{(16 \times 12)^2} = -0.1953E$$

$$k_{22} = \frac{4E(1,200)}{16(12)} + \frac{4E(7,200)}{50(12)} = 25E + 48E = 73E$$

$$k_{12} = k_{21} = 24E$$

$$k_{32} = -\frac{6E(1,200)}{(16 \times 12)^2} = -0.1953E$$

$$k_{33} = \frac{12E(1,200)}{(16 \times 12)^3} + \frac{12E(1,200)}{(16 \times 12)^3} = 0.004069E$$

$$k_{13} = k_{31} = -0.1953E$$

$$k_{23} = k_{32} = -0.1953E$$

The inverse of the stiffness matrix is also shown in Figure 9-11. Again the elements represent rotations or lateral displacements with no artificial restraint or freedom.

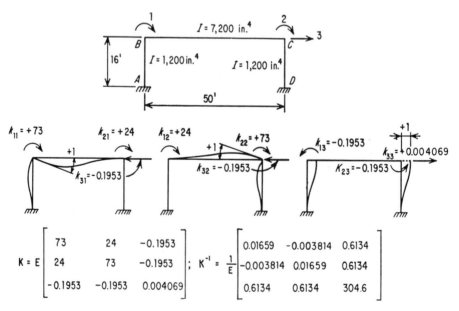

$$K = E \begin{bmatrix} 73 & 24 & -0.1953 \\ 24 & 73 & -0.1953 \\ -0.1953 & -0.1953 & 0.004069 \end{bmatrix} ; \quad K^{-1} = \frac{1}{E} \begin{bmatrix} 0.01659 & -0.003814 & 0.6134 \\ -0.003814 & 0.01659 & 0.6134 \\ 0.6134 & 0.6134 & 304.6 \end{bmatrix}$$

Figure 9-11.   Stiffness Matrix and Inverse for Fixed Frame

9.7   Stiffness and Flexibility Matrices: Trusses

In Chapter 8, continuous trusses were analyzed by the force method, solving simultaneous equations containing flexibility coefficients of the type shown in Figure 9-6, Similar flexibility coefficients were used to analyze internally indeterminate trusses. Consequently, the matrix formulation of the truss problem, using the force method, is identical to that for the beam problem.

In the present section we will develop a stiffness matrix for use with the displacement method of analysis. An element of this matrix will represent a joint force component developed when a unit displacement is introduced at the same joint or at an immediately adjacent joint, with all other joint displacements prevented.

Figure 9-12(a) shows, in the xy-plane, a bar ab of length L, area A, and modulus of elasticity E, subjected to a small unit movement in the positive x-direction at end b with end a held in position. The orientation of the bar is defined by the x- and y-coordinates shown in parentheses. The unit movement introduces a change in length in ab of

$$\Delta L = \frac{x_b - x_a}{L}$$

and an axial force of

$$F = \left(\frac{AE}{L}\right)\Delta L = \left(\frac{AE}{L}\right)\left(\frac{x_b - x_a}{L}\right)$$

Calling the horizontal component of force F_{xx}, and the vertical component F_{yx},

$$F_{xx} = \left(\frac{AE}{L}\right)\left(\frac{x_b - x_a}{L}\right)^2 ; \qquad F_{yx} = \left(\frac{AE}{L}\right)\left(\frac{x_b - x_a}{L}\right)\left(\frac{y_b - y_a}{L}\right) \qquad (9.18)$$

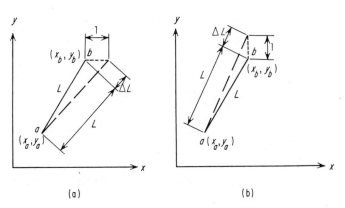

(a)   (b)

Figure 9-12.   Identification Sketch

The components of force at point a are equal to the components at point b but are of opposite sign.

In Figure 9-12(b) a unit movement in the positive y-direction is imposed on point b. Calling the vertical component of force F_{yy} and the horizontal component F_{xy}, we obtain in the same manner as before,

$$F_{yy} = \left(\frac{AE}{L}\right)\left(\frac{y_b - y_a}{L}\right)^2 ; \qquad F_{xy} = F_{yx} \qquad (9.19)$$

The components of force at a are again equal to those at b but of opposite sign.

If positive unit horizontal and vertical movements are introduced at a with b held in position, x_a and x_b, and y_a and y_b will be interchanged in all the preceding expressions. All force components, however, will remain unchanged in both magnitude and sign.

Suppose two or more bars frame into a displaced joint j. Then if the far ends of the bars are designated as i_1, i_2, and so forth, the stiffness coefficients at j are, from Equations (9.18) and (9.19),

$$
\left.
\begin{aligned}
k_{xx} &= \sum_{i_1,i_2,\cdots} \left(\frac{AE}{L^3}\right)_{ji} (x_j - x_i)^2 \\[2mm]
k_{yy} &= \sum_{i_1,i_2,\cdots} \left(\frac{AE}{L^3}\right)_{ji} (y_j - y_i)^2 \\[2mm]
k_{xy} = k_{yx} &= \sum_{i_1,i_2,\cdots} \left(\frac{AE}{L^3}\right)_{ji} (x_j - x_i)(y_j - y_i)
\end{aligned}
\right\} \qquad (9.20a)
$$

where the summation includes all bars framing into joint j. For three-dimensional truss frameworks it is necessary to include the following additional stiffness coefficients:

$$
\left.
\begin{aligned}
k_{zz} &= \sum_{i_1,i_2,\cdots} \left(\frac{AE}{L^3}\right)_{ji} (z_j - z_i)^2 \\[2mm]
k_{yz} = k_{zy} &= \sum_{i_1,i_2,\cdots} \left(\frac{AE}{L^3}\right)_{ji} (y_j - y_i)(z_j - z_i) \\[2mm]
k_{zx} = k_{xz} &= \sum_{i_1,i_2,\cdots} \left(\frac{AE}{L^3}\right)_{ji} (z_j - z_i)(x_j - x_i)
\end{aligned}
\right\} \qquad (9.20b)
$$

At each adjacent joint i held fixed in position, the stiffness coefficients involve only the opposite end of a member framing into the displaced joint j, and they are

$$
\left.
\begin{aligned}
k_{xx} &= -\left(\frac{AE}{L^3}\right)_{ji} (x_j - x_i)^2 \\[2mm]
k_{yy} &= -\left(\frac{AE}{L^3}\right)_{ji} (y_j - y_i)^2 \\[2mm]
k_{zz} &= -\left(\frac{AE}{L^3}\right)_{ji} (z_j - z_i)^2 \\[2mm]
k_{xy} = k_{yx} &= -\left(\frac{AE}{L^3}\right)_{ji} (x_j - x_i)(y_j - y_i) \\[2mm]
k_{yz} = k_{zy} &= -\left(\frac{AE}{L^3}\right)_{ji} (y_j - y_i)(z_j - z_i) \\[2mm]
k_{zx} = k_{xz} &= -\left(\frac{AE}{L^3}\right)_{ji} (z_j - z_i)(x_j - x_i)
\end{aligned}
\right\}
\tag{9.21}
$$

Equations (9.20) can be written in matrix form as follows:

$$
\begin{bmatrix}
k_{xx} & k_{xy} & k_{xz} \\
k_{yx} & k_{yy} & k_{yz} \\
k_{zx} & k_{zy} & k_{zz}
\end{bmatrix}
= \sum_{i_1,i_2,\cdots} \left(\frac{AE}{L^3}\right)_{ji}
\begin{bmatrix}
(x_j - x_i) \\
(y_j - y_i) \\
(z_j - z_i)
\end{bmatrix}
\left[(x_j - x_i) \;\; (y_j - y_i) \;\; (z_j - z_i) \right]
\tag{9.20c}
$$

The matrix formulation of Equations (9.21) is

$$
\begin{bmatrix}
k_{xx} & k_{xy} & k_{xz} \\
k_{yx} & k_{yy} & k_{yz} \\
k_{zx} & k_{zy} & k_{zz}
\end{bmatrix}
= -\left(\frac{AE}{L^3}\right)_{ji}
\begin{bmatrix}
(x_j - x_i) \\
(y_j - y_i) \\
(z_j - z_i)
\end{bmatrix}
\left[(x_j - x_i) \;\; (y_j - y_i) \;\; (z_j - z_i) \right]
\tag{9.21b}
$$

Figure 9-13(a) shows a very simple, two-dimensional truss. For ease of identification, the x- and y-components of joint forces and joint displacements are numbered, using odd numbers for the x-direction and even numbers for the y-direction. Thus the stiffness coefficient k_{45} represents the force component in the y-direction at U_1 resulting from a unit displacement of L_2 in the x-direction. The numbers enclosed in parentheses are the x- and y-coordinates measured from L_0, which is taken as the origin of axes.

A stiffness matrix for a planar truss is generally of the order $2n \times 2n$, where n represents the number of joints in the truss. For a three-dimensional truss,

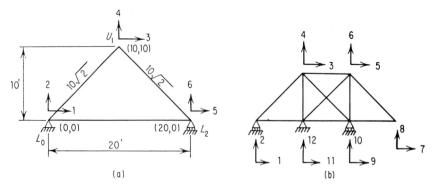

Figure 9-13.   *Identification Sketches for Matrix Formulation*

the matrix is $3n \times 3n$. In the truss of Figure 9-13(a), support conditions are such that no vertical or horizontal movement can occur at L_0, and no vertical movement can occur at L_2. As a result, all stiffness coefficients involving the subscripts, 1, 2, and 6 are eliminated, and the stiffness matrix becomes

$$\mathbf{K} = \begin{bmatrix} k_{33} & k_{34} & k_{35} \\ k_{43} & k_{44} & k_{45} \\ k_{53} & k_{54} & k_{55} \end{bmatrix}$$

in which the individual stiffness coefficients can be evaluated by means of Equations (9.20) and (9.21). Thus, from Equations (9.20),

$$k_{33} = \frac{AE}{10\sqrt{2}} \left(\frac{10 - 0}{10\sqrt{2}} \right)^2 + \frac{AE}{10\sqrt{2}} \left(\frac{10 - 20}{10\sqrt{2}} \right)^2 = (2) \frac{AE}{20\sqrt{2}}$$

$$k_{44} = \frac{AE}{10\sqrt{2}} \left(\frac{10 - 0}{10\sqrt{2}} \right)^2 + \frac{AE}{10\sqrt{2}} \left(\frac{10 - 0}{10\sqrt{2}} \right)^2 = (2) \frac{AE}{20\sqrt{2}}$$

$$k_{34} = \frac{AE}{10\sqrt{2}} \left(\frac{10 - 0}{10\sqrt{2}} \right)\left(\frac{10 - 0}{10\sqrt{2}} \right) + \frac{AE}{10\sqrt{2}} \left(\frac{10 - 20}{10\sqrt{2}} \right)\left(\frac{10 - 0}{10\sqrt{2}} \right) = 0$$

$$k_{55} = \frac{AE}{20} \left(\frac{20 - 0}{20} \right)^2 + \frac{AE}{10\sqrt{2}} \left(\frac{20 - 10}{10\sqrt{2}} \right)^2 = (2.414) \frac{AE}{20\sqrt{2}}$$

$$k_{43} = k_{34}$$

From Equations (9.21),

$$k_{35} = -\frac{AE}{10\sqrt{2}} \left(\frac{20 - 10}{10\sqrt{2}} \right)^2 = (-1) \frac{AE}{20\sqrt{2}}$$

$$k_{45} = -\frac{AE}{10\sqrt{2}} \left(\frac{20 - 10}{10\sqrt{2}} \right)\left(\frac{10 - 10}{10\sqrt{2}} \right) = (1) \frac{AE}{20\sqrt{2}}$$

$$k_{53} = k_{35}$$

$$k_{54} = k_{45}$$

276

The stiffness matrix for the truss in Figure 9-13(a) becomes

$$\mathbf{K} = \frac{AE}{20\sqrt{2}} \begin{bmatrix} 2 & 0 & -1 \\ 0 & 2 & 1 \\ -1 & 1 & 2.414 \end{bmatrix}$$

If we invert the stiffness matrix we obtain

$$\mathbf{K}^{-1} = \frac{10}{AE} \begin{bmatrix} 1.914 & -0.5 & 1 \\ -0.5 & 1.914 & -1 \\ 1 & -1 & 2 \end{bmatrix}$$

The elements of this matrix are flexibility coefficients which represent the movements of the joints due to unit forces applied successively at the locations and directions designated as 3, 4, and 5 with no artificial restraint or freedom. These flexibility coefficients could also be obtained directly by one of the methods of Chapter 6.

For the simple structure considered, it is not too much more difficult to obtain the above flexibility coefficients directly. As more joints are added, however, the amount of work involved becomes much greater. This is particularly true if the truss is statically indeterminate. On the other hand, stiffness coefficients can always be obtained by means of the simple arithmetic computations indicated by Equations (9.20) and (9.21), and statical indeterminateness in no way complicates their calculation.

The statically indeterminate truss of Figure 9-13(b) has three joints that can move in any direction in the xy plane, two joints at which movement is restricted to one direction, and one joint at which no movement can take place. The square stiffness matrix will have $3(2) + 2(1) + 0 = 8$ rows and columns. Coefficients containing the subscripts 2, 10, 11, and 12 do not appear in the matrix. All coefficients are determined exactly as for the truss in Figure 9-13(a).

9.8   Matrix Analysis of Continuous Beams

Before proceeding, it should be understood that we will be doing what was done in Chapter 7, except that we now solve the simultaneous equations by inverting the matrix of the coefficients. As will be pointed out, however, matrix formulation is advantageous for use with a digital computer, particularly when a large number of loading patterns must be considered.

Figure 9-14 shows the loaded beam analyzed in Chapter 7 by the force method (Figure 7-2) and the displacement method (Figure 7-5). In Figure 9-14 we proceed by the displacement method, assuming a solution satisfying geometry (fixed ends at B, C, and D). The errors in statics are the unbalanced moments at B, C, and D. We have already determined the appropriate stiffness matrix for a continuous beam of four spans and constant moment of inertia in Figure 9-4 (see also Figure 7-5) and inverted it in Figure 9-5. Thus Equation (9.17) becomes

$$
\begin{bmatrix} D_b \\ D_c \\ D_d \end{bmatrix} = \frac{L}{EI} \begin{bmatrix} 0.15476 & -0.04167 & 0.01190 \\ -0.04167 & 0.14583 & -0.04167 \\ 0.01190 & -0.04167 & 0.15476 \end{bmatrix} \begin{bmatrix} -25.0 \\ -133.3 \\ -66.7 \end{bmatrix}
$$

and, performing the indicated multiplications we obtain

$$
D_b = 0.891 \frac{L}{EI}; \qquad D_c = -15.62 \frac{L}{EI}; \qquad D_d = -5.07 \frac{L}{EI}
$$

These values are the rotations at the interior supports. They are identical to the values obtained in Figure 7-5. Correction moments at the end of each span can now be obtained by multiplying these rotations by the appropriate

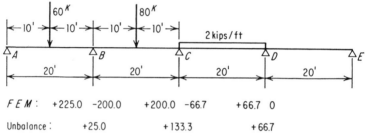

FEM :   +225.0 -200.0   +200.0 -66.7   +66.7 0

Unbalance :   +25.0   +133.3   +66.7

Figure 9-14.   Displacement Method

moment stiffness and carry-over factors for the individual members (see Figure 9-4). In general, we can obtain a correction moment, say m_{bc}, as

$$
m_{bc} = K_{bc} D_b + C_{cb} K_{cb} D_c \tag{9.22}
$$

in which K represents moment stiffness of an individual member, and C represents the carry-over factor.

For analysis by digital computer it is convenient to combine expressions such as Equation (9.22) in matrix form. For the problem under consideration we have

$$
\begin{bmatrix} m_{ba} \\ m_{bc} \\ m_{cb} \\ m_{cd} \\ m_{dc} \\ m_{de} \end{bmatrix} = \begin{bmatrix} K_{ba} & 0 & 0 \\ K_{bc} & K_{cb}C_{cb} & 0 \\ K_{bc}C_{bc} & K_{cb} & 0 \\ 0 & K_{cd} & K_{dc}C_{dc} \\ 0 & K_{cd}C_{cd} & K_{dc} \\ 0 & 0 & K_{de} \end{bmatrix} \begin{bmatrix} D_b \\ D_c \\ D_d \end{bmatrix}
$$

in which $K_{ba} = K_{de} = 3EI/L$, all other values of K are equal to $4EI/L$, and all values of C are equal to 0.5. Using these values of K and C and the previously determined values of D, and then performing the indicated matrix multiplication, the correction moments are

$$m_{ba} = +2.7 \text{ ft-kips}$$

$$m_{bc} = -27.7$$

$$m_{cb} = -60.7$$

$$m_{cd} = -72.6$$

$$m_{dc} = -51.5$$

$$m_{de} = -15.2$$

These values are identical to those obtained in Section 7.4.

The final moments are obtained by adding the correction moments to the assumed (fixed-end) moments, as follows:

$$M_{ba} = +225.0 + 2.7 = +227.7 \text{ ft-kips}$$

$$M_{bc} = -200.0 - 27.7 = -227.7$$

$$M_{cb} = +200.0 - 60.7 = +139.3$$

$$M_{cd} = -66.7 - 72.6 = -139.3$$

$$M_{dc} = +66.7 - 51.5 = +15.2$$

$$M_{de} = 0 - 15.2 = -15.2$$

If end A or E were fixed completely or partially, the same procedure would be used but with appropriate stiffness and carry-over factor.

Notice that for any other pattern of loading it is only necessary to replace the column vector P and then perform the indicated multiplications. As the number of loading patterns increases, the matrix method becomes more and more attractive.

The beam and loading in Figure 9-15 are identical to those in Figure 7-1.

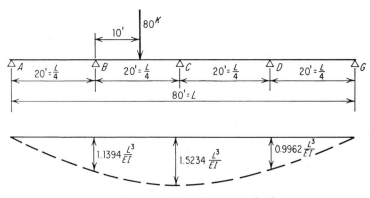

Figure 9-15.   Force Method

As in the latter figure, we proceed by the force method, assuming a solution satisfying statics (zero reactions at B, C, and D). The errors in geometry are the resulting displacements at B, C, and D, and they have the values determined in Figure 7-1. The flexibility matrix, shown in Figure 9-6, has already been inverted (Figure 9-7). Equation (9.16) becomes

$$\begin{bmatrix} X_b \\ X_c \\ X_d \end{bmatrix} = \frac{EI}{L^3} \begin{bmatrix} 630.86 & -603.44 & 246.86 \\ -603.44 & 877.73 & -603.44 \\ 246.86 & -603.44 & 630.86 \end{bmatrix} \begin{bmatrix} -1.1394 \\ -1.5234 \\ -0.9962 \end{bmatrix} \frac{L^3}{EI}$$

Performing the indicated multiplications we obtain

$$X_b = -45.5 \text{ kips}; \qquad X_c = -48.4 \text{ kips}; \qquad X_d = +9.5 \text{ kips}$$

These values are the corrections to the asssumed reactions at B, C, and D. They are identical to those in Figure 7-1 but are of opposite sign because the unit forces in Figure 9-6 were assumed downward rather than upward as in Figure 7-1. Since the assumed reactions were all zero, X_b, X_c, and X_d represent the actual reactions, acting exactly as in Figure 7-1.

For any other loading it is only necessary to change the values in the column vector Δ. If the beam is on elastic supports (see Section 7.3), it is necessary to modify the flexibility coefficients in Figure 9-6 accordingly.

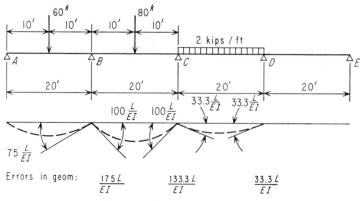

Figure 9-16.   Force Method

The beam and loads in Figure 9-16 are identical to those in Figure 9-14. We now, however, make an analysis by the force method. A solution satisfying the statical requirements is obtained by assuming the structure to be cut at all supports. The resulting end rotations of all members are identical to those in Figure 7-2 except that they are one-twentieth as large since they are now expressed in terms of L. Since the deflected structure must be continuous, errors in geometry equal to the sums of the end slopes at each joint must be corrected without upsetting the statical balance of the assumed solution.

The flexibility matrix for this structure is shown in Figure 9-8. Its inverse is shown in Figure 9-9. Thus

$$\begin{bmatrix} X_b \\ X_c \\ X_d \end{bmatrix} = \frac{3EI}{7L} \begin{bmatrix} 3.75 & -1.00 & 0.25 \\ -1.00 & 4.00 & -1.00 \\ 0.25 & -1.00 & 3.75 \end{bmatrix} \begin{bmatrix} -175 \\ -133.3 \\ -33.3 \end{bmatrix} \frac{L}{EI}$$

and the moments at the supports are

$$X_b = -228 \text{ ft-kips};\qquad X_c = -139 \text{ ft-kips};\qquad X_d = -15 \text{ ft-kips}$$

In this problem, a negative sign for moment indicates that it acts opposite to the corresponding unit applied moment in Figure 9-8.

It is easier to obtain the stiffness matrix of Figure 9-4 than the flexibility matrix of either Figure 9-6 or Figure 9-8. However, solution by displacement method does not yield moments or forces directly. On the other hand, the displacement method directly yields actual joint rotations, thus facilitating the determination of deflections if they are desired.

In the general case of three-dimensional frameworks, with out-of-plane members or branches framing into the joints, it is necessary to determine the unbalanced moments and stiffness coefficients with respect to three orthogonal axes. In order to do this, one must first obtain fixed-end moments and stiffnesses of the individual out-of-plane members or branches. Procedures for computing such values are available.[1] Of course, larger matrices result, but the scheme of analysis is identical to that for plane structures.

9.9   Matrix Analysis of Frames

Figure 9-17(a) shows the rigid frame of Figure 9-10 subjected to a 50-kip vertical load and a 24-kip horizontal load. We assume a solution satisfying geometry—that is, we assume joints B and C fixed against rotation and translation. The fixed-end moments and forces shown in (b) are consistent with this assumption. The errors in statics resulting from the assumed solution are shown in (c). They consist of the unbalanced moments at B and C, and of the force of 16.5 kips to the left (24-kip load minus the 7.5-kip reaction for AB fixed at B and simply supported at A) required to prevent translation in the assumed solution.

The errors in statics, but with opposite sign, are the elements of the column vector which, when multiplied by $\mathbf{K}^{-1}$ shown in Figure 9-10, yields the column vector of joint rotations at B and C, and translation at C. Thus

$$\begin{bmatrix} D_1 \\ D_2 \\ D_3 \end{bmatrix} = \frac{1}{E} \begin{bmatrix} 0.01647 & -0.00397 & 2.085 \\ -0.00397 & 0.01647 & 0.6145 \\ 2.085 & 0.6145 & 1,277 \end{bmatrix} \begin{bmatrix} 1,278 \\ -2,250 \\ 16.5 \end{bmatrix} = \frac{1}{E} \begin{bmatrix} 64.38 \\ -31.99 \\ 22,350 \end{bmatrix}$$

[1] James Michalos, *Theory of Structural Analysis and Design* (New York: Ronald, 1958).

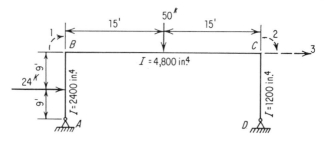

(a) Loaded Frame, with Reference System

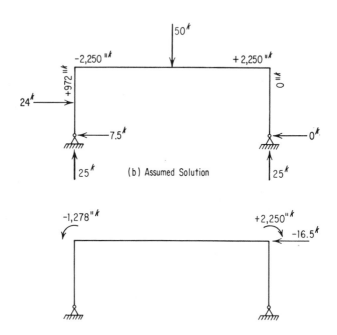

(b) Assumed Solution

(c) Resulting Errors in Statics

Figure 9-17. Analysis of Rigid Frame by Displacement Method

in which $D_1 = 64.38/E$ is the clockwise rotation at B, $D_2 = -31.99/E$ is the counterclockwise rotation at C, and $D_3 = 22,350/E$ is the translation of BC to the right.

The correction moments are obtained by multiplying the D values by the appropriate relationships, obtained in the following paragraph, for individual members, between rotation, moment, displacement, and force, as follows:

$$m_{ba} = 64.38(33.33) + 22,350(-0.1543) = -1,300 \text{ in.-kips}$$

$$m_{bc} = 64.38(53.33) - 31.99(26.66) = +2,580 \text{ in.-kips}$$

$$m_{cb} = -31.99(53.33) + 64.38(26.66) = +10 \text{ in.-kips}$$

$$m_{cd} = -31.99(16.66) + 22,350(-0.0772) = -2,260 \text{ in.-kips}$$

If a digital computer is used, it is convenient to use matrix multiplication for this operation, as illustrated for Figure 9-14 in Section 9.8. All the stiffnesses for individual members actually include a factor E which cancels the $1/E$ multiplier of the D terms when the correction moments are evaluated. The stiffnesses used were obtained as follows:

$$33.33 = 3(2{,}400)/(18 \times 12)$$
$$-0.1543 = -3(2{,}400)/(18 \times 12)^2$$
$$53.33 = 4(4{,}800)/(30 \times 12)$$
$$26.66 = 2(4{,}800)/(30 \times 12)$$
$$16.66 = 3(1{,}200)/(18 \times 12)$$
$$-0.0772 = -3(1{,}200)/(18 \times 12)^2$$

Adding the correction moments to the assumed moments, we obtain the actual moments (rounded to the nearest 10 in.-kips)

$$M_{ba} = 972 - 1{,}300 \qquad = -330 \text{ in.-kips}$$
$$M_{bc} = -2{,}250 + 2{,}580 = +330 \text{ in.-kips}$$
$$M_{cb} = 2{,}250 + 7 \qquad = +2{,}260 \text{ in.-kips}$$
$$M_{cd} = 0 - 2{,}260 \qquad = -2{,}260 \text{ in.-kips}$$

If in Figure 9-17(a) there were also a horizontal applied load at B or C, the only difference would be that we would include it in determining the unbalanced force in (c). For example, if a load of $+20$ kips were applied at B, the third element in the "load" column would become $+16.5 + 20.0 = +36.5$. Nothing else would change.

Matrix analysis can be used for any frame, regardless of loading, number of spans, or number of stories. The stiffness matrix is formulated just as for Figure 9-10. For n degrees of freedom of rotation or translation, the resulting matrix is of order $n \times n$. When a digital computer is available, this method is particularly suitable for the analysis of structures with many degrees of freedom and/or many loading conditions. If change in length due to axial load is considered important, as it may be in columns of multistory frames, this effect can be accounted for by including the appropriate additional elements in the stiffness matrix.

9.10 Matrix Analysis of Trusses

In Chapter 8 statically indeterminate trusses were analyzed by the force method, using flexibility coefficients such as those in Figure 9-7. A matrix analysis for such trusses can be made by inverting the flexibility matrix, exactly as for continuous beams.

The displacement method of analysis can be applied to any truss, regardless of whether it is statically indeterminate or not. For a statically determinate truss it would appear ridiculous to do so because the stresses can be obtained straightforwardly by simple computations of statics. On the other hand, if it is also desired to obtain joint displacements for many loading patterns, and if a digital computer can be used, there may be an advantage in the use of the displacement method.

The availability of a digital computer will be a factor in deciding whether the displacement method or the force method is to be used in the analysis of statically indeterminate trusses. For example, the truss in Figure 9-13(b) is statically indeterminate in the second degree. If a force method is used, it is necessary to solve two simultaneous equations. If a displacement method is used, there would be eight simultaneous equations (8×8 matrix). Although the stiffness coefficients of the displacement method are much more easy to obtain than the flexibility coefficients of the force method, the force method would generally be chosen if only a desk calculator were available. If a digital computer is used in conjunction with a matrix inversion program, then the displacement method could have advantages.

The displacement method could be preferable to the force method even if a digital computer were not to be used. This would be true when a statically indeterminate truss has many members framing into a relatively few joints. An example of this would be a structure such as that in Figure 9-18. This

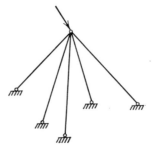

Figure 9-18.   Structure with One Movable Joint

structure is statically indeterminate three times and, by force method, would require the solution of three simultaneous equations. Since only the loaded joint can move, two simultaneous equations result by displacement method.

For the general case of a truss, we have, by the displacement method,

$$\mathbf{D} = \mathbf{K}^{-1}\mathbf{P}$$

or

$$
\begin{bmatrix} D_1 \\ D_2 \\ \cdot \\ \cdot \\ \cdot \\ D_n \end{bmatrix}
=
\begin{bmatrix} k_{11} & k_{12} \cdots & k_{1n} \\ k_{21} & k_{22} \cdots & k_{2n} \\ \cdot & \cdot \ \cdots & \cdot \\ \cdot & \cdot \ \cdots & \cdot \\ \cdot & \cdot \ \cdots & \cdot \\ k_{n1} & k_{n2} \cdots & k_{nn} \end{bmatrix}^{-1}
\begin{bmatrix} P_1 \\ P_2 \\ \cdot \\ \cdot \\ \cdot \\ P_n \end{bmatrix}
\qquad (9.23)
$$

in which **D** represents joint displacements and **P** represents the errors in statics, but with opposite sign, associated with the assumed solution that satisfies geometry. The solution assumed is that no displacement occurs at any of the joints of the truss. Then what is wrong with statics at each joint are the forces that must be applied to prevent displacement. In each case these will be equal and opposite to the applied loads. Therefore P is now equal to the load, and with the *same* sign.

With the displacements determined, the total force, F, in any bar ji can be obtained as

$$F_{ji} = \left(\frac{AE}{L^2}\right)_{ji} [(x_j - x_i)(D_{jx} - D_{ix}) + (y_j - y_i)(D_{jy} - D_{iy})$$

$$+ (z_j - z_i)(D_{jz} - D_{iz})] \quad (9.24)$$

in which D_{jx} represents the displacement of end j in the x-direction, and so forth. In the two-dimensional problem the z terms drop out. Equation (9.24) can be rewritten in matrix form as follows.

$$F_{ji} = \left(\frac{AE}{L^2}\right)_{ji} [(x_j - x_i) \quad (y_j - y_i) \quad (z_j - z_i)] \begin{bmatrix} (D_{jx} - D_{ix}) \\ (D_{jy} - D_{iy}) \\ (D_{jz} - D_{iz}) \end{bmatrix} \quad (9.24a)$$

As an example, we solve the simple problem indicated in Figure 9-19. This is the truss of Figure 9-13(a), for which we have already obtained the stiffness

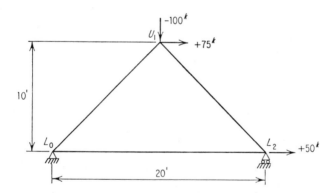

Figure 9-19.   Loaded Truss

matrix and inverted it. The positive directions for joint forces and displacements are shown in Figure 9-13(a). Equation (9.23) becomes

$$\begin{bmatrix} D_3 \\ D_4 \\ D_5 \end{bmatrix} = \frac{10}{AE} \begin{bmatrix} 1.914 & -0.500 & 1.000 \\ -0.500 & 1.914 & -1.000 \\ 1.000 & -1.000 & 2.000 \end{bmatrix} \begin{bmatrix} +75 \\ -100 \\ +50 \end{bmatrix} = \frac{10}{AE} \begin{bmatrix} 243.55 \\ -278.90 \\ 275.00 \end{bmatrix}$$

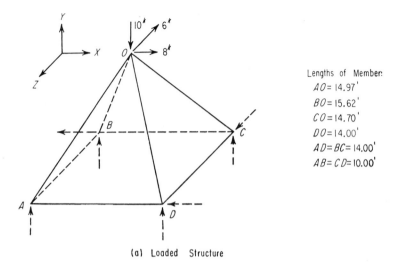

Lengths of Member:
$AO = 14.97'$
$BO = 15.62'$
$CO = 14.70'$
$DO = 14.00'$
$AD = BC = 14.00'$
$AB = CD = 10.00'$

(a) Loaded Structure

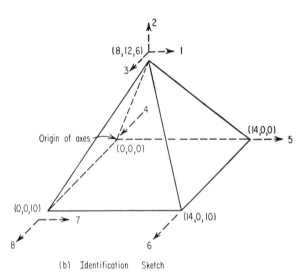

(b) Identification Sketch

Figure 9-20. Three-Dimensional Truss

From Equation (9.24) the force in bar U_1L_2 is

$$U_1L_2 = \frac{AE}{200}[(20 - 10)(275.00 - 243.55) + (0 - 10)(0 + 278.90)]\frac{10}{AE}$$

$$= -123.7 \text{ kips}$$

Similarly, $L_0U_1 = -17.7$ kips, and $L_0L_2 = +137.5$ kips. Positive sign indicates tension.

Trusses are generally analyzed as if the members at the joints were connected

286

by means of frictionless pins. Actually, they are almost invariably rigidly connected at each joint, and this induces bending stresses in addition to the axial forces normally computed, even though all loads are applied at the joints. These so-called secondary stresses generally have negligible effect on the axial forces, reducing them by a small amount. See Section 12.8.

If loads are applied directly to the bars, between joints of the truss, compute the fixed-end moments and corresponding fixed-end forces at the ends of each member. At each joint obtain the total unbalanced moment and the total unbalanced force (along each reference axis). The load vector, $\mathbf{P}$, in Equation (9.23) will now include these unbalanced forces and moments (but with opposite sign) in addition to any forces applied directly to the joint. Of course, the stiffness matrix must now include flexural stiffness coefficients at the joints.

The space truss and the loading in Figure 9-20(a) are identical to that in Figure 4-4. The dashed arrows in (b) indicate, in the positive directions, the degrees of freedom of the joints. With the origin of axes at point B, the co-ordinates (x, y, and z) of each joint are shown in parentheses.

The coefficients of the 8×8 stiffness matrix, evaluated through use of Equations (9.20) and (9.21), are tabulated in the eight rows and eight columns of Table 9-1. For example, $k_{35} = 0.01133$ is found in row 3, column 5, and is

TABLE 9-1 Stiffness Matrix

	1	2	3	4	5	6	7	8
1	0.06032	0.004092	0.0004722	-0.01260	-0.01133	-0.008746	-0.01908	0.009538
2	0.004092	0.1785	0.009756	-0.01889	0.02266	0.01749	-0.02861	0.01431
3	0.0004722	0.009756	0.03138	-0.009446	0.01133	-0.005831	0.009538	-0.004769
4	-0.01260	-0.01889	-0.009446	0.109446	0	0	0	-0.1000
5	-0.01133	0.02266	0.01133	0	0.08276	0	0	0
6	-0.008746	0.01749	-0.005831	0	0	0.105831	0	0
7	-0.01908	-0.02861	0.009538	0	0	0	0.09050	-0.009538
8	0.009538	0.01431	-0.004769	-0.1000	0	0	-0.009538	0.104769

equal to k_{53} in row 5, column 3. In order to obtain absolute values of the coefficients of the stiffness matrix, it would be necessary to multiply each tabulated coefficient by AE, expressed in foot units. In what follows, the areas of all bars are assumed equal. Since this structure is statically determinate (see Section 4.4), any set of areas used would result in the same values of bar stress. This would not, of course, be true for a statically indeterminate truss.

The stiffness matrix in Table 9-1 was inverted by digital computer to obtain the matrix in Table 9-2. The tabulated coefficients are all multiples of $1/AE$. The displacements, D, of the joints of the truss are obtained, as before, from multiplication of the matrix inverse by the load vector, $\mathbf{P}$, as follows:

$$
\begin{bmatrix} D_1 \\ D_2 \\ D_3 \\ D_4 \\ D_5 \\ D_6 \\ D_7 \\ D_8 \end{bmatrix} = \mathbf{K}^{-1} \begin{bmatrix} 8.0 \\ -10.0 \\ -6.0 \\ 0.0 \\ 0.0 \\ 0.0 \\ 0.0 \\ 0.0 \end{bmatrix} = \begin{bmatrix} 143.46 \\ -56.23 \\ -366.91 \\ -342.67 \\ 85.26 \\ 0.93 \\ 14.48 \\ -347.84 \end{bmatrix} \frac{1}{AE}
$$

From Equation (9.24) we can now obtain stresses in all bars. For example, for bar OA,

$$
F = \frac{1}{(14.97)^2} [(8 - 0)(143.46 - 14.48) + (12 - 0)(-56.23 - 0)
$$
$$
+ (6 - 10)(-366.91 + 347.84)]
$$
$$
= 1.93 \text{ kips}
$$

All bar forces are identical to those computed in Section 4.4. With bar forces

TABLE 9-2 Inverse of Stiffness Matrix

	1	2	3	4	5	6	7	8
1	19.55	0.1505	1.914	10.00	2.374	1.696	4.841	8.275
2	0.1505	6.510	-1.278	2.769	-1.586	-1.133	2.425	1.903
3	1.914	-1.278	65.83	65.83	-8.400	3.996	-0.0003220	65.83
4	10.00	2.769	65.83	148.1	-8.401	3.996	11.23	144.1
5	2.374	-1.586	-8.400	-8.401	13.99	-0.004394	-0.001209	-8.401
6	1.696	-1.133	3.996	3.996	-0.004394	9.996	-0.0007286	3.996
7	4.841	2.425	-0.0003220	11.23	-0.001209	-0.0007286	14.02	11.22
8	8.275	1.903	65.83	144.1	-8.401	3.996	11.22	150.0

known, the reactions can be obtained from summations of forces at each support point. For any other system of loading, only the load vector is changed.

All calculations, from determination of stiffness coefficients to computation of bar forces and reactions, can be programmed for a digital computer. The procedure illustrated in connection with Figure 9-20 is a perfectly general one for three-dimensional trusses.

Problems

9.1. For the matrices

$$A = \begin{bmatrix} 5 & 0 & -1 \\ 3 & -2 & 4 \end{bmatrix}; \quad B = \begin{bmatrix} 2 & 1 \\ 0 & -4 \\ 3 & 6 \end{bmatrix}; \quad C = \begin{bmatrix} 1 & 2 & 3 \\ -4 & 2 & 6 \\ 5 & 0 & -7 \end{bmatrix}; \quad D = \begin{bmatrix} 5 \\ -2 \\ 3 \end{bmatrix};$$

evaluate the following matrix products: (a) AB; (b) BA; (c) AD; (d) CD

9.2. Determine the inverse of the following matrices by use of the cofactor approach:

$$A = \begin{bmatrix} 4 & 5 \\ 10 & 16 \end{bmatrix}; \quad B = \begin{bmatrix} 8 & 7 \\ 7 & 8 \end{bmatrix}; \quad C = \begin{bmatrix} 1.20 & 0.40 & -0.02 \\ 0.40 & 1.40 & -0.03 \\ -0.02 & -0.03 & 0.002833 \end{bmatrix}$$

$$Ans.: \ C^{-1} = \begin{bmatrix} 0.9746 & -0.1695 & 5.0856 \\ -0.1695 & 0.9534 & 8.8997 \\ 5.0856 & 8.8997 & 483.1286 \end{bmatrix}$$

9.3. Compute the elements of the inverse of the matrices in Problem 9.2 by use of pivotal condensation.

9.4. Find the eigenvalues for the following matrices of Problem 9.2:
(a) matrix A (Ans.: $\lambda_1 = 19.27$; $\lambda_2 = 0.73$.);
(b) matrix B (Ans.: $\lambda_1 = 15$; $\lambda_2 = 1$.).

9.5. Use matrix iteration to evaluate the *highest* eigenvalues of the matrices in Problem 9.4.

9.6. Solve the following simultaneous equations by use of the inverse of the matrix of coefficients and by pivotal condensation:
(a) $4X_1 + 5X_2 = 3$
$10X_1 + 16X_2 = 4$
(b) $27X_1 + 14X_2 + 4X_3 = 39$
$14X_1 + 8X_2 + 2.5X_3 = 20$
$4X_1 + 2.5X_2 + X_3 = 5$ (Ans.: $X_1 = 1$; $X_2 = 2$; $X_3 = -4$.)

9.7. Solve the following equations by use of the Gauss–Seidel iteration method:
(a) $10X_1 + 4X_2 = 40$
$2X_1 + 7X_2 = -23$
(b) $20X_1 + 8X_2 + 4X_3 + X_4 = 56$
$5X_1 + 40X_2 + 8X_3 + 5X_4 = 162$
$6X_1 + 8X_2 + 30X_3 + 6X_4 = -88$
$8X_1 + 12X_2 + 10X_3 + 50X_4 = 404$
(Ans.: $X_1 = 2$; $X_2 = 4$; $X_3 = -6$; $X_4 = 8$.)

9.8. Determine the stiffness matrix of the continuous beam of Figure 9-4 if support A is fixed against rotation.

9.9. Construct the stiffness matrix for the beam shown in Figure 7-10 using the following values of moment of inertia for the spans: $I_{AB} = 4I$; $I_{BC} = 3I$;

$$I_{CD} = 2I. \quad Ans.: \ K = \frac{EI}{30} \begin{bmatrix} 24 & 6 \\ 6 & 18 \end{bmatrix}.$$

9.10. Invert the stiffness matrix of Problem 9.9 and show the physical significance of the elements of the inverse on a sketch of the continuous beam.

9.11. Evaluate the elements of the stiffness matrix for the rigid frame of:

(a) Figure 7-20;

(b) Figure 7-22.

$$Ans.\ for\ (b)\colon\ \mathbf{K} = E \begin{bmatrix} 1.20 & 0.40 & -0.02 \\ 0.40 & 1.40 & -0.03 \\ -0.02 & -0.03 & 0.002833 \end{bmatrix}$$

9.12. Construct the stiffness matrix for the truss of Problem 8-1(a).

9.13. Determine the final moments at all supports for the continuous beam and loading of Figure 7-10 by a matrix method of analysis utilizing the stiffness matrix of Problem 9.9 and its inverse from Problem 9.10.

9.14. Analyze the beam of Figure 7-10 for the following loading conditions:

(a) all spans loaded with a uniformly distributed load of 5 kips/ft;

(b) a single concentrated load of 100-kips, located in span BC 10 ft to the right of support B.

9.15. Analyze the rigid frame of Figure 9-11 by a matrix method of analysis for the moments at all joints due to a single concentrated horizontal load of 20-kips applied to the right at joint B.

9.16. Use a matrix method of analysis to determine the moments at all joints of the loaded rigid frame of:

(a) Figure 7-20;

(b) Figure 7-22 (see Problem 11 for $\mathbf{K}$ and Problem 2 for $\mathbf{K}^{-1}$).

9.17. Determine the values of all bar forces for the loaded truss of Problem 9.12 by inverting the stiffness matrix. ($Ans.\colon\ L_0U_1 = +33.1^k;\ L_0L_1 = +16.6^k.$)

Chapter 10

Arches and Rings

Statically determinate (three-hinged) arches were treated in Chapters 2 and 3. Statically indeterminate arches and rings are considered in the present chapter. The pressure line, introduced in Chapter 2, is reexamined, particularly with respect to its application to approximate analysis and its relationship to exact analysis. Exact methods of analysis are presented and applied.

10.1 The Pressure Line

The pressure line can be defined as a curve or series of straight segments that represent successive resultants of all forces (loads and reactions) acting on a structure. It is a string polygon, but one that "fits" the structure. A pressure line "fits" the axis of a member when the angle changes corresponding to the pressure line balance. To be in balance, the angle changes in a loaded hingeless arch or rigid frame must satisfy the following conditions of geometry:

$$\theta = \int d\theta = 0 \tag{10.1}$$

$$\Delta_x = \int y \, d\theta = 0 \tag{10.2}$$

$$\Delta_y = \int x \, d\theta = 0 \tag{10.3}$$

Equation (10.1) states that the sum of all the angle changes along the structure must be equal to zero. Equations (10.2) and (10.3) express the condition that there be no relative displacement of one end of the arch with respect to the other. Equations (10.1) and (10.3) were used in Chapter 7 to express the geometric requirements for a fixed-end beam. The necessity of now satisfying three equations of geometry is consistent with the fact that a hingeless arch is statically indeterminate in the third degree.

If the structure is elastic, then, from Equation (6.3), and neglecting the effects of shear and axial force, Equations (10.1) to (10.3) become

$$\theta = \int \frac{M}{EI} ds = 0 \tag{10.4}$$

$$\Delta_x = \int y \frac{M}{EI} ds = 0 \tag{10.5}$$

$$\Delta_y = \int x \frac{M}{EI} ds = 0 \tag{10.6}$$

The effects of shear on displacements in an arch of practical dimensions are infinitesimal. The student can quickly verify that the shortening of an element, ds, of the arch due to the action of the axial thrust, N, is

$$\Delta(ds) = \frac{N}{AE} ds \tag{a}$$

Furthermore, this shortening results in an additional angle change

$$d\theta = \frac{N}{AEr} ds \tag{b}$$

in which r is the radius of the arch axis at the element under consideration. The total displacements projected along the X-axis and along the Y-axis due to rib shortening will be, using Equations (a) and (b),

$$\Delta_x = \int \frac{N}{AE} dx - \int y \frac{N}{AEr} ds \tag{c}$$

$$\Delta_y = \int \frac{N}{AE} dy + \int x \frac{N}{AEr} ds \tag{d}$$

and the total rotation due to the same cause will be

$$\theta = \int \frac{N}{AEr} ds \tag{e}$$

Equations (10.4) through (10.5) now become

$$\theta = \int \frac{M}{EI} ds - \int \frac{N}{AEr} ds = 0 \tag{10.4a}$$

$$\Delta_x = \int y \frac{M}{EI} ds - \int \frac{N}{AE} dx + \int y \frac{N}{AEr} ds = 0 \tag{10.5a}$$

$$\Delta_y = \int x \frac{M}{EI} ds - \int \frac{N}{AE} dy - \int x \frac{N}{AEr} ds = 0 \tag{10.6a}$$

The inclusion of the rib shortening effects would substantially complicate

all subsequent development. Even if we omitted expression (e), whose effect
is of a secondary order compared to expressions (c) and (d), the work would
still be quite complicated. Investigations have shown, however, that even the
effect of expressions (c) and (d) is significant only in the case of flat arches that
are comparatively thick. Consequently, we will base all future development on
Equations (10.4) through (10.6) and correct for rib shortening (or similar
effects, such as temperature change) as explained in Section 10.7. As a rough
guide, such corrections are significant only for rise-to-span ratios less than,
say, 0.2 unless extremely thick ribs are used.

In Chapter 6 it was found convenient to treat angle changes as forces
along their axes of rotation. Displacements could then be computed as
moments of these "forces" about the line of displacement. As a result of
the analogy between computations of geometry and computations of statics,
Equations (10.4), (10.5), and (10.6) are automatically satisfied if, treating
angle changes as forces, we satisfy the following conditions of statical equilibrium:

$$\sum F \ = 0 \tag{10.7}$$

$$\sum M_x = \sum Fy = 0 \tag{10.8}$$

$$\sum M_y = \sum Fx = 0 \tag{10.9}$$

in which the forces, F, are the angle changes (m/EI per unit length of the
structure) applied normal to the plane of the structure, and M_x and M_y are
analogous moments equal to Δ_x and Δ_y, respectively.

Figure 10-1(a) shows a trial pressure line for a concentrated load, W,
placed on a hingeless arch. Bending moments are represented by vertical
ordinates between pressure line and the arch axis. The numerical value of the
moment at any section is determined as the product of the horizontal thrust
and the vertical ordinate, η, at the section. The values of horizontal thrust
and bending moment are found exactly as for three-hinged arches. See
Equations (2.2) and (2.3), and Figures 2-2 and 2-3.

The angle change per unit length at any section is obtained by dividing
the bending moment at that section by EI. Since only relative angle changes
are necessary for our present purpose, we can divide bending moments by
relative values of I. The angle changes corresponding to the trial pressure line
must be such that Equations (10.4), (10.5), and (10.6) are satisfied. Or, treating
the angle changes as forces normal to the plane of the arch, it is necessary to
satisfy the analogous expressions of Equations (10.7), (10.8), and (10.9).

The resultant angle changes, or "forces," corresponding to the areas
between pressure line and axis of the arch, assuming constant I, are indicated
by crosses in Figure 10-1(a). Since the angle changes occur along the arch
axis, the position of these resultants is that corresponding to the distribution of
analogous forces along an arc. The magnitude of each resultant "force" is
equal to the area between the pressure line and the arch axis. If the pressure
line in Figure 10-1(a) is correct, then the final resultant of all positive forces

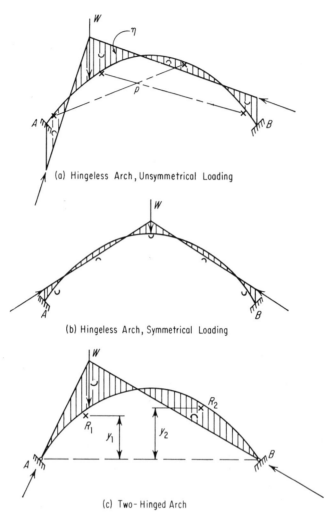

(a) Hingeless Arch, Unsymmetrical Loading

(b) Hingeless Arch, Symmetrical Loading

(c) Two-Hinged Arch

Figure 10-1.   Pressure Lines

(corresponding to tension on the inner fibers of the arch) must be equal and opposite to the total resultant of all negative forces. Furthermore, these final positive and negative resultants must be colinear at some point p. Equations (10.7), (10.8), and (10.9) are then automatically satisfied.

Strictly speaking, since the angle changes occur along the curved rib, and since the distance along a segment of arc is somewhat greater than its horizontal projection, the resultant angle changes are a little greater than the areas between axis and pressure line. This has no practical bearing on the use of the pressure line for approximate results. However, it is of interest to note that, as will be shown in Section 10.2, for a so-called secant variation in I the resultant angle changes are exactly equal to the areas between pressure line and arch.

Figure 10-1(b) shows a pressure line for symmetrical loading. Again, the resultant of the positive forces must be equal, opposite, and colinear with the resultant of the negative forces.

The reader must keep in mind that angle changes vary inversely with I. Consequently, the pressure line tends to move away from sections with greater relative values of moment of inertia in order to satisfy the requirements stated in Equations (10.4) through (10.6). As would be expected, this results in increased moments at stiff sections.

A pressure line for a two-hinged arch is shown in Figure 10-1(c). Equations (10.4) and (10.6), or Equations (10.7) and (10.9) are not applicable because unknown rotations occur at hinges A and B. However, Equation (10.5) or Equation (10.8), with y measured to a straight line joining the hinges, is all that is necessary to test a trial pressure line, and this is consistent with the fact that the two-hinged arch has only one degree of statical indeterminateness. Thus, in (c), it is necessary that

$$R_1 y_1 = R_2 y_2$$

in which R_1 and R_2 represent, respectively, the resultant of the positive "forces" and the resultant of the negative "forces."

Once the correct position of the pressure line is determined, the rotations at A and B can be found, by means of Equations (10.7) and (10.9), as the reactions at A and B normal to the plane of the arch.

10.2   Analysis by Direct Solution of Equations of Geometry

Figure 10-2 shows a hingeless arch with arbitrary loading. The moment and reactions at A are taken as the indeterminate quantities. The bending moment at the element ds, with tension on the inner surface of the arch taken as positive, is

$$M = M_A + V_A x + H_A y + m_0 \tag{10.10}$$

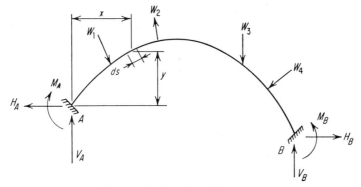

Figure 10-2.   Hingeless Arch

in which m_0 represents the moment of any loads applied to the left of the element under consideration.

Equations (10.4) through (10.6) can now be written as

$$\int_A^B (M_A + V_A x + H_A y + m_0) \frac{ds}{EI} = 0 \tag{10.11}$$

$$\int_A^B (M_A + V_A x + H_A y + m_0)y \frac{ds}{EI} = 0 \tag{10.12}$$

$$\int_A^B (M_A + V_A x + H_A y + m_0)x \frac{ds}{EI} = 0 \tag{10.13}$$

Integration of these equations is generally quite difficult or even impossible. For numerical solutions, integration is replaced by summation, using finite elements, Δs, as follows:

$$M_A \sum \frac{\Delta s}{EI} + V_A \sum x \frac{\Delta s}{EI} + H_A \sum y \frac{\Delta s}{EI} + \sum m_0 \frac{\Delta s}{EI} = 0 \tag{10.14}$$

$$M_A \sum y \frac{\Delta s}{EI} + V_A \sum xy \frac{\Delta s}{EI} + H_A \sum y^2 \frac{\Delta s}{EI} + \sum m_0 y \frac{\Delta s}{EI} = 0 \tag{10.15}$$

$$M_A \sum x \frac{\Delta s}{EI} + V_A \sum x^2 \frac{\Delta s}{EI} + H_A \sum xy \frac{\Delta s}{EI} + \sum m_0 x \frac{\Delta s}{EI} = 0 \tag{10.16}$$

Application of these equations to the solution of problems is illustrated at the end of Section 10.3, after the identical equations are obtained through use of the force method of analysis.

For the usual case of gravity loading, a negative value will be obtained for H_A, indicating it acts in the opposite direction to that shown in Figure 10-2. If a rotation, θ, or displacement, Δ_x or Δ_y, is known or assumed to take place, this value replaces the zero on the right-hand side of the corresponding equation.

In the two-hinged arch in Figure 10-3, the reactions have been resolved

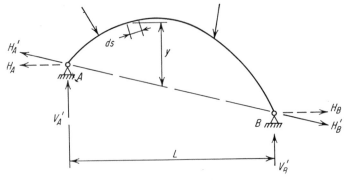

Figure 10-3. Two-Hinged Arch

into vertical components, V_A' and V_B', and into components, H_A' and H_B', along line AB. The vertical components are identical to those that would result if the structure were simply supported. The horizontal components of reaction, H_A and H_B, are indicated by broken arrows.

Equation (10.5) is the only applicable equation of geometry for the two-hinged arch, but y must be measured from arch axis to line AB. As previously explained, this is necessary in order to eliminate the unknown rotations at the hinges. The bending moment at an element ds is

$$M = m_0 + H_A y \tag{10.17}$$

in which m_0 now represents the bending moment for the structure *simply supported* at A and B. That is, the moment m_0 is that resulting from V_A' and the applied loads to the left of the element under consideration. Consequently, Equation (10.5) becomes

$$\Delta_x = \int_A^B y(m_0 + H_A y) \frac{ds}{EI} = 0$$

and we obtain

$$H_A = -\frac{\displaystyle\int_A^B y m_0 (ds/EI)}{\displaystyle\int_A^B y^2 (ds/EI)} \tag{10.18}$$

For computational purposes it is generally necessary to replace integration by summation, as follows:

$$H_A = -\frac{\sum y m_0 (\Delta s/EI)}{\sum y^2 (\Delta s/EI)} \tag{10.19}$$

With H_A known, H_B and the actual vertical reaction components for the arch, V_A and V_B, can be obtained by statics. If a horizontal displacement is known or assumed to take place, then Δ_x is not zero and its value must be subtracted from the numerator of Equations (10.18) and (10.19).

If it is assumed that the moment of inertia, I, varies with the secant of the slope angle of the arch axis, and if I_c is the moment of inertia at the crown,

$$I = I_c \frac{ds}{dx}$$

and

$$\frac{ds}{I} = \frac{dx}{I_c} \tag{10.20}$$

Substituting dx/I_c for ds/I in Equations (10.11), (10.12), and (10.13), or in Equation (10.18), greatly simplifies the integration. For most practical problems, however, the shape of the arch axis and the variation in moment of inertia are such that summation is resorted to rather than integration.

If secant variation is assumed, the moment areas in Figure 10.1 exactly represent the angle changes because integration is now performed along the X-axis rather than along the rib.

10.3　Analysis by Force Method

In this section we apply the force method of analysis, in which we assume a solution satisfying statics and superimpose corrections on the resulting errors in geometry. It is shown that the resulting equations are identical to those obtained in Section 10.2.

In Figure 10-4 it has been assumed that the arch is cantilevered from support B, and the resulting errors of geometry at A are the change in slope, θ, and the displacements Δ_x and Δ_y. Unit values of moment, horizontal force, and vertical force are then applied successively at end A, and the resulting rotations and displacements determined. These quantities are all designated

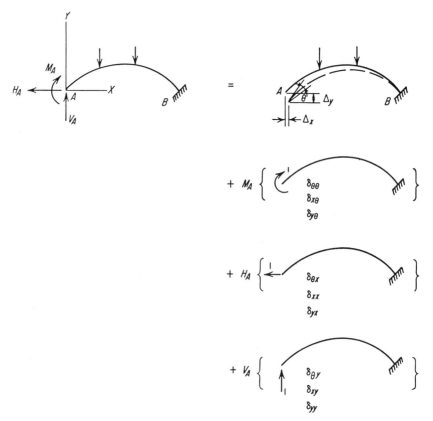

Figure 10-4.　Force Method of Analysis

by δ, with appropriate double subscripts, the first of which identifies the rotation or displacement, and the second of which identifies the cause. For example, $\delta_{\theta\theta}$ is a rotation due to unit moment, $\delta_{x\theta}$ is a displacement in the x-direction due to unit moment, and δ_{yx} is a vertical displacement due to unit horizontal force.

In the same manner as for continuous beams and trusses, we can write

$$\theta + M_A\delta_{\theta\theta} + H_A\delta_{\theta x} + V_A\delta_{\theta y} = 0 \qquad (10.21)$$

$$\Delta_x + M_A\delta_{x\theta} + H_A\delta_{xx} + V_A\delta_{xy} = 0 \qquad (10.22)$$

$$\Delta_y + M_A\delta_{y\theta} + H_A\delta_{yx} + V_A\delta_{yy} = 0 \qquad (10.23)$$

Expressions for evaluating all displacements and rotations in Equations (10.21) through (10.23) can be written immediately from the integral expressions in Equations (10.4) through (10.6) by inserting the appropriate values of M. These values are $M = m_0$ for finding the errors in geometry, θ, Δ_x, and Δ_y; $M = 1$ for determining rotations and displacements due to applied unit moment; $M = y$ for determining rotations and displacements due to applied unit horizontal force; and $M = x$ for rotations and displacements resulting from applied unit vertical force. The expressions for rotations and displacements become

$$
\left.
\begin{aligned}
\theta &= \int_A^B \frac{m_0}{EI}\,ds\,; \qquad \Delta_x = \int_A^B y\,\frac{m_0}{EI}\,ds\,; \qquad \Delta_y = \int_A^B x\,\frac{m_0}{EI}\,ds \\[2mm]
\delta_{\theta\theta} &= \int_A^B \frac{ds}{EI}\,; \qquad \delta_{\theta x} = \delta_{x\theta} = \int_A^B y\,\frac{ds}{EI}\,; \qquad \delta_{\theta y} = \delta_{y\theta} = \int_A^B x\,\frac{ds}{EI} \\[2mm]
\delta_{xx} &= \int_A^B y^2\,\frac{ds}{EI}\,; \qquad \delta_{xy} = \delta_{yx} = \int_A^B xy\,\frac{ds}{EI}\,; \qquad \delta_{yy} = \int_A^B x^2\,\frac{ds}{EI}
\end{aligned}
\right\} \quad (10.24)
$$

Identical expressions can be obtained through application of the principle of virtual work.

If the expressions (10.24) are substituted for the rotations and displacements in Equations (10.21) through (10.23), we again obtain Equations (10.11) through (10.13). For numerical solutions we use Equations (10.14) through (10.16), as explained previously.

Although this is not a book on design, a few comments pertaining to design are pertinent at this point. An arch is designed primarily to support its dead load plus the live load to which it will be subjected. The most economical structure is one in which bending moments are minimized. If the arch is given the shape of the dead load pressure line, then under dead load no bending moments will result except those due to rib shortening, temperature, and other volume changes. If for reasons of esthetics or economy it is desired to maintain minimum thickness at the crown, with a progressive increase in thickness toward the springings, stresses at the crown due to volume changes must be minimized. This can be accomplished by using a shape of arch axis that lies between the dead load polygon and a parabola—that is, an arch axis corresponding to the string polygon for dead load (nonuniform) plus, perhaps, one half of the live load (uniformly distributed).

The parabolic, fixed arch of constant section in Figure 10-5 is loaded with a concentrated force of 10 kips applied vertically downward, 70 ft from end A. For computational purposes the arch has been divided into twenty segments of 5-ft horizontal projection.

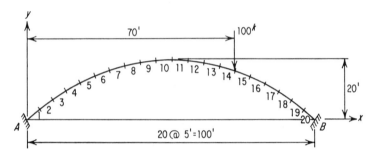

Figure 10-5. Loaded Arch

The coefficients of M_A, V_A, and H_A in Equations (10.14) through (10.16) are evaluated in Table 10-1. The values of m_0 were obtained by assuming the arch cantilevered from B. As E and I are constant, E is omitted from the tabulation and I is conveniently taken as one. Equations (10.14) through (10.16) become

$$109.9M_A + 5,495V_A + 1,417H_A - 53,550 = 0$$

$$1,417M_A + 70,853V_A + 22,280H_A - 358,433 = 0$$

$$5,495M_A + 372,358V_A + 70,853H_A - 4,829,825 = 0$$

from which

$$M_A = \quad 451.9 \text{ ft-kips}$$

$$V_A = \quad 22.05 \text{ kips}$$

$$H_A = -82.76 \text{ kips}$$

The negative value of H_A indicates that the horizontal thrust acts opposite to the direction shown in Figure 10-2. With these values at A known, moments, shears, and thrusts can be evaluated anywhere along the arch by computations of statics. In this manner, for example, we obtain

$$M_B = -343.1 \text{ ft-kips}$$

$$V_B = \quad 77.95 \text{ kips}$$

$$H_B = -82.76 \text{ kips}$$

TABLE 10-1 Tabulation for Arch Analysis

Sect	Δs	I	$\frac{\Delta s}{I}$	x	y	$x\frac{\Delta s}{I}$	$y\frac{\Delta s}{I}$	$xy\frac{\Delta s}{I}$	$x^2\frac{\Delta s}{I}$	$y^2\frac{\Delta s}{I}$	m_0	$m_0\frac{\Delta s}{I}$	$xm_0\frac{\Delta s}{I}$	$ym_0\frac{\Delta s}{I}$
1	6.29	1	6.29	2.5	1.95	15.7	12.3	30	39	24				
2	6.05	1	6.05	7.5	5.55	45.4	33.6	252	340	186				
3	5.83	1	5.83	12.5	8.75	72.9	51.0	637	911	446				
4	5.64	1	5.64	17.5	11.55	98.7	65.1	1,140	1,727	751				
5	5.46	1	5.46	22.5	13.95	122.8	76.2	1,713	2,763	1,063				
6	5.32	1	5.32	27.5	15.95	146.3	84.9	2,333	4,023	1,354				
7	5.20	1	5.20	32.5	17.55	169.0	91.3	2,966	5,492	1,602				
8	5.10	1	5.10	37.5	18.75	191.3	95.6	3,586	7,173	1,792				
9	5.04	1	5.04	42.5	19.55	214.2	98.5	4,187	9,103	1,925				
10	5.02	1	5.02	47.5	19.95	238.5	100.1	4,758	11,328	1,997				
11	5.02	1	5.02	52.5	19.95	263.6	100.1	5,258	13,839	1,997				
12	5.04	1	5.04	57.5	19.55	289.8	98.5	5,665	16,663	1,925				
13	5.10	1	5.10	62.5	18.75	318.8	95.6	5,977	19,925	1,792				
14	5.20	1	5.20	67.5	17.55	351.0	91.3	6,160	23,692	1,602				
15	5.32	1	5.32	72.5	15.95	385.7	84.9	6,151	27,963	1,354	-250	-1,330	-96,425	-21,213
16	5.46	1	5.46	77.5	13.95	423.2	76.2	5,903	32,798	1,063	-750	-4,100	-317,750	-57,195
17	5.64	1	5.64	82.5	11.55	465.3	65.1	5,374	38,387	751	-1,250	-7,070	-583,275	-81,658
18	5.83	1	5.83	87.5	8.75	510.1	51.0	4,463	44,633	446	-1,750	-10,200	-892,500	-89,250
19	6.05	1	6.05	92.5	5.55	559.6	33.6	3,105	51,763	186	-2,250	-13,600	-1,258,000	-75,480
20	6.29	1	6.29	97.5	1.95	613.3	12.3	1,195	59,796	24	-2,750	-17,250	-1,681,875	-33,637
TOTALS	109.9		5,495				1,417	70,853	372,358	22,280		-53,550	-4,829,825	-358,433

The pressure line is shown in Figure 10-6. It is readily constructed to scale by connecting ordinates at A, B, and the load point which are obtained by dividing bending moment by horizontal thrust at the particular point, as illustrated at B in the figure.

If the arch were hinged at A and B, the value of H_A could be obtained from Equation (10.19) providing the values of m_0 were those corresponding to simple supports at A and B.

The coefficients of M_A, H_A, and V_A in Equations (10.14) through (10.16)

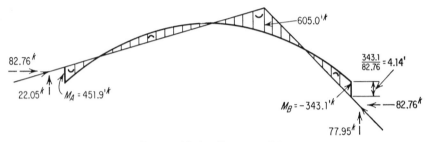

Figure 10-6.   Pressure Line

and in Equations (10.21) through (10.23) are flexibility coefficients, and the solution in matrix form is (see Chapter 9)

$$\mathbf{X} = \mathbf{F}^{-1}\Delta \qquad (10.25)$$

in which $\mathbf{X}$ represents a column vector consisting of M_A, V_A, and H_A, $\mathbf{F}$ represents the flexibility matrix, and Δ represents a column vector consisting of θ, Δ_x, and Δ_y, but with opposite signs. A matrix formulation is advantageous when many patterns of loading must be considered.

The maximum compressive and tensile stresses at any section in the arch are readily determined from the familiar expression

$$\sigma = \frac{N}{A} \pm \frac{Mc}{I} \qquad (10.26)$$

in which N is the axial force at the section. See the end of Section 10.9 for use of kern moments.

10.4   The Elastic Center

Equations (10.14) through (10.16) were obtained by setting the origin of the coordinate axes at end A of the arch. A study of those equations reveals that a substantial simplification would result if

$$\sum x \frac{\Delta s}{EI} = 0 \quad \text{and} \quad \sum y \frac{\Delta s}{EI} = 0$$

This can be done, as shown in Figure 10-7, by imagining an infinitely stiff arm, rigidly connected at A, with its other end located at the origin of a new set of axes, Y_c and X_c, which satisfies

$$\sum x_c \frac{\Delta s}{EI} = 0 \quad \text{and} \quad \sum y_c \frac{\Delta s}{EI} = 0 \tag{10.27}$$

in which the subscript c indicates that distances are now measured from Y_c and X_c. The indeterminate forces and moments are now h_c, v_c, and m_c, and they can be related to H_A, V_A, and M_A.

If $\Delta s/EI$ is considered to represent an area, then Equations (10.27) are identical to the familiar statements defining centroidal axes, and the axes

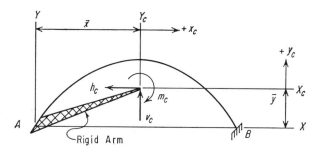

Figure 10-7.   The Elastic Center

labeled X_c and Y_c in Figure 10-7 are the centroidal axes of the elastic areas, $\Delta s/EI$. These axes can be located in the usual manner, with respect to *any* originally assumed system of axes, as follows:

$$\bar{x} = \frac{\sum x(\Delta s/EI)}{\sum (\Delta s/EI)} \tag{10.28}$$

$$\bar{y} = \frac{\sum y(\Delta s/EI)}{\sum (\Delta s/EI)} \tag{10.29}$$

Equations corresponding to Equations (10.14) through (10.16) now become simply

$$m_c \sum \frac{\Delta s}{EI} + \sum m_0 \frac{\Delta s}{EI} = 0 \tag{10.30}$$

$$v_c \sum x_c y_c \frac{\Delta s}{EI} + h_c \sum y_c^2 \frac{\Delta s}{EI} + \sum m_0 y_c \frac{\Delta s}{EI} = 0 \tag{10.31}$$

$$v_c \sum x_c^2 \frac{\Delta s}{EI} + h_c \sum x_c y_c \frac{\Delta s}{EI} + \sum m_0 x_c \frac{\Delta s}{EI} = 0 \tag{10.32}$$

The physical significance of this simplification is that, with the axes located so as to satisfy Equations (10.27), v_c and h_c do not contribute to rotation of one end of the arch with respect to the other, and m_c does not contribute to displacements. Equations (10.30) through (10.32) can also be obtained through application of the force method (Figure 10-4) by applying all forces and moments at the elastic center.

From Equation (10.30),

$$m_c = -\frac{\sum m_0(\Delta s/EI)}{\sum (\Delta s/E)I}$$ (10.33)

and from Equations (10.31) and (10.32),

$$h_c = -\frac{\sum y_c m_0(\Delta s/EI) - \dfrac{\sum x_c y_c(\Delta s/EI)}{\sum x_c{}^2(\Delta s/EI)} \sum x_c m_0(\Delta s/EI)}{\sum y_c^2(\Delta s/EI) - \dfrac{\sum x_c y_c(\Delta s/EI)}{\sum x_c{}^2(\Delta s/EI)} \sum x_c y_c(\Delta s/EI)}$$ (10.34)

$$v_c = -\frac{\sum x_c m_0(\Delta s/EI) - \dfrac{\sum x_c y_c(\Delta s/EI)}{\sum y_c^2(\Delta s/EI)} \sum y_c m_0(\Delta s/EI)}{\sum x_c{}^2(\Delta s/EI) - \dfrac{\sum x_c y_c(\Delta s/EI)}{\sum y_c{}^2(\Delta s/EI)} \sum x_c y_c(\Delta s/EI)}$$ (10.35)

If, as is most often the case, the arch is symmetrical about the Y_c axis, then $\sum x_c y_c(\Delta s/EI) = 0$, and the expressions for h_c and v_c become

$$h_c = -\frac{\sum y_c m_0(\Delta s/EI)}{\sum y_c{}^2(\Delta s/EI)}$$ (10.36)

$$v_c = -\frac{\sum x_c m_0(\Delta s/EI)}{\sum x_c{}^2(\Delta s/EI)}$$ (10.37)

The assumed solution need not be that of a member cantilevered from end B. We can assume simple supports at A and B, or any other solution which corresponds to a stable, statically determinate structure. Of course, the values of m_0 in Equations (10.33) through (10.37) must be those resulting from the assumed solution.

With the values of moment, horizontal force, and vertical force at the elastic center known, correction moments, m_i, and correction forces, h_i and v_i, due to m_c, h_c, and v_c can be obtained by statics for any section along the arch, as follows:

$$m_i = m_c + h_c y_c + v_c x_c$$ (10.38)

$$h_i = h_c$$ (10.39)

$$v_i = v_c$$ (10.40)

The final moments and forces at any section of the structure are obtained by adding corrections to the values corresponding to the assumed solution, as follows:

$$M = m_0 + m_i \tag{10.41}$$

$$H = h_0 + h_i \tag{10.42}$$

$$V = v_0 + v_i \tag{10.43}$$

Positive M indicates tension of the inner surface of an arch or ring. Positive H indicates tensile horizontal component of force acting on an element of the structure, and positive V indicates positive shear acting on the element. Thus V_B as shown in Figure 10-2 is negative, whereas all other reactions and end moments are positive.

We now solve the problem in Figure 10-5 through use of Equations (10.33), (10.36), and (10.37). Again we assume the arch cantilevered from B. Making use of Table 10-1, we first locate the centroid, by means of Equations (10.28) and (10.29), as follows:

$$\bar{x} = \frac{5,495}{109.9} = 50.000 \text{ ft}$$

$$\bar{y} = \frac{1,417}{109.9} = 12.893 \text{ ft}$$

However, instead of now determining distances x_c and y_c for use in Equations (10.36) and (10.37), we can still make use of the original x- and y-distances by modifying those equations to read

$$h_c = - \frac{\sum ym_0(\Delta s/EI) - \bar{y} \sum m_0(\Delta s/EI)}{\sum y^2(\Delta s/EI) - \bar{y}^2 \sum (\Delta s/EI)} \tag{10.36a}$$

$$v_c = - \frac{\sum xm_0(\Delta s/EI) - \bar{x} \sum m_0(\Delta s/EI)}{\sum x^2(\Delta s/EI) - \bar{x}^2 \sum (\Delta s/EI)} \tag{10.37a}$$

From Table 10-1, and using the values of $\bar{x}$ and $\bar{y}$ previously determined, the values of h_c and v_c are obtained as

$$h_c = - \frac{-358,433 - (12.893)(-53,550)}{-22,280 - (12.893)^2(109.9)} = -82.76 \text{ kips}$$

$$v_c = - \frac{-4,829,825 - (50.000)(-53,550)}{372,358 - (50.000)^2(109.9)} = 22.05 \text{ kips}$$

From Equation (10.33),

$$m_c = - \frac{-53,550}{109.9} = 487.3 \text{ ft-kips}$$

Then, from Equations (10.38) through (10.40), at A

$$m_i = 487.3 + (-82.76)(-12.893) + (22.05)(-50.000) = 451.6 \text{ ft-kips}$$

Throughout the arch, from Equations (10.39) and (10.40),

$$h_i = -82.76 \text{ kips}$$

$$v_i = 22.05 \text{ kips}$$

The final values at A are, from Equations (10.41) through (10.43),

$$M = 0 + 451.6 = 451.6 \text{ ft-kips}$$
$$H = 0 + (-82.76) = -82.76 \text{ kips}$$
$$V = 0 + 22.05 = 22.05 \text{ kips}$$

Values at any other section can now be determined by statics, or exactly as at A by first evaluating m_i at the section. For example, at B

$$m_i = 487.3 + (-82.76)(-12.893) + (22.05)(50.000) = 2,656.6 \text{ ft-kips}$$

Then the final values at B are

$$M = -3,000 + 2,656.6 = -343.4 \text{ ft-kips}$$
$$H = 0 + (-82.76) = -82.76 \text{ kips}$$
$$V = -100 + 22.05 = -77.95 \text{ kips}$$

where $-3,000$ is the value of m_0 at B, and 0 and -100 are, respectively, the values of h_0 and v_0. The value of v_0 is negative because it acts upward (negative shear) at B.

If there is a perfect hinge in the arch, it is equivalent to an infinite value of $\Delta s/EI$. Therefore the elastic center is located at the hinge of a one-hinged arch or on a line connecting the hinges of a two-hinged arch. In the latter case Equation (10.36) becomes identical to Equation (10.19). The values of m_0, however, must be for the structure considered simply supported at A and B. A hinged structure cannot be cantilevered from its hinged end.

10.5 The Column Analogy

Consider a short strut or column subjected to an eccentric load, P. If plane sections remain plane, and if stress is proportional to strain, the stress, σ, at any point of the cross section of the short column is defined by the following equation of a plane:

$$\sigma = a + bx_c + cy_c \qquad (10.44)$$

in which the distances x_c and y_c are measured from the centroidal axes of the cross section.

The constant, a, and the coefficients, b and c, in Equation (10.44) can be evaluated by application of the three conditions of statical equilibrium. Thus, letting dA represent a differential area of the cross section, the first condition of equilibrium gives

$$P = \int \sigma \, dA$$
$$= a\int dA + b\int x_c \, dA + c\int y_c \, dA$$

But, by definition of a centroid,

$$\int x_c \, dA = 0$$

$$\int y_c \, dA = 0$$

Therefore,

$$P = a \int dA \qquad\qquad \textbf{(a)}$$

A second condition of equilibrium gives

$$M_y = \int \sigma x_c \, dA$$

$$= a \int x_c \, dA + b \int x_c^2 dA + c \int x_c y_c \, dA$$

$$M_y = b I_y + c I_{xy} \qquad\qquad \textbf{(b)}$$

Similarly, we obtain

$$M_x = b I_{xy} + c I_x \qquad\qquad \textbf{(c)}$$

From Equation (a)

$$a = \frac{P}{\int dA} = \frac{P}{A} \qquad\qquad \textbf{(10.45)}$$

and from Equations (b) and (c), solved simultaneously,

$$b = \frac{M_y - (I_{xy}/I_x)M_x}{I_y - (I_{xy}/I_x)I_{xy}} = \frac{M_y'}{I_y'} \qquad\qquad \textbf{(10.46)}$$

$$c = \frac{M_x - (I_{xy}/I_y)M_y}{I_x - (I_{xy}/I_y)I_{xy}} = \frac{M_x'}{I_x'} \qquad\qquad \textbf{(10.47)}$$

Equation (10.44) now becomes

$$\sigma = \frac{P}{A} + \frac{M_y'}{I_y'} x_c + \frac{M_x'}{I_x'} y_c \qquad\qquad \textbf{(10.48)}$$

from which we can compute the stress at any point in the cross section of a short column, regardless of shape of cross section, making use of any orthogonal pair of axes whose origin is at the centroid of the section. There is no need to locate principal axes.

If the cross section is symmetrical with respect to one of the centroidal axes, then I_{xy}, the product of inertia, is equal to zero. Equation (10.48) then becomes the familiar equation

$$\sigma = \frac{P}{A} + \frac{M_y}{I_y} x_c + \frac{M_x}{I_x} y_c \qquad\qquad \textbf{(10.49)}$$

Now reinspect Equations (10.33) through (10.35) and observe that if the angle changes, $m_0 \Delta s / EI$, are treated as forces, and values of $\Delta s / EI$ treated as differential areas, those equations are identical, except for sign, to Equations (10.45) through (10.47). Consequently, the same relationship holds between

Equation (10.38) and Equation (10.49), and the correction moment, m_i, in an arch is equal, but of opposite sign, to the stress, σ, on an imaginary column cross section loaded with the "forces" $m_0 \Delta s / EI$. Thus, we can write for the correction moments and forces

$$m_i = \frac{P}{A} + \frac{M_x'}{I_x'} y_c + \frac{M_y'}{I_y'} x_c \qquad (10.50)$$

$$h_i = \frac{M_x'}{I_x'} \qquad (10.51)$$

$$v_i = \frac{M_y'}{I_y'} \qquad (10.52)$$

in which

$$A = \sum \frac{\Delta s}{EI} = \sum dA \qquad P = \sum m_0 \, dA$$

$$I_x' = I_x - \frac{I_{xy}}{I_y} I_{xy} \qquad M_x' = M_x - \frac{I_{xy}}{I_y} M_y$$

$$I_y' = I_y - \frac{I_{xy}}{I_x} I_{xy} \qquad M_y' = M_y - \frac{I_{xy}}{I_x} M_x$$

where

$$I_x = \sum y_c^2 \, dA = \sum y^2 \, dA - \bar{y}^2 \sum dA \qquad M_x = \sum y_c m_0 \, dA = \sum y m_0 \, dA - \bar{y} \sum m_0 \, dA$$

$$I_y = \sum x_c^2 \, dA = \sum x^2 \, dA - \bar{x}^2 \sum dA \qquad M_y = \sum x_c m_0 \, dA = \sum x m_0 \, dA - \bar{x} \sum m_0 \, dA$$

$$I_{xy} = \sum x_c y_c \, dA = \sum xy \, dA - \bar{x}\bar{y} \sum dA$$

in which x and y can be measured from any pair of orthogonal axes, and

$$\bar{y} = \frac{\sum y \, dA}{A}$$

$$\bar{x} = \frac{\sum x \, dA}{A}$$

When symmetry exists, $I_{xy} = 0$ and all prime symbols are dropped from Equations (10.50) to (10.52).

The cross-sectional area, A, of the column is equivalent, in the arch, to the total of the angle changes that result from the application of a unit moment at the elastic center. The moments of inertia, I_x' and I_y', of the column are equivalent to the displacements at the elastic center of the arch resulting from unit forces applied in the x- and y-directions, respectively. P represents the total load on the column and is equivalent to the total of the angle changes in the arch consistent with the assumed solution. The terms M_x' and M_y' represent bending moments about centroidal axes in the column. They are equivalent to the displacements at the elastic center of the arch that result from the assumed solution.

Do not confuse I with I_x, I_y, and I_{xy}. The term I represents a moment of inertia of the section of the actual structure. The terms I_x, I_y, and I_{xy} represent moments of inertia of the imaginary column cross section.

To account for the difference in signs between Equations (10.45) through (10.47) and Equations (10.33) through (10.35), we now *subtract* the correction moments and forces from the assumed moments and forces to obtain the final values. That is

$$M = m_0 - m_i \tag{10.53}$$

$$H = h_0 - h_i \tag{10.54}$$

$$V = v_0 - v_i \tag{10.55}$$

Since Equations (10.50) through (10.52) are equivalent to Equations (10.38) through (10.40), the question naturally arises as to the importance, if any, of the column analogy. The analogy is a formalization of the important pressure line concept, in which angle changes are treated as forces. The requirements of geometry for an arch are automatically satisfied when we satisfy the conditions of statics in a short, imaginary column. The analysis of a statically indeterminate arch is consequently reduced to the familiar pattern of computations for combined axial and flexural stress. Finally, the column analogy permits vizualization of the stress condition of the cross section of the column, and thus of the bending moments in the arch.

10.6 Application of the Column Analogy

The loaded arch in Figure 10-5 is analyzed by column analogy in Figure 10-8, using tabulated sums from Table 10-1. The analogous column is shown loaded with the "forces," m_0/EI, corresponding to the assumed solution (arch cantilevered from B). The thickness anywhere along the cross section of an analogous column is equal to $1/EI$. Therefore, the intensity of applied force is m_0, and a force per unit area in the column is equivalent to a bending moment in the arch. The properties (A, I_x, and I_y) and the loads and moments (P, M_x, and M_y) were determined with the aid of the tabulated sums of Table 10-1. The reader should observe that although in Figure 10-8 we have proceeded exactly as if we were solving an elementary problem in combined axial and bending stress, nonetheless we have made computations identical to those previously made using the concept of the elastic center.

The computational procedure used in connection with Figure 10-8 is also identical to one that would be used in determining pressures under a footing

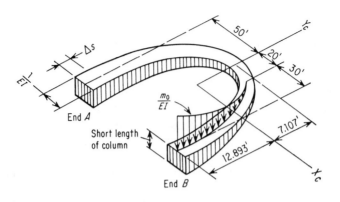

Properties of Section:

$$dA = \frac{\Delta s}{EI}$$

$$A = \Sigma dA = 109.9$$

$$\bar{y} = \frac{\Sigma y \, dA}{A} = \frac{1,417}{109.9} = 12.893'$$

$$I_x = 22,280 - (12.893)^2 (109.9) = 4,012$$

$$I_y = 372,358 - (50)^2 (109.9) = 97,608$$

Loads on Section:

$$P = \Sigma m_0 \frac{\Delta s}{EI} = \Sigma m_0 dA = -53,550$$

$$M_x = -358,433 - 12.893 (-53,550) = 331,996$$

$$M_y = -4,829,825 - 50 (-53,550) = -2,152,325$$

$$m_i = \frac{P}{A} + \frac{M_x}{I_x} y_c + \frac{M_y}{I_y} x_c$$

$$(m_i)_B = \frac{-53,550}{109.9} + \frac{331,996}{4,012} (-12.893) + \frac{-2,152,325}{97,608} (50) = -2656.6^{'k}$$

$$h_i = \frac{M_x}{I_x} = \frac{331,996}{4,012} = 82.76^k$$

$$v_i = \frac{M_y}{I_y} = \frac{-2,152,325}{97,608} = -22.05^k$$

$$M_B = m_0 - m_i = -3,000 - (-2,656.6) = \underline{343.4^{'k}}$$

$$H = h_0 - h_i = 0 - 82.76 = \underline{-82.76^k}$$

$$V_B = v_0 - v_i = -100 - (-22.05) = \underline{77.95^k}$$

Figure 10-8. Application of Column Analogy

with the same dimensions and in constant contact with a foundation material that is capable of resisting tensile stress.

As a result of symmetry of structure and loading, only one half of the rigid frame in Figure 10-9 is subdivided into segments. Properties of the analogous column, and loads on it, are obtained by doubling the sums obtained from the tabulated values. All computations are by slide rule.

Since, if friction is neglected, a hinge is incapable of resisting moment, it is given a value of $I = 0$ and, consequently, dA for a hinge is infinite and P/A is equal to zero. In addition, the centroid of the column cross section is on a line passing through the hinges, making I_y infinite and M_y/I_y equal to zero. Thus,

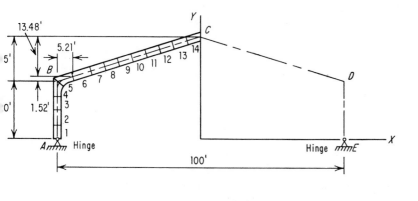

Sect.	Δs	I	dA	x	y	$y\,dA$	y^2dA	m_0	$m_0\,dA$	$ym_0\,dA$
hinge	—	0	∞	−50.0	0	0	0	0	0	0
1	5.00	1.00	5.00	−50.0	2.5	13	30	0	0	0
2	5.00	1.00	5.00	−50.0	7.5	38	280	0	0	0
3	4.66	1.00	4.66	−50.0	12.3	57	710	0	0	0
4	4.80	1.54	3.12	−49.9	17.2	54	930	0	0	0
5	5.00	1.35	3.70	−47.2	20.6	76	1,570	136	500	10,300
6	6.80	0.92	7.40	−41.6	22.5	166	3,750	385	2,850	64,100
7	5.00	0.92	5.43	−36.0	24.2	131	3,180	605	3,290	79,600
8	5.00	0.92	5.43	−31.2	25.6	139	3,560	765	4,160	106,500
9	5.00	0.92	5.43	−26.4	27.1	147	3,990	902	4,900	132,800
10	5.00	0.92	5.43	−21.6	28.5	155	4,420	1,017	5,520	157,500
11	5.00	0.92	5.43	−16.8	30.0	163	4,900	1,110	6,030	180,900
12	5.00	0.92	5.43	−12.0	31.4	170	5,340	1,178	6,400	201,000
13	5.00	0.92	5.43	− 7.2	32.8	178	5,850	1,224	6,650	218,000
14	5.00	0.92	5.43	− 2.4	34.3	186	6,400	1,242	6,750	231,800
Σ:		∞				1,673	44,910			1,382,500
						x2=	x2 =			x2 =
						3346	89,820			2,765,000

$$h_i = \frac{2,765,000}{89,820} = 30.8^k$$

$$(m_i)_B = (m_i)_D = 30.8\,(20) = 616^{'k}$$

$$(m_i)_C = 30.8\,(35) = 1,078^{'k}$$

$$H = 0 - 30.8 = \underline{-30.8}^{k}$$

$$M_B = M_D = 0 - 616 = \underline{-616}^{'k}$$

$$M_C = 1,250 - 1,078 = \underline{172}^{'k}$$

Figure 10-9. Analysis of Two-Hinged Frame

311

it is not necessary to tabulate values of $x^2\,dA$ and $xm_0\,dA$, and the expression for correction moment reduces to

$$m_i = \frac{M_x}{I_x}\,y_c = h_i y_c \tag{10.56}$$

which is identical to Equation (10.19) except for sign. If the structure were unsymmetrical, it would be necessary to include $x\,dA$, $xy\,dA$, $x^2\,dA$, and $xm_0\,dA$ in the tabulation. Then,

$$m_i = \frac{M_x'}{I_x'}\,y_c = h_i y_c \tag{10.57}$$

As we are using segments of finite length Δs, the expression $I_x = \sum y^2\,dA$ is not strictly correct. Rather, we should add corrections for the moment of inertia of each segment about its own centroidal axis. This correction is important only for relatively long segments close to the centroidal axes of the column section. For example, for segment 10 the correction would be $(\frac{1}{12})(5.43)(1.56)^2 = 1$, where 5.43 is the area, dA, of the segment and 1.56 is its projection on a y-axis. For segment 1, the correction would be $(\frac{1}{12})(5.00)(5.00)^2 = 10$. A few computations such as these quickly indicate that the corrections can be omitted in most cases. Even if segments 6 through 14 were combined into one, in order to shorten the tabulation in Figure 10-9, the correction would still not be critical. However, it would then be necessary to compute $m_0\,dA$ on the basis of the actual distribution of assumed moments rather than as the product of the length of the segment and the value of m_0 at the center of the segment. Furthermore, the value of $m_0\,dA$, in whole or in parts, must then be multiplied by the distance, or distances, to the centroid of the $m_0\,dA$ values. To illustrate, the value of m_0 at the upper end of segment 5 is 250 ft-kips. Then, treating segments 6 through 14 as one segment,

$$dA = 7.40 + 8(5.43) = 50.84$$

and the value of $m_0\,dA$ (in two parts) is

$$(250)(50.84) = 12,710 \qquad \text{(part 1)}$$
$$\tfrac{2}{3}(1,000)(50.84) = 33,890 \qquad \text{(part 2)}$$

These values are multiplied by distances to the centers of gravity of the above "loads" on the column to obtain corresponding values of $ym_0\,dA$. Thus

$$12,710(28.26) = 360,000 \qquad \text{(part 1)}$$
$$33,890(29.95) = 1,012,000 \qquad \text{(part 2)}$$

If the sums of the preceding values for $m_0\,dA$ and $ym_0\,dA$ are substituted for the total values of segments 6 through 14 in Figure 10-9, the results will be the same.

If the frame in Figure 10-9 were fixed at its bases, it would be necessary to compute $\bar{y}$ and to correct the values of I_x and M_x to the centroid. Then

$$A = 144.62$$

$$P = 94,100$$

$$\bar{y} = \frac{3,346}{144.64} = 23.1 \text{ ft}$$

$$I_x = 89,820 - (144.62)(23.1)^2 = 12,600$$

$$M_x = 2,765,000 - (94,100)(23.1) = 585,000$$

and

$$h_i = \frac{585,000}{12,600} = 46.4 \text{ kips}; \qquad H = 0 - 46.4 = -46.4 \text{ kips}$$

$$m_{iA} = \frac{94,100}{144.62} + 46.4(-23.1) = -418 \text{ ft-kips};$$
$$M_A = 0 - (-418) = 418 \text{ ft-kips}$$

$$m_{iB} = \frac{94,100}{144.62} + 46.4(-3.1) = 508 \text{ ft-kips}; \qquad M_B = 0 - 508 = -508 \text{ ft-kips}$$

$$m_{iC} = \frac{94,100}{144.62} + 46.4(11.9) = 1,203 \text{ ft-kips};$$
$$M_C = 1,250 - 1,203 = 47 \text{ ft-kips}$$

The effect of externally applied moments, such as those resulting from brackets supporting crane girders, is incorporated by including these moments in the assumed distribution of m_0. Bending moments along the projecting cantilever itself are, of course, not included.

Completely closed frames or rings can be readily analyzed by column analogy. A statically possible solution (a ring is generally assumed cut at a section) is assumed, and the work proceeds exactly as in the foregoing.

The student should reflect on the fact that the problems of obtaining satisfactory answers from a set of simultaneous equations have not been eliminated. The column analogy and its mathematical equivalent, the method of the elastic center, represent the solution of the three simultaneous equations which express the requirements of geometry. An adequate number of significant figures must be used in the computations in order to obtain reasonably precise results. Generally, the smaller the corrections to the assumed solution, the smaller the errors in the final values. Consequently, the closer the assumed solution is to the correct solution, the smaller is the precision of computation required. Of course, if one could assume the correct pressure line to begin with, all corrections would vanish.

A solution is correct if the final values of bending moment, M, satisfy the following requirements of geometry:

$$\sum M \, dA = 0$$

$$\sum xM \, dA = 0$$

$$\sum yM \, dA = 0$$

The student should establish that these requirements are essentially satisfied in the illustrative examples that have been discussed. Only the last requirement is applicable to a structure with two hinges.

10.7   Volume Changes and Movements at Supports

Change in length along the axis of the structure can result from rise or drop in temperature, axial shortening due to the thrust (rib shortening), concrete shrinkage, or creep. These effects can be studied by estimating or computing the relative displacements at the supports which would occur if the structure were free to move, and then determining the forces and moments necessary to restore the structure to its actual support condition. These displacements are positive if they are consistent with positive directions of H and V. A solution is readily obtained from the column analogy by setting M_x equal and opposite to the imaginary horizontal displacement and M_y equal and opposite to the imaginary vertical displacement. Since only displacements have been imposed, $P = 0$.

If there is a relative movement between supports because of foundation conditions, M_x and M_y then represent actual displacements. If a rotation occurs at a support because of foundation conditions, P is equal to the rotation, and M_x and M_y are computed as the moments of this "load." Values of M_x, M_y, and P are positive if they are consistent with positive directions of H, V, and M at the supports.

A uniform change in temperature would produce, if movement could occur freely, a relative horizontal displacement between supports of an amount

$$\Delta_x = \varepsilon TL \qquad (10.58)$$

in which ε represents the coefficient of thermal expansion, T is the temperature change, and L is the horizontal distance between supports. If the supports are not at the same elevation, there will, in addition, be a relative vertical displacement of

$$\Delta_y = \varepsilon TD \qquad (10.59)$$

in which D represents the difference in elevation between the two supports. Consistent with the sign convention adopted for M_x and M_y, $M_x = -\Delta_x$ and $M_y = -\Delta_y$. The horizontal and vertical forces due to temperature change are then

$$H_T = \frac{M_x}{I_x}; \qquad V_T = \frac{M_y}{I_y} \qquad (10.60)$$

Assume that for the arch in Figure 10.5, $\varepsilon = 6 \times 10^{-6}$ and $T = -50°$. For this drop in temperature,

$$\Delta_x = -(6 \times 10^{-6})(50)(100) = -3 \times 10^{-2} \text{ ft}$$

Then, remembering that EI was, for convenience, omitted from all properties and loads in Figure 10-8,

$$H_T = \frac{M_x}{I_x} = \frac{3 \times 10^{-2}}{4,012/EI} = 7.47 \times 10^{-6} EI \text{ kips}$$

and the bending moment at any point along the arch axis is

$$M_T = 7.47 \times 10^{-6} EI y_c \text{ ft-kips}$$

The bending moment at the crown is $7.47 \times 10^{-6} EI(7.107) = 53.1 \times 10^{-6} EI$ ft-kips, and the bending moment at the springings is $7.47 \times 10^{-6} EI(-12.893)$ $= -96.3 \times 10^{-6} EI$ ft-kips. The values of E and I must be expressed in feet and kips in order to be consistent with the values for M_x, I_x, and y_c.

The pressure line for a temperature drop of $50°$ is shown in (a) of Figure 10-10. Since there are no loads on the arch, the pressure line consists of one

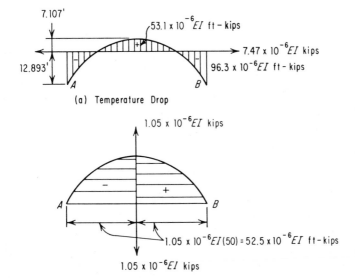

(a) Temperature Drop

(b) Settlement at B

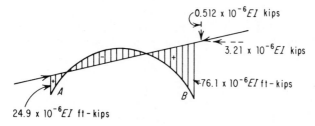

(c) Counterclockwise Rotation at B

Figure 10-10.   Pressure Lines for Volume Changes and Support Movements

straight segment. Also, since M_T is equal to zero when y_c is equal to zero, the pressure line must pass through the elastic center of the arch (centroid of the analogous column).

As explained in Section 10.1, the effect of rib shortening is generally introduced as a correction to the primary analysis. The change in length of an element, ds, as a result of axial thrust, N, is $(N/AE)ds$ and the change in length projected on the X-axis is $(N/AE)dx$, in which A is now the cross-sectional area of the rib. The total change in length along the X-axis, if the arch were free to move at its supports, would be

$$\Delta_x = \int \frac{N}{AE} \, dx$$

The axial thrust, N, at any section is equal to $H \cos \alpha + V \sin \alpha$, where α is the angle made by the arch axis and the X-axis.

The effect of rib shortening can be important in flat arches, particularly for dead load and distributed live load. Under such loading, the pressure line nearly coincides with the arch axis and moments are relatively small compared to thrust. As a result of the pressure line lying close to the axis for loading for which rib shortening is important, N can be closely approximated as $H/\cos \alpha$. Then, since $dx = \cos \alpha \, (ds)$,

$$\Delta_x = \int \frac{H}{AE} \, ds$$

In the terminology of the column analogy,

$$M_x = -\Delta_x = -\int \frac{H}{AE} \, ds \qquad\qquad (10.61)$$

and the horizontal thrust due to rib shortening is

$$H_s = \frac{M_x}{I_x} \qquad\qquad (10.62)$$

The reader should remember that Equation (10.61) is an approximation, based on the assumption that $N = H/\cos \alpha$. Other assumptions have been made in order to obtain a workable expression for rib shortening, whether as the correction represented by Equation (10.62) or for use in Equations (10.4a) through (10.6a). For example, H has been assumed as equal to N, thus resulting in

$$M_x = -\int \frac{H}{AE} \, dx$$

Also, N has been taken as $H \cos \alpha$, resulting in

$$M_x = -\int \frac{H \cos \alpha}{AE} \, dx$$

We are determining a correction that is generally quite small, and a fairly large difference in its value will be negligible as far as the final value of H is concerned.

Obviously, results for rib shortening can be obtained directly from those for temperature change by multiplying the latter moments and forces by the ratio of the values of M_x.

In the arch of Figure 10-5, H and A are constant throughout. Therefore Equation (10.61) becomes

$$M_x = -\frac{H}{AE} \sum \Delta s$$

Then, with $H = -82.76$ kips, and with $\sum \Delta s = 109.90$ ft (see Table 10-1), we obtain

$$M_x = \frac{9,100}{AE} \text{ ft}$$

and, from Equation (10.62),

$$H_s = \frac{9,100/AE}{4,012/EI} = 2.27 \text{ } I/A \text{ kips}$$

in which A and I are, respectively, the area and moment of inertia of the rib cross section.

If the arch were hinged at its supports, the axis X_c in Figure 10-8 would pass through A and B, and I_x would be $\sum y^2 \, dA = 22,280$. Then, from Equation (10.62),

$$H_s = \frac{9,100/AE}{22,280/EI} = 0.408 \text{ } I/A \text{ kips}$$

Values of H_s and H_T are much smaller in two-hinged arches than in hingeless arches. Values of M_s and M_T at the crown are also smaller but not in the same proportion as H_T because the moment arm is now equal to the full height of the arch. The value of H_s is always positive (producing tension), and the pressure line is identical to that in Figure 10-10(a) except for the numerical values.

In a three-hinged arch, H_T and H_s are equal to zero because the arch is free to accommodate changes in dimension. A straight pressure line cannot be passed through three hinges.

For gravity loading, H is constant throughout the arch. Then, if the slope angle of an element is α, $ds = dx/\cos \alpha$. Equation (10.61) becomes

$$M_x = -\frac{H}{E} \int \frac{dx}{A \cos \alpha} = -H \frac{L}{E} \left(\frac{1}{A \cos \alpha} \right)_m \qquad \textbf{(10.63)}$$

in which $(1/A \cos \alpha)_m$ represents the mean of the reciprocals of all values of

$A \cos \alpha$, the vertical projections of A. Equation (10.63) can generally be approximated quite closely for practical purposes by

$$M_x = -\frac{HL}{E} \frac{1}{(A \cos \alpha)_m} \qquad (10.64)$$

Equation (10.63) or Equation (10.64) enables one to make a quick determination of the effect of rib shortening in arches of either constant or variable section. For example, if from a quick inspection of the arch in Figure 10-5, with A constant, we take the mean value of $\cos \alpha$ as 0.87 (corresponding to $\alpha = 30°$ approximately), then from Equation (10.64),

$$M_x = -\frac{(-82.76)(100)}{E(0.87A)} = \frac{9,500}{AE} \text{ ft}$$

which compares favorably with the value of $9,100/AE$ previously obtained. Remember that we are generally dealing with a small correction. No great precision of computation is meaningful except, possibly, for extremely flat or thick arches that are seldom used.

Since the correction due to rib shortening is made by using the value of horizontal thrust obtained by neglecting this effect, in the case of extremely flat arches it might be desirable to obtain an additional correction due H_s. That is, we may calculate the rib shortening due to rib shortening.

Suppose support B of the arch in Figure 10.5 moves 0.100 ft down relative to support A. Then M_y is positive because the movement is consistent with positive vertical reactions, and

$$V = \frac{M_y}{I_y} = \frac{0.100}{97,608/EI} = 1.05 \times 10^{-6} EI \text{ kips}$$

The pressure line is shown in Figure 10-10(b). Note that the pressure line is again drawn through the elastic center, and $M_B = -M_A = 50V$.

If the arch rotates 0.001 radian counterclockwise at B because of yielding or imperfect fixity, P will be positive because such a rotation corresponds to positive moment. Then (see Figure 10-8)

$$P = 0.001$$

$$M_x = 0.001(-12.893) = -0.012893 \text{ ft}$$

$$M_y = 0.001(50) = 0.050 \text{ ft}$$

and

$$H = \frac{-0.012893}{4,012/EI} = -3.21 \times 10^{-6} EI \text{ kips}$$

$$V = \frac{0.050}{97,608/EI} = 0.512 \times 10^{-6} EI \text{ kips}$$

From Equation (10.50) the bending moment at any section of the arch is

$$M = \frac{0.001 EI}{109.9} + (-3.21 \times 10^{-6} EI) y_c + (0.512 \times 10^{-6} EI) x_c$$

Inserting $y_c = -12.893$ and $x_c = 50$, we obtain $76.1 \times 10^{-6} EI$ ft-kips at B. With $y_c = -12.893$ and $x_c = -50$, the bending moment at A is $24.9 \times 10^{-6} EI$ ft-kips. The pressure line is shown in Figure 10-10(c). Its components are H and V, and then it is located correctly by dividing the moments at A and B by H in order to obtain vertical distances from the arch.

10.8   Stiffness Properties by Column Analogy

In the analysis of continuous beams or continuous arches on slender piers by a displacement method (including moment distribution), it is necessary to know the moments and forces resulting from unit rotations and unit displacements. Such stiffness coefficients for individual arches can be determined exactly as were the effects for rotation or movement of a support in the preceding section. They are further considered in Section 10.10.

The stiffness coefficients for an individual beam are the moment stiffness and carry-over used in the method of moment distribution. These, as well as fixed-end moments, are conveniently determined by column analogy. For a beam, $y_c = 0$, and the expression for correction moment in all cases reduces to

$$m_i = \frac{P}{A} + \frac{M_y}{I_y} x_c \tag{10.65}$$

In Figure 10-11(a), fixed-end moments due to a uniformly distributed load of one kip/ft are determined by assuming the beam simply supported at A and B. The position of the centroid of the analogous cross section is at midpoint by inspection. The tabulated moments of inertia are those at the center of the sections and are in terms of the value, I, at the sections of constant depth. As a result of symmetry of structure and load, $M_y = 0$.

Stiffness K_A (moment at A necessary to produce a unit rotation at A without translation when end B is fixed) is determined in Figure 10-11(b) by applying a load $P = 1$ at A. The carry-over factor, C_{AB}, is the ratio of the moment produced at B to that at A. Because of symmetry, $K_B = K_A$ and $C_{BA} = C_{AB}$.

Sometimes it is desired to determine fixed-end moments due to a moment applied at some intermediate point along a member. In such a case we assume a statically possible distribution of moments (for example, that corresponding to a cantilevered member) and proceed as before.

A beam with an intermediate hinge is handled in a similar manner. The centroidal Y-axis is always located at the hinge, and the area of the analogous column is infinite.

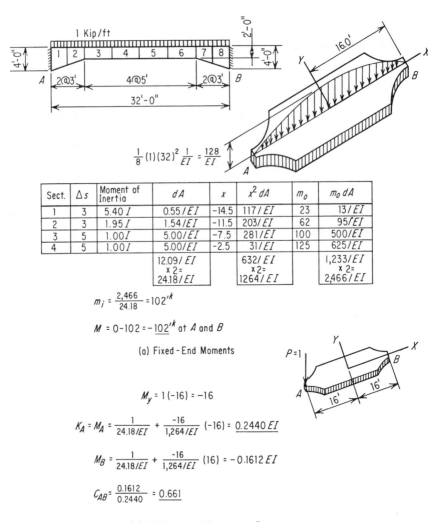

Sect.	Δs	Moment of Inertia	dA	x	$x^2 dA$	m_o	$m_o dA$
1	3	$5.40\,I$	$0.55/EI$	-14.5	$117/EI$	23	$13/EI$
2	3	$1.95\,I$	$1.54/EI$	-11.5	$203/EI$	62	$95/EI$
3	5	$1.00\,I$	$5.00/EI$	-7.5	$281/EI$	100	$500/EI$
4	5	$1.00\,I$	$5.00/EI$	-2.5	$31/EI$	125	$625/EI$
			$12.09/EI$ $\times 2=$ $24.18/EI$		$632/EI$ $\times 2=$ $1264/EI$		$1,233/EI$ $\times 2=$ $2,466/EI$

$$m_i = \frac{2,466}{24.18} = 102'^k$$

$$M = 0-102 = -\underline{102'^k} \text{ at } A \text{ and } B$$

(a) Fixed-End Moments

$$M_y = 1(-16) = -16$$

$$K_A = M_A = \frac{1}{24.18/EI} + \frac{-16}{1,264/EI}(-16) = 0.2440\,EI$$

$$M_B = \frac{1}{24.18/EI} + \frac{-16}{1,264/EI}(16) = -0.1612\,EI$$

$$C_{AB} = \frac{0.1612}{0.2440} = 0.661$$

(b) Stiffness and Carry-over Factor

Figure 10-11. Moments and Properties of Haunched Beam

10.9 Influence Lines

It is sometimes considered necessary (for example, in the design of long-span arch bridges) to use influence lines. Figure 10-12 shows some influence lines for a two-hinged arch. The general shape of the influence line in (b) is readily visualized, from a consideration of Müller-Breslau's principle, as the displaced position of the axis due to a very small relative horizontal displacement of A and B. The precise determination of the influence line is discussed later in this section.

320

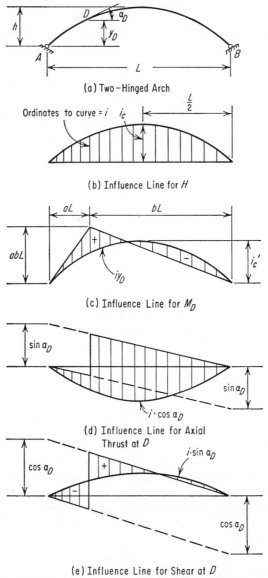

(a) Two-Hinged Arch

Ordinates to curve = i

(b) Influence Line for H

(c) Influence Line for M_D

(d) Influence Line for Axial Thrust at D

(e) Influence Line for Shear at D

Figure 10-12.   Influence Lines for Two-Hinged Arch

Influence lines for moment are obtained by superimposing the effect of H on an influence line for simple-beam moment. This has been done in Figure 10-12(c) for moment at a point D. The effect of the horizontal thrust is obtained by multiplying each ordinate, i, in (b) by the moment arm, y_D, of the horizontal reaction. Influence lines for axial thrust and shear are obtained in a similar manner in (d) and (e) respectively. The method is identical to that used in Figure 3-9 for a three-hinged arch.

Since the moment anywhere along a pressure line must be zero (see Section 2.2), the horizontal thrust due to vertical loading on any arch, hinged or fixed, is

$$H = \frac{m_s}{h'} \qquad\qquad (10.66)$$

in which m_s represents a simple-beam moment and h' is the corresponding height to the pressure line. For a load of unit intensity, distributed uniformly along the horizontal projection of the arch, m_s at midspan is $(\frac{1}{8})L^2$, and

$$H = \frac{1}{8}\frac{L^2}{h'} \qquad\qquad (10.67)$$

where h' is now the total rise of the pressure line (a parabola) between supports. If the arch is assumed parabolic in shape, it will coincide with the pressure line and h' will be equal to the rise, h, of the arch. Then

$$H = \frac{1}{8}\frac{L^2}{h} \qquad\qquad (10.68)$$

As this is the horizontal thrust resulting from a uniform load of unit intensity per unit horizontal length, Equation (10.68) gives the area under the influence line for horizontal thrust in any parabolic arch.

If we assume that the influence line in Figure 10-12(b) is also parabolic, then the area under the influence line is $(\frac{2}{3})i_c L$, in which i_c is the midordinate. Equating this value to the area as expressed by Equation (10.68), we obtain

$$i_c = \frac{3}{16}\frac{L}{h}$$

Approximate influence ordinates, i, at other points can now be obtained on the basis of the assumed parabolic shape of the influence line for H.

For a parabolic arch there is no bending moment (or shear) anywhere if it is uniformly loaded along its horizontal projection. Therefore, the plus area and minus area in (c) must be equal. Equating the area of the triangle to that of the parabola, we obtain

$$i_c' = \tfrac{3}{4}abL$$

The influence ordinates obtained by the above assumptions are generally rather crude approximations because the shape of the influence line will vary with shape of arch and variation in its cross section.

The shape of the influence line for thrust in Figure 10-13(b) is also readily visualized, if we remember that no rotation can take place at the springings of a fixed-end arch. An approximate value for i_c can be obtained by recognizing that the area under the influence line will be roughly $(\frac{1}{2})i_c L$. Equating this to the right-hand side of Equation (10.68) results in

$$i_c = \frac{1}{4}\frac{L}{h}$$

Approximate influence lines for moment are obtained in (c), (d), and (e) by superimposing the effect of H on influence lines for an equivalent fixed-end beam of span L. If the arch is parabolic, there will be no bending moment anywhere along its axis if it is loaded with a uniform load. Therefore, for a parabolic arch the superposition must be such that the plus areas equal the minus areas. The fixed-end beam influence values are those for a beam of

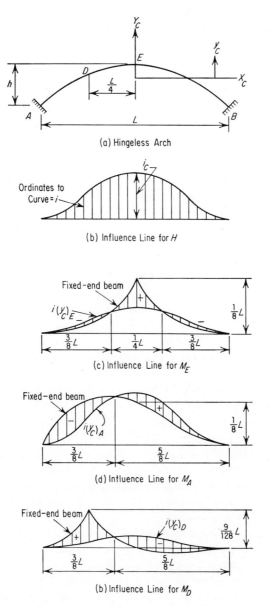

(a) Hingeless Arch

(b) Influence Line for H

(c) Influence Line for M_E

(d) Influence Line for M_A

(b) Influence Line for M_D

Figure 10-13.　Influence Lines for Hingeless Arch

constant section. The use of these values is theoretically correct for an arch with secant variation in moment of inertia.

The influence lines in Figure 10-13 are quite crude, but they are useful in indicating load divides. They show that for uniform live load an acceptable analysis can be made by loading the portions of the structure indicated in the figure. As a matter of fact, maximum live load moments at crown, springing, and quarter-point can all be obtained by superposition of the results of two analyses: one for load on the entire span and one for load on three-eighths of the span.

In the remainder of this section we discuss the determination of exact influence lines. For two-hinged arches they are all obtained from the influence line for H, by superposition as in Figure 10-12. For hingeless arches it is more convenient to plot influence lines independently on a straight base line.

Attention is called to the fact that arch bridges are generally loaded at specific locations by columns supporting an overhead roadway or by hangers supporting a suspended roadway. Influence lines for such structures are composed of straight-line segments between load points.

Influence lines for a particular arch can be conveniently determined by making an analysis, such as that in Figure 10-8, for different locations of a unit load. The analysis in Figure 10-8 is for a load of 100 kips placed as shown in Figure 10-5. Consequently, the influence values for M, H, and V at B are equal to the values in Figure 10-8 divided by 100. This analysis would be repeated for different load positions, using only the right-hand half of the structure because of symmetry.

Influence lines can also be determined by direct application of Müller-Breslau's principle. The influence line for horizontal thrust is obtained by imposing a unit horizontal displacement between supports, and the influence line for vertical reaction is obtained by imposing a unit vertical movement. The influence line for moment at a support is obtained by imposing a unit rotation. In every case the resulting vertical displacements of the arch axis are influence ordinates for vertical loading, and the horizontal displacements are influence ordinates for horizontal loading. This procedure can conveniently be applied by means of the column analogy. For instance, to obtain an influence line for H, set $M_x = 1$, and from M_x/I_x obtain the horizontal thrust necessary to produce the unit displacement. Compute bending moments, M, resulting from this thrust, at each station, and then obtain angle changes, $M(dA)$. With these angle changes, compute vertical displacements (influence ordinates for vertical loading) and horizontal displacements (influence ordinates for horizontal loading).

Exact influence tables and influence lines can be prepared[1] by writing general algebraic expressions for the terms of the column analogy. The integrations involved are quite formidable. Simple, closed expressions are obtainable only for a secant variation in moment of inertia, which permits

[1] James Michalos, *Theory of Structural Analysis and Design* (New York: Ronald, 1958).

integration along the X-axis rather than along the centerline of the arch. For the parabolic arch with secant variation, the following expressions result for H, V, and M at the right support when the arch is subjected to a unit vertical load placed at a distance $bL/2$ to the left of the crown:

$$H = \frac{15}{64}\frac{L}{h}(1 - b^2)^2 \tag{10.69}$$

$$V = \frac{1}{4}(2 + b)(1 - b)^2 \tag{10.70}$$

$$M = \frac{L}{32}(1 - b)^2(5b^2 + 6b + 1) \tag{10.71}$$

in which h is the rise of the arch.

For a two-hinged, parabolic arch with secant variation in I, the following expression for H is obtained when the arch is subjected to a unit vertical load placed at a distance aL from the left support:

$$H = \frac{5}{8}\frac{L}{h}(a - 2a^3 + a^4) \tag{10.72}$$

Influence lines for arches with secant variation are often good approximations for use with arches whose depth increases towards the springings.

As mentioned previously, no such simple expressions result for arches of constant section. Influence tables are necessary. These tables[2] of influence values for parabolic, circular, or semielliptical arches make possible the direct design of arches of constant section. In addition, based on numerical studies, influence lines are available for arches of variable cross section. These simplify the preparation of a preliminary design for final analysis.

For extremely flat arches it may be considered necessary to correct tabulated influence values in order to account for rib shortening. See Section 10.7.

Combined bending and axial stresses, σ_u at the extreme upper fiber and σ_l at the extreme lower fiber of a cross section, can be computed as

$$\sigma_u = \frac{M_l c_u}{I}$$
$$\tag{10.73}$$
$$\sigma_l = \frac{M_u c_l}{I}$$

in which M_l and M_u are, respectively, the bending moments about the lower and upper kern points of the section, c_l and c_u are, respectively, the distances from the centroidal axis of the cross section to the lower and upper extreme fibers, and I is the moment of inertia of the cross section. To determine M_l and M_u, it is necessary to know the location of the kern points. If the cross section

---

[2] Michalos, *op. cit.*

has a vertical axis of symmetry, the kern points are located on it at distances from the centroidal axis equal to

$$k_u = \frac{I}{Ac_l}$$

$$k_l = \frac{I}{Ac_u}$$

$$(10.74)$$

in which A represents the area of the cross section.

Strictly speaking, if Equations (10.73) are to be used to compute stresses, we should first obtain influence lines for moment about the upper and about the lower kern points. Thus, in Figure 10-12(c), a simple-beam influence line for moment at the upper kern point would be combined with corrections $i(y_u)_D$. Similarly, a simple-beam influence line for moment at the lower kern point would be combined with corrections $i(y_l)_D$. Practically, the small added precision that would result is hardly justified in view of the uncertainties in loading and the differences between the analytical model and the real structure.

10.10 Continuous Arches

Continuous arches or continuous gabled frames can be analyzed by the displacement method (or by moment distribution) once we know the stiffness values. Such values are conveniently determined by column analogy in the same manner as in Sections 10.7 and 10.8. Stiffness values for arches of constant section and certain given shapes have been prepared and tabulated.[3] For other arches, they must be determined by analysis.

Figure 10-14(a) shows a series of arches on slender piers. Each arch is identical to that in Figure 10-5, with a constant moment of inertia equal to 1.5 ft⁴. The piers are also of constant section, with moment of inertia equal to 10 ft⁴. The four degrees of freedom at the supports are indicated by broken arrows numbered 1 through 4. The positive sense of rotations, displacements, moments, and forces is as indicated by these arrows. We proceed in a manner similar to that used for rigid frames in Chapter 9.

Moment necessary to rotate one end of a pier through a unit angle, with no translation and the far end fixed, is

$$M = \frac{4EI}{L} = \frac{4(10)E}{20} = 2E = 20{,}000 \times 10^{-4}E$$

At the opposite end, the moment induced is

$$M = \frac{2EI}{L} = 10{,}000 \times 10^{-4}E$$

[3] Michalos, *op. cit.*

Horizontal force resulting from unit rotation at one end of a pier, and moment resulting from unit displacement of one end of a pier are

$$H = -\frac{6EI}{L^2} = -\frac{6(10)E}{(20)^2} = -0.15E = -1,500 \times 10^{-4}E, \text{ at same end}$$

$$= 1,500 \times 10^{-4}E, \text{ at opposite end}$$

$$M = -\frac{6EI}{L^2} = -1,500 \times 10^{-4}E, \text{ at both ends}$$

Horizontal force necessary to displace one end of a pier a unit distance relative to the other end, with no end rotation permitted, is

$$H = \frac{12EI}{L^3} = \frac{12(10)E}{(20)^3} = 0.015E = 150 \times 10^{-4}E$$

At the opposite end, the force induced is

$$H = -150 \times 10^{-4}E$$

Stiffnesses for the arches can be conveniently obtained by column analogy. For the present arches, results for a horizontal displacement (M_x) of 3×10^{-2} ft are available in Figure 10-10(a), and results for a counterclockwise (negative) rotation of 0.001 rad at a support are available in Figure 10-10(c). The effect of unit displacement or unit rotation is determined by ratio. Referring to Figure 10-10—

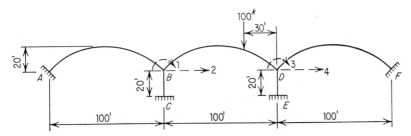

(a) Dimension and Identification Sketch

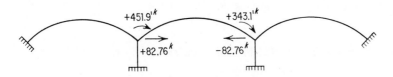

(b) Fixed-End Moments and Horizontal Thrusts

Figure 10-14.   Continuous Arches on Slender Piers

(1) For positive unit displacement at one end, using the positive sense of H and M indicated in Figure 10-14(a):

$$H = \frac{7.47 \times 10^{-6}E(1.5)}{3 \times 10^{-2}} = 3.735 \times 10^{-4}E., \text{ at same end}$$
$$= -3.735 \times 10^{-4}E, \text{ at opposite end}$$

$$M = \frac{96.3 \times 10^{-6}E(1.5)}{3 \times 10^{-2}} = 48.15 \times 10^{-4}E, \text{ at same end}$$
$$= -48.15 \times 10^{-4}E, \text{ at opposite end}$$

(2) For positive unit rotation at one end, remembering that a negative rotation was applied in Figure 10-10(c):

$$H = \frac{3.21 \times 10^{-6}E(1.5)}{0.001} = 48.15 \times 10^{-4}E, \text{ at same end}$$

$$H = -48.15 \times 10^{-4}E, \text{ at opposite end}$$

$$M = \frac{76.1 \times 10^{-6}E(1.5)}{0.001} = 1,141.5 \times 10^{-4}E, \text{ at same end}$$

$$M = -\frac{24.9 \times 10^{-6}E(1.5)}{0.001} = -373.5 \times 10^{-4}E, \text{ at opposite end}$$

The stiffness coefficients at the joints are then obtained by combination of the preceding values for moment and horizontal force in the individual arches and piers. Thus

$$k_{11} = 2(1,141.5 \times 10^{-4}E) + 20,000 \times 10^{-4}E = 22,283 \times 10^{-4}E$$
$$k_{22} = 2(3.735 \times 10^{-4}E) + 150 \times 10^{-4}E = 157.47 \times 10^{-4}E$$
$$k_{12} = k_{21} = 2(48.15 \times 10^{-4}E) - 1,500 \times 10^{-4}E = -1,403.7 \times 10^{-4}E$$
$$k_{31} = k_{13} = -373.5 \times 10^{-4}E$$
$$k_{41} = k_{14} = -48.15 \times 10^{-4}E$$
$$k_{32} = k_{23} = -48.15 \times 10^{-4}E$$
$$k_{42} = k_{24} = -3.735 \times 10^{-4}E$$
$$k_{33} = 2(1,141.5 \times 10^{-4}E) + 20,000 \times 10^{-4}E = 22,283 \times 10^{-4}E$$
$$k_{44} = 2(3.735 \times 10^{-4}E) + 150 \times 10^{-4}E = 157.47 \times 10^{-4}E$$
$$k_{34} = k_{43} = 2(48.15 \times 10^{-4}E) - 1,500 \times 10^{-4}E = -1,403.7 \times 10^{-4}E$$

The stiffness matrix is

$$\mathbf{K} = 10^{-4}E \begin{bmatrix} 22{,}283. & -1{,}403.7 & -373.5 & -48.15 \\ -1{,}403.7 & 157.47 & -48.15 & -3.735 \\ -373.5 & -48.15 & 22{,}283. & -1{,}403.7 \\ -48.15 & -3.735 & -1{,}403.7 & 157.47 \end{bmatrix}$$

The fixed-end moments and horizontal thrusts (from Figure 10.6) are shown in Figure 10-14(b) with signs in accord with the positive directions indicated by broken arrow in Figure 10-14(a). Since there is load on only one span, these fixed-end values are the unbalanced moments and forces—that is, the errors in statics of the assumed fixed-end solution. Therefore, the correction moments and forces required to correct the errors are identical to the values in (b), but with opposite sign, and the "load" vector is

$$\mathbf{P} = \begin{bmatrix} -451.9 \\ -82.76 \\ -343.1 \\ +82.76 \end{bmatrix}$$

The unknown rotations and displacements can be found from

$$\mathbf{D} = \mathbf{K}^{-1}\mathbf{P}$$

All of the following computations were performed by digital computer. Inverting the stiffness matrix, the matrix equation for rotations and displacements becomes

$$\begin{bmatrix} D_1 \\ D_2 \\ D_3 \\ D_4 \end{bmatrix} = \frac{1}{E} \begin{bmatrix} 1.0540 & 9.4942 & 0.16574 & 2.0249 \\ 9.4942 & 149.34 & 2.0249 & 24.495 \\ 0.16574 & 2.0249 & 1.0540 & 9.4942 \\ 2.0249 & 24.495 & 9.4942 & 149.34 \end{bmatrix} \begin{bmatrix} -451.9 \\ -82.76 \\ -343.1 \\ +82.76 \end{bmatrix}$$

and

$$D_1 = -1{,}151./E$$

$$D_2 = -15{,}317./E$$

$$D_3 = 181.6/E$$

$$D_4 = 6{,}159/E$$

With the rotations and displacements known, correction moments and forces at the ends of the members were obtained, making use of the stiffness relationships for individual arches and piers as determined earlier. In matrix notation,

$$
\begin{bmatrix}
H_{BD} = -H_{DB} \\
H_{BA} = -H_{AB} \\
H_{BC} = -H_{CB} \\
H_{DF} = -H_{FD} \\
H_{DE} = -H_{ED} \\
M_{BD} \\
M_{BA} \\
M_{BC} \\
M_{AB} \\
M_{DB} \\
M_{DF} \\
M_{FD} \\
M_{DE} \\
M_{CB} \\
M_{ED}
\end{bmatrix}
= 10^{-4}
\begin{bmatrix}
48.15 & 3.735 & -48.15 & -3.735 \\
48.15 & 3.735 & 0 & 0 \\
1{,}500. & 150. & 0 & 0 \\
0 & 0 & 48.15 & 3.735 \\
0 & 0 & -1{,}500 & 150. \\
1{,}141.5 & 48.15 & -373.5 & -48.15 \\
1{,}141.5 & 48.15 & 0 & 0 \\
20{,}000. & -1{,}500. & 0 & 0 \\
-373.5 & -48.15 & 0 & 0 \\
-373.5 & -48.15 & 1{,}141.5 & 48.15 \\
0 & 0 & 1{,}141.5 & 48.15 \\
0 & 0 & -373.5 & -48.15 \\
0 & 0 & 20{,}000. & -1{,}500. \\
10{,}000. & -1{,}500. & 0 & 0 \\
0 & 0 & 10{,}000. & -1{,}500.
\end{bmatrix}
\begin{bmatrix}
-1{,}151. \\
-15{,}317. \\
181.6 \\
6{,}159.
\end{bmatrix}
=
\begin{bmatrix}
-14.44 \\
-11.26 \\
-57.06 \\
3.17 \\
65.15 \\
-241.6 \\
-205.2 \\
-5.1 \\
116.8 \\
167.1 \\
50.4 \\
-36.4 \\
-560.6 \\
1{,}146. \\
-742.2
\end{bmatrix}
$$

A positive sign for H indicates force acting to the right, and a positive sign for M indicates clockwise moment.

The final end moments and forces were obtained by adding the correction values to the assumed values shown in Figure 10-14(b) as follows:

$$
\begin{bmatrix}
H_{BD} = -H_{DB} \\
H_{BA} = -H_{AB} \\
H_{BC} = -H_{CB} \\
H_{DF} = -H_{FD} \\
H_{DE} = -H_{ED} \\
M_{BD} \\
M_{BA} \\
M_{BC} \\
M_{AB} \\
M_{DB} \\
M_{DF} \\
M_{FD} \\
M_{DE} \\
M_{CB} \\
M_{ED}
\end{bmatrix}
=
\begin{bmatrix}
82.76 \\
0 \\
0 \\
0 \\
0 \\
451.9 \\
0 \\
0 \\
0 \\
343.1 \\
0 \\
0 \\
0 \\
0 \\
0
\end{bmatrix}
+
\begin{bmatrix}
-14.44 \\
-11.26 \\
-57.06 \\
3.17 \\
65.15 \\
-241.6 \\
-205.2 \\
-5.1 \\
116.8 \\
167.1 \\
50.4 \\
-36.4 \\
-560.6 \\
1{,}146. \\
-742.2
\end{bmatrix}
=
\begin{bmatrix}
68.32 \\
-11.26 \\
-57.06 \\
3.17 \\
65.15 \\
210.3 \\
-205.2 \\
-5.1 \\
116.8 \\
510.2 \\
50.4 \\
-36.4 \\
-560.6 \\
1{,}146. \\
-742.2
\end{bmatrix}
$$

All values of H are in kips and all values of M are in ft-kips.

From the horizontal thrusts and end moments, the pressure line can be drawn and bending moments obtained anywhere in the structure. Also, vertical components of force can be computed by statics.

If a digital computer is available, results can be obtained at great speed for innumerable conditions of loading simply by changing the vector **P** to correspond to the various loading conditions. The determination of this vector by, say, column analogy, can also be programmed for the computer.

Problems

10.1.   For the one-hinged parabolic arch, sketch the pressure line and state mathematically the conditions of geometry that must be satisfied, indicating the reference axes. From the pressure line, determine the reactions at A and D and the bending moments at A, B, and D. *Hint:* The origin of axes must be at the hinge. Why?

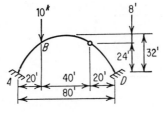

Problem 10-1

10.2. For the two-hinged parabolic arch, proceed as in Problem 1.

10.3. By means of Equations (10.14) through (10.16) determine the reactions and moments at A and B, and draw the pressure line for the parabolic arch of constant section. Divide the arch into 20 segments of equal horizontal projection.   (*Ans.:* $M_B = 32.2$ ft-kips; $V_B = -1.21$ kips; $H_B = -3.70$ kips.)

10.4. Solve Problem 10.3, making use of the elastic center.

10.5. Assume the arch is parabolic, with secant variation in moment of inertia. Use Equation (10.18) to derive Equation (10.72).

10.6. Draw the analogous column and compute its cross-sectional properties without subdividing the members. Apply the column analogy and determine bending moments, axial forces, and shears in the members. *Hint:* Cut one of the members to obtain statically possible solution ("loading"). Which cut results in simplest "loading"?   (*Ans.:* $M_A = M_B = -11.8$ ft-kips; $M_C = M_D = 4.3$ ft-kips.)

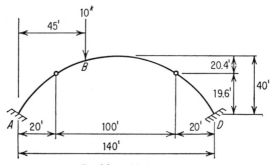

Problem 10-2

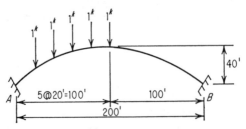

Problem 10-3

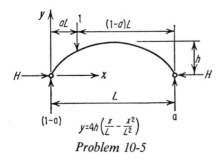

$$y = 4h\left(\frac{x}{L} - \frac{x^2}{L^2}\right)$$

Problem 10-5

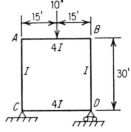

Problem 10-6

10.7. By column analogy determine the pressure line, assuming constant moment of inertia. Do not subdivide members. (*Ans.: H= −6.07 kips.*)

10.8. In Figure 10-5 assume that the relative moments of inertia vary linearly from 1.00 at station 10 to 1.90 at stations 1 and 20. Solve by column analogy and draw the pressure line. Compare this pressure line to that in Figure 10-6.

10.9. In Figure 10-5 assume hinges at A and B. Solve for H by column analogy and draw the pressure line. (*Ans.: H= −79.4 kips.*)

10.10. By column analogy, and without subdividing the members, determine forces and moments. (*Ans.: H= −13.1 kips; M_A= 82.0 ft-kips.*)

10.11. Repeat Problem 10.10, but for a uniform lateral load of 0.3 kip/ft on AB.

10.12. By column analogy determine moments at A, B, C, and D of the closed ring with constant moment of inertia. *Hint:* If ring is cut at D, m_0 at all sections between A and C is equal to $−Wr \sin \theta$. (*Ans.: M_A= M_C=0.318 Wr; M_B= M_D= −0.182 Wr.*)

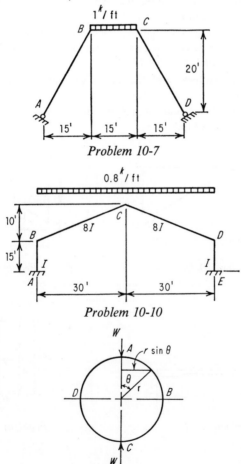

Problem 10-7

Problem 10-10

Problem 10-12

10.13. By column analogy compute H, in terms of EI expressed in inch units, for a uniform temperature rise of 100°F if the coefficient of thermal expansion is 6.5×10^{-6}. Draw the pressure line and check the computed value of H by noting that the total product of the angles changes about the X-axis through the hinge must be equal to the temperature expansion that would take place if the structure were free to move.   (*Ans.: $H = -0.193 \times 10^{-8} EI$.*)

10.14. Assume structure of Problem 10.13 is hingeless. Draw the pressure line and, by column analogy, determine moments at A, B, and C for a relative horizontal movement of B 1 in. to the right, and then for relative downward movement of 1 in.   (*Ans.: $H = 4.94 \times 10^{-9} EI$; $V = 6.94 \times 10^{-10} EI$, with EI in inch units.*)

10.15. Assume that the actual moments of inertia, in inch units, of the rigid frame of Figure 10-9 are 4,460 times those listed and that $E = 30,000,000$ psi. Obtain H and draw the moment diagram for a uniform temperature drop of 60°F if the coefficient of thermal expansion is 6.5×10^{-6}.
(*Ans.: $H = 0.403$ kip.*)

10.16. Determine the fixed-end moments, the stiffnesses, and the carry-over factors if the moment of inertia varies as the depth cubed.   (*Ans.: $FEM_A = 120$ ft-kips; $K_A = 0.200EI$; $C_{AB} = 0.475$.*)

10.17. Compute the stiffness and the carry-over factor.   (*Ans.: $K = 0.3644EI$; $C = 0.756$.*)

10.18. Obtain the fixed-end moment at B and draw the moment diagram.
(*Ans.: $M_B = 0.4$ ft-kip.*)

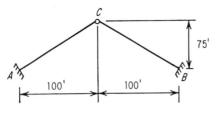

Problem 10-13

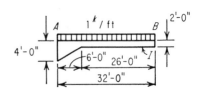

Problem 10-16

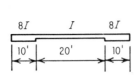

Problem 10-17

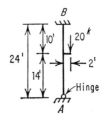

Problem 10-18

Chapter 11

Plastic Analysis

Elastic behavior has served as the basis for the design of virtually all statically indeterminate structures. In recent years, however, plastic behavior has received increasing attention as a basis for design of certain types of steel frame structures, particularly single-story rigid frames under static loading. Some of the arguments advanced for use of plastic design are: easier analysis in comparison to elastic analysis, more realistic factor of safety, and economy through the resulting use of lighter members.

Ease of analysis, in itself, does not appeal to the authors as a valid argument unless it follows directly from a philosophy of design that results in a better structure. As a matter of fact, it should be pointed out that plastic analysis is comparatively easy only for the relatively simple problems to which it is generally applied. On the other hand, as an illustration, the behavior of columns subjected to biaxial bending beyond the elastic range can be awesome to put in analytical form.

A more realistic factor of safety is desirable, but one that is based on some particular failure condition may still have a very narrow range of application. Economy of material, while desirable, does not necessarily mean over-all economy. In structural design, as elsewhere, you generally "get what you pay for." Smaller sizes of members will mean higher stresses under the working loads that are applied throughout the life of the structure. The greater deflections that result might lead to unsatisfactory performance. This can be particularly true if some of the modern steels with extremely high yield strength are used.

It must be remembered that in any design, whether elastic or plastic, the structure is designed to stand—not to fall. Elastic analysis is important in assessing day-by-day performance, although plastic analysis is desirable for an understanding of the mechanism of failure. As the late Professor Hardy Cross used to ask: "How may the structure behave?" To begin to answer this question, a designer must assess the *entire behavior*, elastic, elastic-plastic, and fully plastic, if it is at all possible.

In conclusion, then, plastic analysis should be viewed as the opposite extreme from elastic analysis. It is a part, but only a part, of the story. Failure can also occur in the elastic range because of buckling instability, fatigue, or brittle fracture. In the elastic-plastic range, failure may result from instability. Plastic analysis is applicable only when instability is prevented and fatigue and brittle fracture are not considered possible.

11.1   Ultimate Load and Maximum Strength

An idealized stress-strain diagram for carbon steel is shown in Figure 11-1. The reader should remember that the strain at fracture is fifteen or more times the strain indicated at the end of the plastic range, where strain-hardening commences. The increase in load capacity that accompanies strain-hardening is of no practical importance in design because of the extremely large defor-

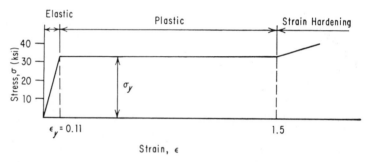

Figure 11-1.   Idealized Stress-Strain Diagram for Carbon Steel

mations that have occurred. Even before strain-hardening begins, the deformations are roughly fifteen times those at yield.

If a minimum yield stress of 33,000 psi is assumed for ordinary carbon steel, then, at a working stress of 20,000 psi, the factor of safety in conventional elastic design is $33,000 \div 20,000 = 1.65$. Suppose a simple beam is subjected to a load that is 1.65 times that which would produce a stress of 20,000 psi in the extreme fibers. The resulting stress would be the yield stress of 33,000 psi, but only at the extreme fibers. Yielding will progress through the entire cross section only after additional load is added. For the commonly used wide-flange shapes this will amount to approximately 12 per cent of the load producing yield at the outer fibers. Thus the overload factor of safety is $(1.65)(1.12) = 1.85$.

Plastic design is based on ultimate load. Generally, the same margin of safety, 1.85, has been adopted for plastic design. Thus the loads applied to the structure in analysis are taken as 1.85 times the working loads. It should be clear that, based on the preceding discussion, plastic design of a statically determinate wide-flange beam would result in a cross section that is almost the same as that obtained on the basis of elastic considerations only. It is in dealing with statically indeterminate beams and frames that a redistribution of bending moment, resulting from the formation of so-called yield hinges, can result in an appreciable saving in material under the conditions stipulated for plastic design.

In the next section we consider plastic bending at a cross section. Then, in the succeeding section, we deal with the formation of yield hinges and the resulting redistribution of bending moments.

.2   Plastic Bending of Beams

Figure 11-2 shows the development of plasticity through the rectangular cross section in (a). In (b) the yield strain, ε_y, and yield stress, σ_y, have been developed at the extreme fibers. The corresponding bending moment is called

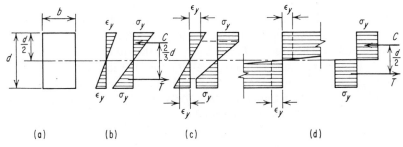

Figure 11-2.   Development of Full Plasticity at a Cross Section

M_y. In (c) the strains have increased beyond ε_y through a portion of the cross section. From Figure 11-1, the corresponding stresses are equal to σ_y, and this is the maximum stress developed. Bending has proceeded in (d) until the strains throughout virtually all of the cross section are extremely large. A stress block with constant stress, σ_y, is obtained as a limit. The bending moment when full plasticity is developed is called M_p.

The compressive force, C, and the tensile force, T, in Figure 11-2(b) are each equal to $(bd/2)(\sigma_y/2)$, and the maximum elastic resisting moment is

$$M_y = \left(\frac{bd}{2}\right)\left(\frac{\sigma_y}{2}\right)\left(\frac{2d}{3}\right) = \sigma_y\left(\frac{bd^2}{6}\right) \tag{11.1}$$

In Figure 11-2(d), $C = T = (bd/2)\sigma_y$, and the plastic resisting moment is

$$M_p = \left(\frac{bd}{2}\right)(\sigma_y)\left(\frac{d}{2}\right) = \sigma_y\left(\frac{bd^2}{4}\right) \tag{11.2}$$

The term $bd^2/6$ in Equation (11.1) is the elastic section modulus, S or I/c. The similar term, $bd^2/4$, in Equation (11.2) is called the plastic modulus, Z.

As with the elastic section modulus, the value of the plastic modulus depends only upon the shape and size of the cross section. With Z known, the plastic resisting moment for any shape can be determined from

$$M_p = \sigma_y Z \tag{11.3}$$

A general expression for Z, for any shape of cross section, is

$$Z = \int_A y \cdot dA \tag{11.4}$$

in which dA represents an infinitesimal cross-sectional area and y is its distance, without regard to sign, from the centroidal axis of the entire cross-section. The integration is performed over the entire cross section, A.

Any shape of cross section can be divided into finite areas, ΔA, with known distances, y, from their centroids to the centroidal axis of the cross section. Then Equation (11.4) becomes

$$Z = \sum_A y \cdot \Delta A \tag{11.5}$$

For a solid rectangular section a comparison of Equation (11.1) with Equation (11.2) shows that the plastic section modulus is 1.5 times the elastic section modulus. Therefore, $M_p = 1.5 \, M_y$. On the other hand, rolled wide-flange sections have much of their area concentrated in their flanges and Z varies between $1.12S$ and $1.15S$. It is generally taken, conservatively, as 12 per cent greater than S. Consequently, M_p is only about 12 per cent greater than M_y. The term *shape factor* is often used to show the effect of shape on M_p. Thus

$$\text{Shape factor} = \frac{M_p}{M_y} = \frac{Z}{S} \tag{11.6}$$

The shape factor is 1.70 for a solid, round cross section and approximately 1.27 for a thin, hollow, tubular cross section.

Shape factors indicate the reserve strength available beyond the initiation of yield at the outer fibers of a cross section. On this basis alone, a solid rectangular section, a solid round section, or a tubular section is better than a wide-flange section. One should remember, however, that, because so much of its area is concentrated at top and bottom, the wide-flange beam can support a much greater load at yield than a solid or tubular section of equal area. Performance and economy give the advantage to wide-flange sections.

The resisting moment, M_{pp}, of a partially plastic section, such as that indicated in Figure 11-2(c), can be found as

$$M_{pp} = \int_A \sigma y \cdot dA \tag{11.7}$$

in which σ varies linearly from zero to σ_y over the elastic portion of the cross section and is equal to σ_y throughout the plastic portions.

Other structural materials, such as aluminium alloys and concrete, do not possess the great ductility evident in Figure 11-1, and fracture occurs at a much lower strain. An ultimate resisting moment for such materials can be determined by replacing the rectangular stress blocks in Figure 11-2 by curved shapes corresponding to the stress-strain diagram of the material.

For reinforced concrete beams the low tensile strength of the concrete is completely discounted, and the tension force is concentrated at the level of the tensile reinforcing steel. The distribution of the compression stresses can be approximated quite closely by some type of parabola. Since reinforced concrete beams are generally underreinforced, failure in bending is due to yielding of the tension steel. Therefore, $T = A_s \sigma_y$, in which A_s is the cross-sectional area of the tensile reinforcement and σ_y is the yield stress of the steel. Furthermore it becomes convenient to replace the parabolic stress distribution by an equivalent rectangular stress block such that the distance from C to T will give the same resisting moment as for the actual stress distribution.

.3   Plastic Hinges and Redistribution of Moment

As the load on the simply supported beam in Figure 11-3 is increased, a value is reached at which yielding of the outer fibers of the cross section under the load commences. The maximum bending moment at that load is equal to M_y. As the load is further increased, the bending moments along the beam also increase until the condition indicated in the figure is reached. The full plastic moment has developed directly beneath the load, and partial plasticity has developed over a length ΔL. The length of this zone of yielding depends upon the type of loading and upon the shape of cross section. The student should verify that for a concentrated load at midspan, $\Delta L = L/3$ for a rectangular cross section (shape factor $= 1.5$) and $\Delta L = 0.107L$ to $0.130L$ for a wide-flange

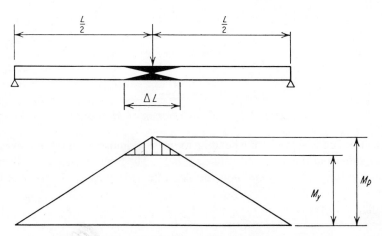

Figure 11-3.   Yield Zone under Concentrated Load

section (shape factor $= 1.12$ to 1.15). What is ΔL when a uniformly distributed load is applied?

For the simple plastic analysis under consideration, it is assumed that all of the plastic rotation is concentrated at a single cross section. The member then behaves as if it were hinged at that section but with a constant resisting moment, M_p, acting on the section.

As stated in Section 11.1, it is redistribution of bending moment in a statically indeterminate structure that leads to a significant increase of strength beyond the elastic limit. Figure 11-4(a) shows a fixed-end beam supporting a uniformly distributed load. Under elastic conditions the bending moments

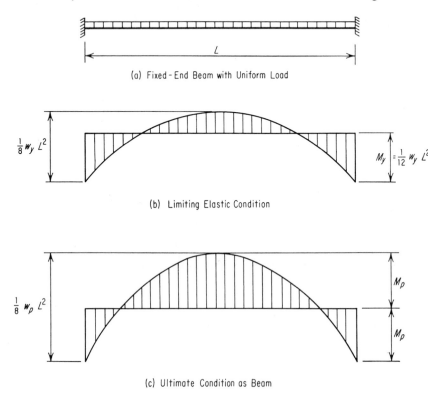

(a) Fixed-End Beam with Uniform Load

(b) Limiting Elastic Condition

(c) Ultimate Condition as Beam

Figure 11-4. Redistribution of Moment

at the fixed ends are twice the bending moment at midspan, and the sum of the latter value and the fixed-end value is $(\tfrac{1}{8})wL^2$. The limiting elastic condition is shown in (b), with the yield moment, M_y, attained under an intensity of load

$$w_y = \frac{12M_y}{L^2} \qquad (11.8)$$

The deflections up to this stage are those of an elastic, fixed-end beam.

As the load is further increased, the full plastic moment, M_p, is developed at the ends. Under still further increase in load the structure acts as a beam with hinged ends but with constant moment, M_p, at the ends. The deflections in this stage are those of an elastic, simply supported beam and, therefore, increase at a faster rate. Finally, an intensity of load, w_p, is reached under which a full plastic hinge develops also at the center section. A mechanism is now formed and the ultimate capacity of the structure as a beam has been reached, with the beam continuing to deflect under constant load. The moment diagram for the ultimate condition is shown in (c). From considerations of statics,

$$2M_p = \tfrac{1}{8}w_p L^2$$

and

$$w_p = \frac{16M_p}{L^2} \qquad\qquad (11.9)$$

From Equations (11.8) and (11.9),

$$\frac{w_p}{w_y} = \frac{4}{3}\frac{M_p}{M_y} = \frac{4}{3} \times \text{shape factor}$$

whereas for a simply supported beam, using Equation (11.6),

$$\frac{w_p}{w_y} = \frac{M_p}{M_y} = \text{shape factor}$$

Redistribution of moment in the fixed-end beam makes possible a one-third increase in collapse load over the simply supported beam of identical cross section.

1.4   Continuous Beams

Collapse of a continuous beam can occur through the formation of a mechanism in any of the spans. In an interior span the failure mechanism is identical to that for the fixed-end beam. In an outer span with one simple support, only two plastic hinges are necessary to form a mechanism. For a span of constant section, the hinges form when the bending moment at the interior supports and at a section somewhere along the span both reach a value of M_p.

Figure 11-5(a) shows the outer span of a continuous beam. In order to obtain a general algebraic expression for locating the plastic hinge in the span, the plastic moment that can be developed has been taken as M_p in the interior of the span and kM_p at support B. The moment diagram when w has reached

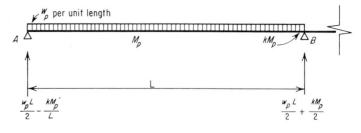

(a) Loaded Outer Span

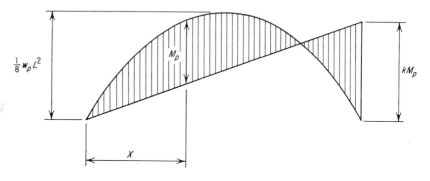

(b) Moment Diagram at Ultimate Load

Figure 11-5. Location of Plastic Hinge in Outer Span of Continuous Beam

the collapse value is shown in (b). The moment at the plastic hinge, located a distance x from A, is

$$\left(\frac{w_p L}{2} - \frac{kM_p}{L}\right)x - \frac{w_p x^2}{2} = M_p$$

from which

$$M_p = \frac{w_p Lx}{2}\left(\frac{L-x}{L+kx}\right) \qquad \textbf{(11.10)}$$

The maximum value of M_p will occur when

$$x = L\sqrt{\frac{1}{k} + \frac{1}{k^2}} - \frac{L}{k} \qquad \textbf{(11.11)}$$

With the value of x known, Equation (11.10) can be used to obtain the required value of M_p for a known load or the collapse load, w_p, for a known value of M_p.

For identical value of plastic moment at a section along the span and at B,

342

k equals one and Equation (11.11) gives $x = 0.414L$ for maximum M_p. The
values of M_p and w_p are then

$$M_p = 0.0857w_pL^2$$

$$w_p = \frac{11.7M_p}{L^2}$$

If $k = \frac{2}{3}$,

$$x = 0.436L$$

$$M_p = 0.0953w_pL^2$$

$$w_p = \frac{10.5M_p}{L^2}$$

For $k = \frac{3}{2}$,

$$x = 0.387L$$

$$M_p = 0.0750w_pL^2$$

$$w_p = \frac{13.3M_p}{L^2}$$

Observe that the value of x decreases as k increases. Furthermore, a small
change in the value of x will yield virtually identical values of M_p and w_p in
each case.

Expressions similar to Equation (11.10) can be written for other types of
loading. In each case the criterion is that the plastic moment develop at enough
sections to form a mechanism in the span under consideration. Generally, a
good enough value of x can be obtained from a plot of the bending moment
diagram by altering the position of the straight closing line until the required
ratio of maximum positive and maximum negative moment is obtained.

Figure 11-6(a) shows a uniformly loaded, three-span beam of constant
section, with a plastic modulus of 300 in.³ Assume that $\sigma_y = 36$ ksi. Then,
from Equation (11.3), $M_p = 36\ (300) = 10,800$ in.-kips, or 900 ft-kips.

The moment diagram consistent with the formation of a mechanism in
span AB is shown in (b). From the previously developed expression for $k = 1$,
the collapse load in span AB and, by symmetry, in span CD is

$$w_p = \frac{11.7(900)}{(30)^2} = 11.7 \text{ kips}/ft$$

The moment diagram consistent with formation of a mechanism in span BC
is shown in (c). The plastic moment is

$$900 = \frac{1}{2}\left[\frac{w_p(40)^2}{8}\right]$$

and

$$w_p = 9 \text{ kips}/ft$$

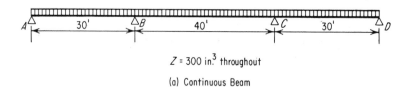

$Z = 300$ in.^{3} throughout

(a) Continuous Beam

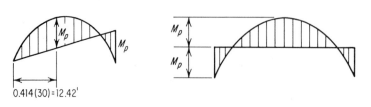

$0.414(30) = 12.42'$

(b) Mechanism in Span AB

(c) Mechanism in Span BC

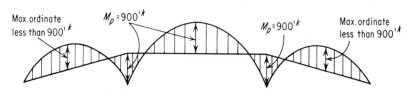

Max. ordinate less than $900'^k$

$M_p = 900'^k$

$M_p = 900'^k$

Max. ordinate less than $900'^k$

(d) Moment Diagram after Development of Mechanism

Figure 11-6. Plastic Analysis of Continuous Beam

This collapse load is smaller than that obtained for the end spans. If the loading is kept uniform on all three spans, failure will occur at a value of 9 kips/ft by formation of a mechanism in span BC. The moment diagram after development of the collapse mechanism is shown in Figure 11-6(d).

No special problem is presented if load intensities are different for individual spans. If concentrated loads are included, it must be remembered that, in plastic analysis, superposition is not valid. One must work with the moment diagram of the entire loading on the span.

Suppose that the beam in Figure 11-6(a) is reinforced by cover plates at B and C so that $k = \frac{3}{2}$. Then in spans AB and CD,

$$w_p = \frac{13.3 M_p}{L^2} = \frac{13.3(900)}{(30)^2}$$

$$w_p = 13.3 \text{ kips/ft}$$

In span BC,

$$\tfrac{3}{2} M_p + M_p = \tfrac{1}{8} w_p (40)^2$$

from which

$$w_p = \tfrac{1}{80} M_p = \tfrac{1}{80}(900)$$

$$w_p = 11.25 \text{ kips/ft}$$

344

This is the collapse load for the uniformly loaded beam, provided the cover plates are long enough so that the bending moment nowhere exceeds the available plastic capacity.

In design, the collapse loading, w_p, is chosen by applying an overload factor to the expected working load. Assume that it is desired to select a beam of constant section, with the spans shown in Figure 11-6(a) for a uniformly distributed collapse load of 9 kips/ft. For spans AB and CD,

$$M_p = 0.0857(9)(30)^2 = 695 \text{ ft kips}$$

For span BC,

$$M_p = (\tfrac{1}{2})(\tfrac{1}{8})(9)(40)^2 = 900 \text{ ft kips}$$

Using the greater value of M_p, Equation (11.3) becomes

$$900(12) = 36Z$$

and

$$Z = 300 \text{ in.}^3$$

which is, of course, the value previously used in the analysis to determine the same collapse load used in this design procedure. With the required value of Z known, the designer can divide it by the shape factor to obtain the required elastic section modulus.

11.5   Use of Virtual Displacements

The principle of virtual displacements (Section 1.14) can be used for plastic analysis. Figure 11-7(a) shows the same uniformly loaded continuous beam as Figure 11-6(a). The potential failure mechanism of span AB, allowed to operate through a virtual movement, is shown in Figure 11-7(b). The total external virtual work, W_e, done by the ultimate distributed load, moving through an average distance of $\Delta/2$, noting that $\Delta = 7.278\theta$, is

$$W_e = 30w_p\left(\frac{\Delta}{2}\right) = 109.1w_p\theta$$

The total internal virtual work, W_i, done by the plastic moments is

$$W_i = M_p\theta + M_p(\tfrac{12.42}{30}\theta) = 1.414M_p\theta$$

Equating the external work to the internal work,

$$109.1w_p\theta = 1.414M_p\theta$$

$$w_p = 0.0130M_p$$

The term θ always cancels. With $M_p = 900$ ft-kips, we obtain

$$w_p = 11.7 \text{ kips/ft}$$

as in the preceding section.

The failure mechanism in span BC is illustrated in Figure 11-7(c). If we now equate external work to internal work, we have

$$40w_p\left(\frac{10\,\theta}{2}\right) = M_p\frac{\theta}{2} + M_p\theta + M_p\frac{\theta}{2}$$

and

$$w_p = 0.0100M_p$$

With $M_p = 900$ ft-kips, we again obtain

$$w_p = 9 \text{ kips/ft}$$

This is the collapse load.

Analysis by virtual work is often referred to as the mechanism method of analysis. The student should verify that if he places the internal hinge at any location other than those shown in Figure 11-7, a larger value of w_p will be obtained. As a result, this procedure is commonly called an upper bound

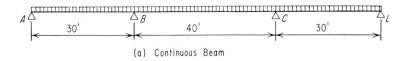

(a) Continuous Beam

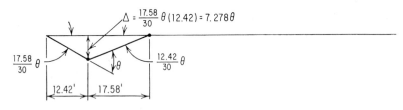

(b) Mechanism in Span AB

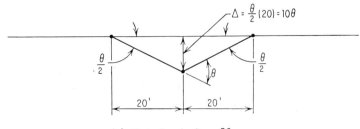

(c) Mechanism in Span BC

Figure 11-7.   Analysis by Virtual Work

method. A value of w_p that is the correct value or slightly above it can always be found by trying different positions of the interior plastic hinge. Remember that a small shift in the position of this hinge will make no practical difference.

The student should use this method to analyze a beam with cover plates at B and C, when $k = \frac{3}{2}$, and compare results with those obtained in Section 11.6. Of course they should be identical.

11.6 Two-Hinged Frames

The analysis of a two-hinged frame subjected to vertical loading is the same as for a three-span beam. Thus for a frame of constant section, with load W at midspan, $M_p = WL/8$, and plastic hinges form at the ends of the beam and under the load. If the columns have a smaller plastic modulus than the beam, plastic hinges will form at the tops of the columns rather than at the ends of the beam. Under any circumstance, the sum of the plastic moment under the load and those at the ends of the beam or top of columns must be $WL/4$.

The frame in Figure 11-8(a) is subjected to a lateral load as well as a vertical

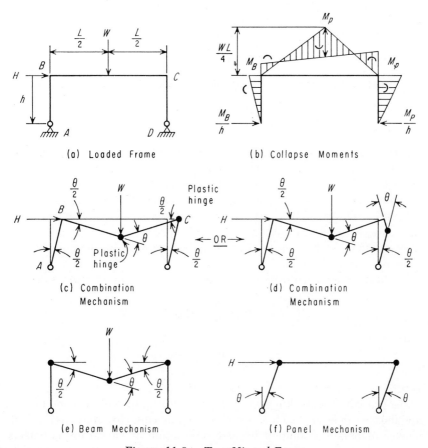

(a) Loaded Frame

(b) Collapse Moments

(c) Combination Mechanism

(d) Combination Mechanism

(e) Beam Mechanism

(f) Panel Mechanism

Figure 11-8. Two-Hinged Frame

load. The collapse moments are shown in (b), and they correspond to the mechanism in (c). From the moment diagram,

$$M_p = \frac{WL}{4} - \frac{M_B + M_p}{2} \tag{a}$$

From $\sum F_x = 0$,

$$H + \frac{M_B}{h} - \frac{M_p}{h} = 0 \tag{b}$$

Eliminating M_B from Equations (a) and (b), we get

$$M_p = \frac{WL}{8} + \frac{Hh}{4} \tag{11.12}$$

If the moment capacity of the beam is greater than for the columns, the hinge at C occurs in the column, as shown in Figure 11-8(d). The procedure is, however, identical. Suppose that the plastic moment for the beam is $2M_p$ and that for the columns is M_p. Equation (a) becomes

$$2M_p = \frac{WL}{4} - \frac{M_B + M_p}{2}$$

and Equation (b) remains as before. Then, eliminating M_B,

$$M_p = \frac{WL}{12} + \frac{Hh}{6} \tag{11.13}$$

If H in Figure 11-8 is large in comparison with W, the sign of M_B, and consequently the direction of the horizontal reaction, M_B/h, at A can change. This will, however, in no way affect Equations (11.12) and (11.13).

Expressions similar to Equations (11.12) and (11.13) can be obtained for different positions of the vertical load or for several loads acting simultaneously. No such formulas are required, however. In any case it is only necessary to draw the moment diagram and allow M_p to be developed at two sections.

Application of virtual work to the mechanism in Figure 11-8(d) results in

$$H\left(\frac{\theta}{2}h\right) + W\left(\frac{\theta}{2}\frac{L}{2}\right) = 2M_p\theta + M_p\theta$$

and

$$M_p = \frac{WL}{12} + \frac{Hh}{6}$$

as before.

The procedure of working with the moment diagram and the conditions of equilibrium can be applied to more involved problems. However, it is generally simpler to obtain a solution through application of virtual displacements, even though several mechanisms are tried in order to insure obtaining the

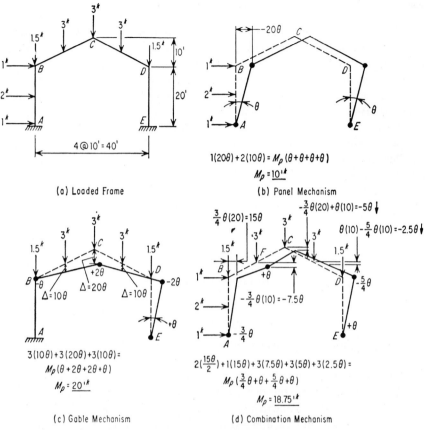

$1(20\theta) + 2(10\theta) = M_p(\theta + \theta + \theta + \theta)$

$M_p = 10^{\prime k}$

(a) Loaded Frame

(b) Panel Mechanism

$3(10\theta) + 3(20\theta) + 3(10\theta) =$

$M_p(\theta + 2\theta + 2\theta + \theta)$

$M_p = 20^{\prime k}$

(c) Gable Mechanism

$2(\frac{15\theta}{2}) + 1(15\theta) + 3(7.5\theta) + 3(5\theta) + 3(2.5\theta) =$

$M_p(\frac{3}{4}\theta + \theta + \frac{5}{4}\theta + \theta)$

$M_p = 18.75^{\prime k}$

(d) Combination Mechanism

Figure 11-9. Gable Frame

correct value. Figure 11-8(e) shows an elementary beam mechanism. An elementary panel mechanism is shown in (f). The student should use virtual work to show that the required M_p for either of these mechanisms is less than that for the combination mechanism.

1.7 Hingeless Frames

A gabled, hingeless frame of constant section is shown in Figure 11-9(a). A panel mechanism is assumed in (b), and the calculation of the corresponding value of M_p is shown below it. Vertical loads do not contribute to external virtual work because there are no vertical displacements. If loads other than vertical are placed on the rafters, the horizontal components of these loads must be included in the expression for external virtual work.

A gable mechanism is assumed in Figure 11-9(c). If the virtual rotation at E is taken as θ, the corresponding rotations at B, C, and D are quickly found by treating the rotations as forces normal to the plane of the frame and satisfying the requirements of statical equilibrium. Thus rotation at C is determined

349

by taking moments about line BD, and rotations at B and D are then found by taking moments about lines DE and BA, respectively. The original position of the frame is used. Virtual movements are considered so small, however, that identical results would be obtained using the displaced position. Positive rotation indicates increase in interior angle, and negative sign indicates decrease. However, signs have no significance in computing internal virtual work performed by the plastic moments, M_p. All such moments act in the same way as the rotations, and all products of moment and rotation are additive.

Alternatively, the rotations can be determined by first locating the instantaneous center of rotation. This is located at the intersection of original lines BC and DE.

For the combination mechanism in Figure 11-9(d), a virtual rotation θ is imposed at E. The corresponding rotation at A is found by taking moments about line FD. It is convenient to use the vertical components of distance to this line from E and from A. Thus,

$$\theta(20) + (\text{Rotation at } A)(20 + \tfrac{20}{3}) = 0$$

and

$$\text{Rotation at } A = -\tfrac{3}{4}\theta$$

Then, taking moments about DE, rotation at F is equal to $+\theta$. From moments about AE, rotation at D is $-(\tfrac{5}{4})\theta$. Displacements are then determined as products of rotations and distances, from either end of the structure, as shown in the figure. Although the displaced position of line AD is outside of the original position, this is due to lateral displacement to the right. The 3-kip load on CD has actually moved downward. If it had moved upward, the external virtual work performed by this load would be negative and would have to be subtracted from the external virtual work performed by the other loads.

The biggest value of M_p is the 20 ft-kips of the gable mechanism, and design must be based on it. If the lateral loads are relatively large, the combination mechanism will dictate the design. Generally speaking, we can say that the critical mechanism is that which results in large movements accompanied by as small a sum of plastic hinge rotations as possible.

Problems

11.1. In Figure 11-6 assume that in addition to the uniformly distributed load, w_p, there is a concentrated load at midspan AB and at midspan BC. Take the value of these concentrated loads as $60w_p$ in AB and $40w_p$ in BC. Determine the value of w_p. (*Ans.*: $w_p = 3$ kips/ft.)

11.2. The moment capacity at the knees is two times that of the remainder of the structure. Derive the expression for M_p. Check through use of virtual displacements. (*Ans.*: $M_p = \tfrac{5}{18} WL$.)

11.3. Sketch the pressure line for this two-hinged frame and, letting the moment at
 B, C, and D become M_p, obtain an expression for M_p directly.

$$\left(Ans.: M_p = \frac{wL^2}{16 + 8(f/h)} \cdot \right)$$

11.4. Repeat Problem 11.3, but making use of beam failure mechanism indicated by
 dashed lines.

11.5. Work problem of Figure 11-9 with hinges at A and E.

11.6. Rework problem of Figure 11-9 on the assumption that the moment capacity
 at the knees, B and D, is twice that of the remainder of the structure.

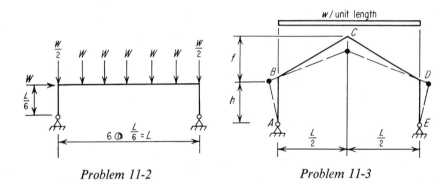

Problem 11-2   Problem 11-3

Chapter 12

Buckling, Stress Intensification, and Secondary Stresses

Buckling and stress intensification, including secondary stresses, are treated in this chapter. The structures considered are centrally loaded columns, beam-columns (including continuous beams with axial load), frames, and trusses. The emphasis is on numerical methods and on concepts of particular relevance in design, although the reader is reminded that this is not a book on design.

12.1 Elastic Buckling of Centrally Loaded Columns

The reader will remember that Euler's formula for the critical load at which a perfectly elastic, perfectly straight, centrally loaded column with pinned ends and constant cross section suddenly bends is

$$P_{cr} = \frac{\pi^2 EI}{L^2} \tag{12.1}$$

This sudden bending occurs because, when the critical load is reached, the column is in a form of unstable equilibrium. Even though the column is perfectly straight and the applied load is perfectly central (conditions that can never be attained actually) the imposition of the slightest lateral force will produce a deflection that increases progressively if the axial load is greater than

P_{cr}. If the axial load is less than P_{cr}, then the deflection will disappear when the lateral force is removed. Thus the critical load can be defined as that which will just maintain a deflected configuration.

From the relationship $I = Ar^2$, in which A is the area and r is the radius of gyration of the cross section of the column, the average stress at the Euler buckling load is determined from Equation (12.1) as

$$\sigma_{cr} = \frac{P_{cr}}{A} = \frac{\pi^2 E}{(L/r)^2} \qquad (12.2)$$

Euler's formula is applicable to any axially loaded bar of constant cross section, regardless of end boundary conditions provided we use the "equivalent" column length, KL, between points of inflection of the buckled shape. Equations (12.1) and (12.2) then become

$$P_{cr} = \frac{\pi^2 EI}{(KL)^2} \qquad (12.3)$$

$$\sigma_{cr} = \frac{\pi^2 E}{(KL/r)^2} \qquad (12.4)$$

Values of K for several buckled shapes are shown in Figure 12-1. Generally good estimates of K for individual members of frameworks can often be obtained by sketching the deflected structure. Observe that in Figure 12-1(f) the value of K will be greater than two if the top of the column is not perfectly fixed. Thus it is very important to exercise care with frames in which the beam connecting the columns is relatively flexible. As the stiffness of the beam

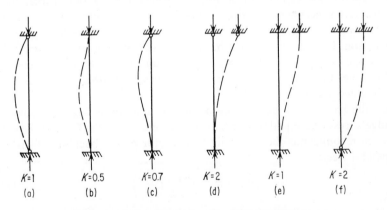

$K=1$ $K=0.5$ $K=0.7$ $K=2$ $K=1$ $K=2$
(a)   (b)   (c)   (d)   (e)   (f)

Figure 12-1. Equivalent-Length Coefficients

approaches zero, the value of K of the column in its translated position will approach infinity.

Actually, care must be exercised in using all values of K shown in Figure 12-1, except that in (a), because conditions of fixity are rarely ideal. Theoretical values of K should be increased by perhaps 10 per cent for each end that is considered fixed for analytical purposes.

12.2   Plastic Buckling of Centrally Loaded Columns

If the stress, σ_{cr}, obtained from Equation (12.4) exceeds the proportional limit of the material, P_{cr} obtained from Equation (12.3) is incorrect. The correct critical load is obtained by using the tangent modulus, E_t, instead of the elastic modulus, E. Then

$$P_{cr} = \frac{\pi^2 E_t I}{(KL)^2}\qquad (12.5)$$

and

$$\sigma_{cr} = \frac{\pi^2 E_t}{(KL/r)^2}\qquad (12.6)$$

From the stress-strain curve for the material, a column strength graph or table can be prepared,[1] by means of Equations (12.4) and (12.6), relating stress, σ_{cr}, to slenderness ratio, KL/r.

Equations (12.5) and (12.6) are directly applicable to structural aluminum alloys. They are not applicable to structural steels because of the presence of high residual stresses resulting from the manufacturing process. A stress-strain curve must be determined using a stub column section, rather than a small coupon specimen, in order to obtain values of the tangent modulus that incorporate the effects of residual stress and variation in yield strength across the section. In addition, it must be recognized that, in a steel column, if the sum of the average applied stress and the residual stress at a point exceeds the yield value, the material at this point supplies no further resistance to the bending accompanying buckling.

On the basis of the above considerations, and conservatively assuming a residual stress level equal to one half of the yield point, the Column Research Council recommends the following formula for plastic buckling of ordinary structural steel:

$$\sigma_{cr} = \sigma_y - \frac{\sigma_y^2}{4\pi^2 E}\left(\frac{KL}{r}\right)^2\qquad (12.7)$$

in which σ_y is the ASTM specification yield point in tension. The formula is conservative for high-strength steels. The same type of parabolic curve was proposed by J. B. Johnson, somewhere about 1890, after a study of test data. The "Johnson Parabola" has been widely used.

Because of the presence of residual stress, the effective stress-strain curve for

---

[1] Column Research Council of Engineering Foundation, *Guide to Design Criteria for Metal Compression Members*, 1960.

steel, obtained from a stub column section, departs from linearity at a stress level much below σ_y. The average value of the residual stress was conservatively taken as $0.5\,\sigma_y$ in obtaining Equation (12.7), and departure from linearity then occurs at an effective proportional limit of $\sigma_y - 0.5\sigma_y = 0.5\sigma_y$. Therefore, Equation (12.4), for elastic buckling, should be used when $\sigma_{cr} < 0.5\sigma_y$; Equation (12.7), for plastic buckling, should be used when $\sigma_{cr} > 0.5\sigma_y$. At $\sigma_{cr} = 0.5\sigma_y$, Equations (12.4) and (12.7) are identical.

At a value of $\sigma_{cr} = 0.5\sigma_y$, Equation (12.4) yields, for ordinary structural steel, approximately 130 for KL/r. For low-alloy steels it yields approximately 110. The Euler formula is, therefore, applicable only when KL/r exceeds these values. For design purposes, a load factor of about 2 should be applied to the basic column formulas of Sections 12.1 and 12.2. For example, the American Institute of Steel Construction Specifications for building design recommends a factor of safety that varies from 1.67 when L/r equals zero to 1.92 for L/r in the range governed by Euler buckling. The increase in factor of safety with increase in L/r is justified by the fact that effects of accidental curvature and variations in effective slenderness ratio are more important in slender columns.

Obviously, since the value of E is essentially the same for all steels, there is no advantage in using the higher strength, low-alloy steels for columns when KL/r exceeds 110 or so. As these steels are more expensive, there is actually no advantage, on a cost basis, at even substantially lower values. It should be pointed out, however, that the use of compression members of high-strength steels has been found advantageous for heavy members (low KL/r values) in bridges and buildings.

12.3   Numerical Procedure for Determining Elastic Buckling Loads of Columns

The differential equation for a member subjected to bending is

$$EI\frac{d^2y}{dx^2} = -M \qquad (12.8)$$

For a pinned-end member subjected only to axial load at its ends, as in Figure 12-2, this becomes

$$EI\frac{d^2y}{dx^2} = -Py \qquad (12.9)$$

This equation is satisfied by a sine curve, and the solution for the critical value of P leads to Euler's formula.

For more complicated cases, such as columns with intermediate axial load and with variable section, the solution of Equation (12.9) can become extremely complicated and laborious. In such cases solutions can be obtained more readily through use of the energy method. The strain energy of bending of an assumed buckled shape is equated to the work done by the load moving through the small relative displacement resulting from curvature of the column. The resulting critical load is an upper-bound value, but very good approximations to the true value will result if the assumed deflected shape agrees reasonably with the exact shape.

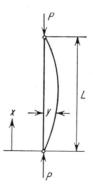

Figure 12-2.   Pin-Ended Column

For the complicated cases mentioned in the preceding paragraph, the use of a method of successive approximations is simplest. The procedure consists of the following steps:

1. Assume a deflected shape ($y = y_0$).
2. Compute the resulting bending moments along the column ($M = Py_0$).
3. Using moments of step 2, compute new deflections ($y_1 = k(Py_0/EI)L^2$, in which k is a constant depending upon the shape assumed in step 1).
4. Set $y_1 = y_0$, and solve for P to obtain the first approximation to the critical load:

$$(P_{cr})_1 = \frac{1}{k}\frac{EI}{L^2}$$

Values of y_1 are generally determined at several points along the column. Unless all values of y_0/y_1 are identical, we do not have the correct buckled shape, and the value of P_{cr} will be different for each pair of y_0 and y_1. The biggest value will be an upper bound solution and the lowest value will be a lower bound solution. If further accuracy is required, the procedure is repeated with the deflections y_1, or multiples thereof, as the assumed deflections in step 1.

If instead of setting $y_1 = y_0$, we set $\sum y_1 = \sum y_0$, which is equivalent to setting $(y_1)_{ave} = (y_0)_{ave}$, we obtain a first approximation to the critical load that is quite close to the actual value. Of course, if the assumed shape is identical to the correct one, the true critical load is obtained from one cycle of the procedure. For example, the correct deflected shape in Figure 12-2 is a sine curve. Then, at any section, the deflection due to moments Py_0 is

$$y_1 = \frac{1}{\pi^2}\frac{Py_0}{EI}L^2$$

Setting $y_1 = y_0$,

$$P_{cr} = \frac{\pi^2 EI}{L^2}$$

If, instead of a sine curve, a parabola had been assumed, the critical load, based on midlength deflections only, would be obtained as follows:

$$y_1 = \frac{5}{48} \frac{P y_0 L^2}{EI}$$

and from $y_1 = y_0$,

$$P_{cr} = 9.6 \frac{EI}{L^2} = (0.986) \frac{\pi^2 EI}{L^2}$$

If y_0 is assumed constant (rectangular deflected shape), the student should verify that, on the basis of midlength deflections only,

$$P_{cr} = 8 \frac{EI}{L^2} = (0.810) \frac{\pi^2 EI}{L^2}$$

Similarly, he should verify that if y_0 is assumed to increase linearly to midlength (triangular deflected shape),

$$P_{cr} = 12 \frac{EI}{L^2} = (1.21) \frac{\pi^2 EI}{L^2}$$

He should also observe that in every case

$$y_1 = \frac{P}{P_{cr}} y_0 \tag{12.10}$$

If deflections are computed at several places, an average value of P_{cr} will be determined which more nearly approaches the true value.

Returning to the method of successive approximations, it is evident that the work involved is essentially that of computing deflections. Except for simple deflected shapes and for columns of constant EI, the determination of deflections with a fair degree of accuracy is quite laborious. Consequently, it is desirable to set up an automatic procedure that will always work and will yield quite accurate values of deflections at several stations along a member. In 1898, L. Vianello used a graphical method to obtain solutions. Subsequently, F. Engesser, A. S. Niles, and R. V. Southwell made contributions. In 1943, Newmark[2] presented a numerical procedure by means of which deflections can be closely approximated by substituting concentrated angle changes at several stations along the member for the actual angle changes. Values for the so-called equivalent concentrated angle changes are readily

[2] N. M. Newmark, "Numerical Procedure for Computing Deflections, Moments, and Buckling Loads," *Transactions*, ASCE, **108** (1943), p. 1161.

obtained by assuming either a linear or a parabolic distribution of the actual angle changes between each station.

Figure 12-3(a) shows a portion of a diagram of angle changes, M/EI, that vary linearly between stations. Equivalent concentrated angle changes are obtained as reactions for simple beams of span ΔL loaded with the angle changes.

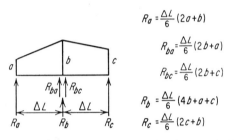

$$R_a = \frac{\Delta L}{6}(2a+b)$$

$$R_{ba} = \frac{\Delta L}{6}(2b+a)$$

$$R_{bc} = \frac{\Delta L}{6}(2b+c)$$

$$R_b = \frac{\Delta L}{6}(4b+a+c)$$

$$R_c = \frac{\Delta L}{6}(2c+b)$$

(a) Segmental Diagram of Angle Changes

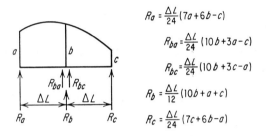

$$R_a = \frac{\Delta L}{24}(7a+6b-c)$$

$$R_{ba} = \frac{\Delta L}{24}(10b+3a-c)$$

$$R_{bc} = \frac{\Delta L}{24}(10b+3c-a)$$

$$R_b = \frac{\Delta L}{12}(10b+a+c)$$

$$R_c = \frac{\Delta L}{24}(7c+6b-a)$$

(b) Smooth Diagram of Angle Changes

Figure 12-3.   Formulas for Equivalent Concentrated Angle Changes

The equivalent concentrated angle changes in Figure 12-3(b) are exact for parabolic distribution of angle change. Deflection computed at a station by means of these values will, therefore, be exact under such a condition. Since any curve can be approximated quite closely by a series of parabolic segments, the values listed are quite accurate for any curve. If sufficient stations are used, a segmental pattern will also closely approximate any curve.

12.4   Buckling Loads by Numerical Procedure

The critical load for a column with constant EI is determined in Figure 12-4. The assumed deflected shape is composed of straight line segments approximating a parabola, but any other set of deflections, y_0, could have been chosen. Because of symmetry, only one half of the column need be considered. The

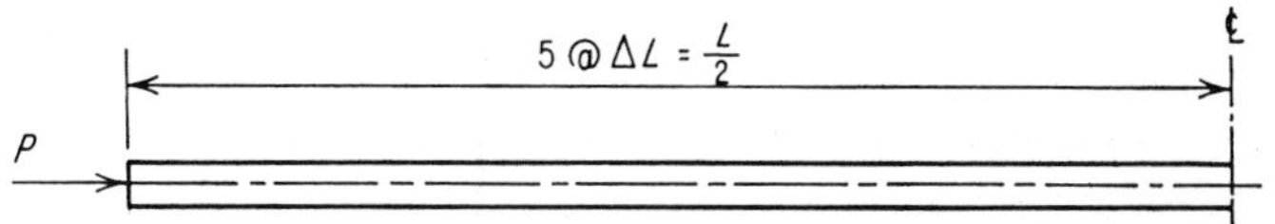

$$5 @ \Delta L = \frac{L}{2}$$

Sta:	0	1	2	3	4	5	Common Factor
y_0:	0	36	64	84	96	100	P
M:	0	36	64	84	96	100	P
M/EI:	0	-36	-64	-84	-96	-100	P/EI
R:	-6	-35	-62	-83	-95	-98	$P(\Delta L)/EI$
Average slope:	324	289	227	144	49		$P(\Delta L)/EI$
y_1:	0	324	613	840	984	1033	$P(\Delta L)^2/EI$
y_0/y_1:		0.111	0.105	0.100	0.098	0.097	$EI/P(\Delta L)^2$

$$\frac{\Sigma y_0}{\Sigma y_1} = \frac{2(36+64+84+96)+100}{2(324+613+840+984)+1{,}033}\;\frac{EI}{P(\Delta L)^2} = 0.1007\frac{EI}{P(\Delta L)^2}$$

$$\text{Set}\quad 0.1007\frac{EI}{P(\Delta L)^2} = 1$$

$$\therefore\; P_{cr} = 0.1007\frac{EI}{(\Delta L)^2} = 10.07\frac{EI}{L^2}$$

$$\text{or,}\; P_{cr} = 1.02\,\pi^2\frac{EI}{L^2}$$

Figure 12-4. Column with Constant EI

equivalent concentrated angle changes, R, are determined from the relationships in Figure 12-3(a). Thus,

$$\text{at sta. 0}:\; R_a = \frac{\Delta L}{6}(2a+b) = \frac{\Delta L}{6}[0+(-36)] = -6(\Delta L)$$

$$\text{at sta. 1}:\; R_b = \frac{\Delta L}{6}(4b+a+c) = \frac{\Delta L}{6}[4(-36)+0+(-64)] = -35(\Delta L)$$

The formula for R_b is used at all remaining stations.

Deflections y_1 can be found as moments due to the concentrated angles treated as loads, but it is easier to accomplish this by means of the average slopes between stations. By symmetry, the average slope on each side of the column midpoint must be $\frac{98}{2}$, or 49. Successive slopes are obtained by addition of the numerical values of the equivalent concentrated angle changes. These slopes are, of course, identical to simple-beam shears resulting from loads equal to the concentrated angle changes. Values of y_1 are obtained by successive addition of the slopes multiplied by ΔL.

Through use of the ratio $\Sigma y_0/\Sigma y_1$, a first approximation of the buckling load is obtained which is only 2 per cent greater than the known Euler value, even though individual values of the ratio y_0/y_1 indicate a spread of more than 10 per cent between upper- and lower-bound values. A repetition of the procedure, using values of y_1, or proportional values, will yield an even more exact value of P_{cr}. If the formulas in Figure 12-3(b) for a smooth deflected curve were used, the first approximation to the critical load would be $9.98EI/L^2$, or $1.01\pi^2 EI/L^2$.

The tapered column in Figure 12-5 is symmetrical about its midlength and has a circular cross section ($I \propto d^4$). Relative values of I, in terms of the end value, I_0, are used. A parabolic deflected shape has been assumed, and the formulas of Figure 12-3(b) are applied to obtain the equivalent concentrated angle changes. Thus,

$$\text{at sta. 0}: \quad R_a = \frac{\Delta L}{24}(7a + 6b - c) = \frac{\Delta L}{24}[0 + 6(-246) - (-309)]$$

$$= -49(\Delta L)$$

$$\text{at sta. 1}: \quad R_b = \frac{\Delta L}{12}(10b + 3c - a) = \frac{\Delta L}{12}[10(-246) + 0 + (-309)]$$

$$= -230(\Delta L)$$

The formula for R_b is used at all subsequent stations.

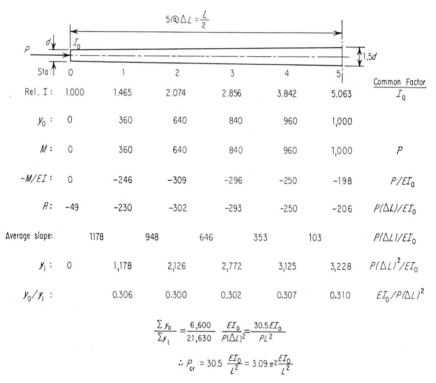

							Common Factor
Rel. I:	1.000	1.465	2.074	2.856	3.842	5.063	I_0
y_0:	0	360	640	840	960	1,000	
M:	0	360	640	840	960	1,000	P
-M/EI:	0	-246	-309	-296	-250	-198	P/EI_0
R:	-49	-230	-302	-293	-250	-206	$P(\Delta L)/EI_0$
Average slope:		1178	948	646	353	103	$P(\Delta L)/EI_0$
y_1:	0	1,178	2,126	2,772	3,125	3,228	$P(\Delta L)^2/EI_0$
y_0/y_1:		0.306	0.300	0.302	0.307	0.310	$EI_0/P(\Delta L)^2$

$$\frac{\Sigma y_0}{\Sigma y_1} = \frac{6,600}{21,630} \frac{EI_0}{P(\Delta L)^2} = \frac{30.5 EI_0}{PL^2}$$

$$\therefore P_{cr} = 30.5 \frac{EI_0}{L^2} = 3.09\,\pi^2 \frac{EI_0}{L^2}$$

Figure 12-5.   Tapered Column

The student should make a second approximation to the buckling load by using the values y_1 as assumed deflections. The exact answer, from a solution of the differential equation, is $30.3 EI_0/L^2$. Note how close the answer is after only one approximation.

The stepped column in Figure 12-6 has an intermediate axial load applied at midheight where the sudden change of cross section takes place. A constant shear of $61.8P/\Delta L$ is introduced by the intermediate load acting on a moment

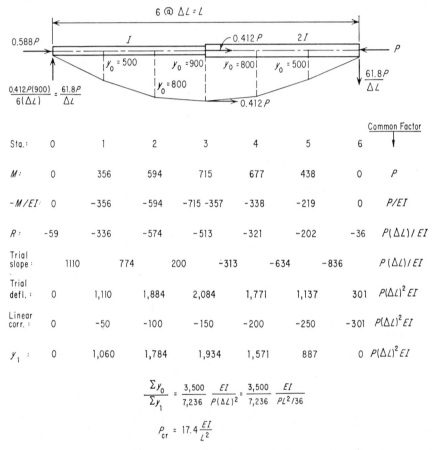

Figure 12-6.   *Stepped Column with Intermediate Load*

arm of $y_0 = 900$. The bending moments corresponding to this shear must be added to those due to the end axial loads.

The assumed deflected shape is segmental, and the equivalent concentrated angle changes are determined from the formulas for R_a and R_b in Figure 12-3(a). Notice that at the point of sudden change in cross section two values of M/EI are obtained, by dividing $M = 715$ by I and $2I$, respectively. Therefore, there is a sudden change in ordinate from 715 to 357 in the diagram of angle changes. The equivalent concentrated angle change is obtained as the sum of the values R_c and R_a, as follows:

$$R_c = \frac{\Delta L}{6}(2c + b) = \frac{\Delta L}{6}[2(-715) + (-594)] = -337.3(\Delta L)$$

$$R_a = \frac{\Delta L}{6}(2a + b) = \frac{\Delta L}{6}[2(-357) + (-338)] = -175.3(\Delta L)$$

$$R_c + R_a = -513(\Delta L)$$

The equivalent concentrated angle changes are not symmetrical about the midlength, and average slopes cannot now be found directly. Instead, assume any value of end slope (1,110 in this case) and add successive equivalent concentrated angle changes to obtain trial deflections. This results in a deflection of 301 at the right-hand end, when in fact, it must be zero. A linear correction is then applied so as to make the end value zero. Add the linear corrections to the trial deflections to obtain the desired values, y_1. It is emphasized that any value of end slope may be assumed. The value in this case resulted from an arbitrary split (200 and 313) of the midpoint equivalent concentrated angle change in an attempt to keep the linear corrections small.

The exact value for P_{cr} is $16.66EI/L^2$. If a smooth, deflected shape is assumed, the first approximation is found to be $16.74EI/L^2$, which is, of course, a better value than that obtained in Figure 12-6. A second approximation in Figure 12-6 would lead to an improved value but still not as good as one obtained using the formulas in Figure 12-3(b). Of course, as more stations are used, values obtained by either assumption will converge to the same value.

For use in design, the buckling load should be reduced by a factor of about 2 to obtain the allowable load. If, however, the buckling load produces stresses, $\sigma_{cr} = P_{cr}/A$, greater than the proportional limit, the analysis is not acceptable. It is possible to include the tangent modulus effect, which will vary along the column, and obtain a solution by numerical methods. For most practical purposes, however, the allowable load can be approximated using P_{cr} from the buckling analysis and modifying Equation (12.7) as follows:

$$\sigma_{all.} = \frac{1}{2}\left[\sigma_y - \frac{\sigma_y^2}{4\pi^2 E}\left(\frac{L}{r}\right)^2\left(\frac{\pi^2}{C}\right)\right]$$

to obtain

$$\sigma_{all.} = \frac{1}{2}\left[\sigma_y - \frac{\sigma_y^2}{4CE}\left(\frac{L}{r}\right)^2\right] \qquad (12.11)$$

in which $\sigma_{all.}$ is the allowable stress and $C = P_{cr}L^2/EI$. To illustrate, if σ_{cr} in Figure 12-5 is greater than the proportional limit, Equation (12.11) becomes

$$\sigma_{all.} = \frac{1}{2}\left[\sigma_y - \frac{\sigma_y^2}{4(30.5)E}\left(\frac{L}{r}\right)^2\right]$$

in which r is the radius of gyration corresponding to I_0.

The numerical procedure can be extended to fixed-end columns. For example, if a column is fixed at one end, proceed as follows:

1. Assume deflections, y_0, for column fixed at one end and hinged at the other. Compute moments due to axial loads, and find deflections, y_1, and end rotation, ϕ_1, resulting from these moments.
2. Find deflections, y_a, and end rotation, ϕ_a, due to the linear distribution of moments resulting from application of an arbitrary moment at the fixed end.
3. Add $(-\phi_1/\phi_a)(y_a)$ to y_1 to obtain deflections y_1'.
4. A first approximation to the critical load is obtained, as before, from $\sum y_0/\sum y_1'$.

2.5 Matrix Formulation

The determination of the critical load for a column can be formulated as follows:

$$\mathbf{FR} = \lambda\mathbf{Y} \tag{12.12}$$

in which $\mathbf{F}$ is a flexibility matrix and $\mathbf{R}$ is a column vector of equivalent concentrated angle changes such that the matrix product $\mathbf{FR}$ is equal to some multiple, λ, of the column vector of deflections, $\mathbf{Y}$, which is consistent with $\mathbf{R}$. This is essentially the eigenvalue formulation of Equation (9.12) of Section 9.3, except that the column vectors on either side of Equation (12.12) are not identical. Instead, the elements of vector $\mathbf{R}$ are functions of the elements of vector $\mathbf{Y}$.

Values of deflections are assumed, and values of the equivalent concentrated angle changes composing $\mathbf{R}$ are determined exactly as in Section 12.4. The elements of the flexibility matrix, $\mathbf{F}$, are deflections due to *unit angle change* and are independent of variation in cross section. These flexibility coefficients can be determined once and for all, for any particular subdivision of the span, by computing them as moments at each station due to a unit "load" placed at one station at a time. In Figure 12-7 they have been determined at the one-sixth points of the span.

The problem in Figure 12-6 is now reworked, using the flexibility matrix determined in Figure 12-7. The column vector, $\mathbf{R}$, consists of values of R, excluding the end stations, from Figure 12-6, but divided by 6 because the flexibility coefficients are in terms of L rather than ΔL. The matrix product $\mathbf{FR}$ is

$$\frac{L}{36}\begin{bmatrix} 5 & 4 & 3 & 2 & 1 \\ 4 & 8 & 6 & 4 & 2 \\ 3 & 6 & 9 & 6 & 3 \\ 2 & 4 & 6 & 8 & 4 \\ 1 & 2 & 3 & 4 & 5 \end{bmatrix}\begin{bmatrix} 56. \\ 95.7 \\ 85.5 \\ 53.5 \\ 33.7 \end{bmatrix}\frac{PL}{EI} = \begin{bmatrix} 1060 \\ 1784 \\ 1934 \\ 1571 \\ 887 \end{bmatrix}\frac{PL^2}{36EI}$$

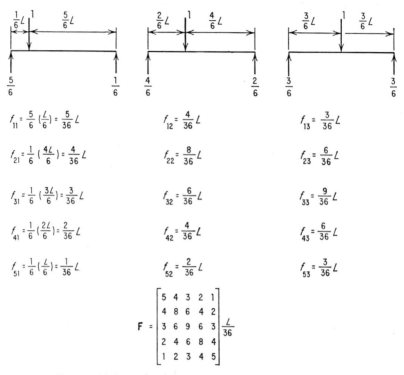

$$f_{11} = \frac{5}{6}\left(\frac{L}{6}\right) = \frac{5}{36}L \qquad f_{12} = \frac{4}{36}L \qquad f_{13} = \frac{3}{36}L$$

$$f_{21} = \frac{1}{6}\left(\frac{4L}{6}\right) = \frac{4}{36}L \qquad f_{22} = \frac{8}{36}L \qquad f_{23} = \frac{6}{36}L$$

$$f_{31} = \frac{1}{6}\left(\frac{3L}{6}\right) = \frac{3}{36}L \qquad f_{32} = \frac{6}{36}L \qquad f_{33} = \frac{9}{36}L$$

$$f_{41} = \frac{1}{6}\left(\frac{2L}{6}\right) = \frac{2}{36}L \qquad f_{42} = \frac{4}{36}L \qquad f_{43} = \frac{6}{36}L$$

$$f_{51} = \frac{1}{6}\left(\frac{L}{6}\right) = \frac{1}{36}L \qquad f_{52} = \frac{2}{36}L \qquad f_{53} = \frac{3}{36}L$$

$$\mathbf{F} = \begin{bmatrix} 5 & 4 & 3 & 2 & 1 \\ 4 & 8 & 6 & 4 & 2 \\ 3 & 6 & 9 & 6 & 3 \\ 2 & 4 & 6 & 8 & 4 \\ 1 & 2 & 3 & 4 & 5 \end{bmatrix} \frac{L}{36}$$

Figure 12-7. Flexibility Matrix for Column Buckling

and Equation (12.12) becomes

$$\begin{bmatrix} 1060 \\ 1784 \\ 1934 \\ 1571 \\ 887 \end{bmatrix} \frac{PL^2}{36EI} = \lambda \begin{bmatrix} 500 \\ 800 \\ 900 \\ 800 \\ 500 \end{bmatrix}$$

The ratios of the corresponding elements of the two column matrices are not exactly alike. A first approximation to the critical load can be obtained, however, by setting $\lambda = 1$ and using the sums of the matrix elements to obtain $P_{cr} = 17.4EI/L^2$, exactly as in Figure 12-6.

If more accuracy is required, the procedure is repeated, using the computed deflection values to obtain a new matrix $\mathbf{R}$. Matrix formulation is convenient for use with a digital computer.

12.6 Beam-Columns

Figure 12-8 shows a member subjected to axial load, P. If deflections, y_0, existed originally, whether due to lateral loads, end moments, or initially

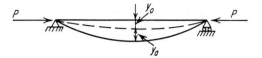

Figure 12-8. Magnification of Deflection by Axial Load

curved shape, additional deflections, y_a, will occur because of the action of P
The maximum deflection at a point will then be

$$y_{max} = y_0 + y_a \qquad \text{(a)}$$

where

$$y_a = y_1 + y_2 + \cdots + y_n \qquad \text{(b)}$$

in which y_1, y_2, etc., are successive increments of y_a, each resulting from the
action of P through the preceding increment of deflection. From Equation
(12.10),

$$\left. \begin{aligned} y_1 &= \frac{P}{P_{cr}} y_0 \\[1em] y_2 &= \frac{P}{P_{cr}} y_1 \\[1em] y_n &= \frac{P}{P_{cr}} y_{n-1} \end{aligned} \right\} \qquad \text{(c)}$$

and Equation (b) becomes

$$y_a = \frac{P}{P_{cr}} (y_0 + y_1 + y_2 + \cdots + y_n)$$

or,

$$y_a = \frac{P}{P_{cr}} (y_0 + y_a)$$

Solving for y_a,

$$y_a = y_0 \frac{1}{\dfrac{P_{cr}}{P} - 1} \qquad \text{(12.13)}$$

Substitution from Equation (12.13) into Equation (a) results in

$$y_{max} = y_0 \frac{1}{1 - \dfrac{P}{P_{cr}}} \qquad \text{(12.14)}$$

in which $1/[1 - (P/P_{cr})]$ represents a magnification factor. Equation (12.14)
is exact if the shape of the original deflected curve is identical to the deflected

365

shape that is consistent with the buckling load, P_{cr}, for the member. Otherwise, expressions (c) cannot be combined. Practically speaking, however, Equation (12.14) can generally be used, regardless of this limitation, to obtain good approximations.

The maximum fiber stress due to P is

$$\sigma_{max} = \frac{P}{A} + \frac{P y_{max}}{I/c} \tag{12.15}$$

If lateral loads are present, bending stress resulting from these loads must be added to the stress obtained by means of Equation (12.15).

Generally, the original deflected shape will not be identical to the pure buckling shape, and, as stated previously, results obtained through use of Equation (12.14) will not be exact. If more exact results are deemed necessary, they can be obtained by a procedure of successive approximations which is illustrated in Figure 12-9.

The values of y_0 in Figure 12-9 are the deflections due to the lateral load

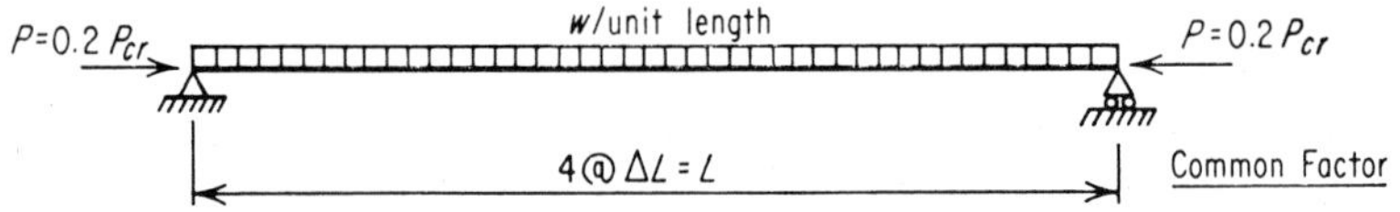

						Common Factor
M_0:	0	1.5	2.0	1.5	0	$w(\Delta L)^2$
$-M_0/EI$:	0	-1.5	-2.0	-1.5	0	$w(\Delta L)^2/EI$
R_0:	-0.292	-1.416	-1.918	-1.416	-0.292	$w(\Delta L)^3/EI$
Average slope:		2.375	0.959	-0.959	-2.375	$w(\Delta L)^3/EI$
y_0:	0	2.375	3.334	2.375	0	$w(\Delta L)^4/EI$
y_a:	0	0.594	0.834	0.594	0	$w(\Delta L)^4/EI$
y_{max}:	0	2.969	4.168	2.969	0	$w(\Delta L)^4/EI$

With $P = 0.2 \dfrac{\pi^2 EI}{(4\Delta L)^2} = \dfrac{0.123 EI}{(\Delta L)^2}$:

M:	0	0.365	0.513	0.365	0	$w(\Delta L)^2$
$-M/EI$:	0	-0.365	-0.513	-0.365	0	$w(\Delta L)^2/EI$
R:	-0.070	-0.347	-0.488	-0.347	-0.070	$w(\Delta L)^3/EI$
Average slope:		0.591	0.244	-0.244	-0.591	$w(\Delta L)^3/EI$
y'_a:	0	0.591	0.835	0.591	0	$w(\Delta L)^4/EI$

Figure 12-9. Beam-Column

only. They are determined exactly as in Section 12.4, but the moments, M_0, are now those resulting from the uniformly distributed load of w per unit length. An estimate is made of the additional deflections, y_a, due to $P = 0.2P_{cr}$ acting on deflections y_0, by means of Equation (12.13). Thus,

$$y_a = y_0 \frac{1}{\dfrac{P_{cr}}{0.2P_{cr}} - 1} = 0.25y_0$$

Values of y_0 and y_a are added to obtain the listed values of y_{max}. The latter are then multiplied by $P = 0.2\pi^2 EI/(4\Delta L)^2$ to obtain moments, M. With values of M known, the usual procedure is used to obtain the corresponding deflections, y_a'. These deflections are found to be virtually identical to the estimated values of y_a, and the final deflections are $y_0 + y_a'$.

If the values of y_a' did not compare favorably with the values of y_a, the latter portion of the procedure would be repeated using moments, M, of $P(y_0 + y_a')$. Generally, values of y_a determined from Equation (12.13) are quite accurate, and it is not necessary to determine values of y_a'.

Beams on elastic supports can be handled in a similar manner. Deflections are assumed. From these, the forces, bending moments, and angle changes are determined. Compute the resulting deflections. If they are not the same as the assumed deflections, repeat the procedure, using the computed deflections as the new assumed values.

In elastic design the stress due to lateral load and axial load on a beam-column, using deflections y_{max}, should not be greater than some value lying between the allowable column stress and the allowable beam stress. Interaction design formulas are generally used to determine whether the stress level is acceptable. A well-known one is that of the American Institute of Steel Construction (AISC):

$$\frac{\sigma_a}{F_a} + \frac{\sigma_b}{F_b} \le 1 \tag{12.16}$$

in which σ_a is P/A, σ_b is Mc/I, and F_a and F_b are, respectively, the allowable axial and bending stresses. To allow for stress intensification due to increase in deflection from y_0 to y_{max}, this interaction formula should be adjusted, by means of Equation (12.14), as follows:

$$\frac{\sigma_a}{F_a} + \frac{\sigma_b}{F_b \left[1 - \left(\dfrac{n\sigma_a}{\sigma_{cr}} \right) \right]} \le 1 \tag{12.17}$$

in which n is a factor of safety of approximately 2.

In ultimate strength design the following interaction formula is applicable:

$$\frac{P}{P_u} + \frac{M}{M_u} \le 1 \tag{12.18}$$

in which P and M are, respectively, the axial thrust and maximum bending moment at failure, P_u is the ultimate possible column load in the absence of lateral load, and M_u is the ultimate possible bending moment in the absence of axial load. To account for stress intensification due to increase in deflection, determine M from

$$M = \frac{M_0}{1 - \dfrac{P}{P_{\mathrm{cr}}}}$$

in which M_0 is the maximum moment associated with deflection y_0.

12.7   Effect of Axial Load on Continuous Beams and Frameworks

As used in moment distribution, stiffness is

$$\text{Stiffness} = S\,\frac{EI}{L} \qquad\qquad \textbf{(12.19)}$$

in which S is a stiffness factor.

For prismatic members with no axial load, $S = 4$ (far end fixed) or $S = 3$ (far end hinged). B. W. James[3] derived expressions for stiffness factor, carry-over factor, C, and fixed-end moment when an axial compression or tension, P, is acting on such members, and they were evaluated by E. E. Lundquist and W. D. Kroll.[4] With these factors known, the moment-distribution calculations for a continuous beam subjected to axial load are performed in the usual way. Convergence is quite good except for compression values of P that approach the critical value. If there is no convergence, an unstable condition is indicated.

The same method of analysis can be used for rigid frames with very slender members. Except for single-span symmetrical frames with symmetrical loading, the axial thrusts in the columns are not known when the analysis is commenced. To determine the stiffness and carry-over factors, these thrusts are assumed. Moment distribution is then performed to obtain moments and accompanying thrusts. If these thrusts differ from the assumed values, they are used to obtain new values of S and C, and the procedure of moment distribution is repeated. Thrusts in the horizontal girders are relatively small, and $S = 4$ and $C = 0.5$ can be used for these members.

Values of S and C are also available[5] for members having infinitely stiff haunches and subjected to axial load. These make possible analysis involving members with haunches or members framing into large gusset plates. The actual haunch or gusset plate is replaced by an equivalent length of infinitely

---

[3] *NACA Technical Note* 534, 1935
[4] *NACA Technical Note* 652, 1938
[5] James Michalos, *Theory of Structural Analysis and Design* (New York: Ronald, 1958).

stiff haunch in order to pick values from the charts. Values for prismatic members are included in these charts as a special case.

If sidesway can occur, corrections must be made for this effect. Fixed-end moments due to a displacement, Δ, of end A of a member with respect to end B are

at A:
$$(S_A + C_{BA}S_B)\frac{EI\Delta}{L^2}$$

$$(12.20)$$

at B:
$$(S_B + C_{AB}S_A)\frac{EI\Delta}{L^2}$$

For symmetrical members, $S_A = S_B$, and $C_{AB} = C_{BA}$.

The translational stiffness, or spring constant, k, is the force necessary to displace laterally the ends of a member a unit distance without rotation. Its value is found by adding the fixed-end moments at A and B (with $\Delta = 1$) from Equations (12.20) and dividing by L. For prismatic members, k can be determined quite accurately as follows:

$$k = N\frac{EI}{L^3}\left(1 - \frac{P}{P_{cr}}\right)$$

$$(12.21)$$

in which $N = 12$ if both ends are fixed, and $N = 3$ if one end is fixed and the other hinged. The expression within the parentheses is a reduction factor which adjusts for the intensification of displacement by axial load, and follows from Equation (12.14). Values of k are important in considering the dynamic response of structures. The important effect of axial load on values of this spring constant cannot be ignored.

Intensification of moments by the action of axial force is important only in quite flexible structures. This has usually meant aircraft structures in the past. However, there is a tendency toward more flexible structures in civil engineering also. A consideration of moment intensification is called for generally only when the magnitude of axial loads and the slenderness of the compression members is such as to result in values of S and C that differ more than slightly from those ordinarily used in moment distribution.

The stability of a triangulated truss framework can be checked by the moment-distribution procedure. For the applied loads (generally the design loads times an overload factor) compute the axial force in each member, and obtain values of S and C from one of the references previously cited. Apply an arbitrary moment to any one of the joints of the truss. Distribute this externally applied moment (with opposite signs) to all members framing into the joint. Carry over moment to the far ends of these members and continue the moment-distribution procedure. If the truss is in stable equilibrium under the applied loads, the moment-distribution process will converge. If the loads are greater than those which would cause buckling, the unbalanced moments will continue to increase.

In design, if the compression members of a frame or truss are proportioned by means of column formulas, using reasonably conservative equivalent lengths, the structure will be stable for the assumed loads and no buckling analysis is required for the structure as a whole. Equivalent length coefficients for several conditions are shown in Figure 12-1. Because of sidesway, the equivalent length of columns in frames is subject to large variation, as mentioned in connection with Figure 12-1(f). For design purposes, charts are available[6] for estimating effective column lengths in frames with or without sidesway.

Intensification of moments and the buckling of flexible arches due to thrust acting on deflections can be studied by a method of successive corrections. For a discussion of the factors involved and for a numerical example of such a study, see Michalos, *Theory of Structural Analysis and Design.*

12.8   Secondary Stresses

Loads applied to the joints of a truss produce only axial force in the members if they are considered to be connected by frictionless pins at the joints. The members in a real truss are generally rigidly connected at the joints, and bending is induced. This is the result of the joint displacement and rotation that accompanies change in length of members due to axial force. The stresses resulting from such bending are referred to as secondary stresses to differentiate them from the so-called primary (axial) stresses. The term *secondary* is appropriate because, although such stresses can be quite large, they are insignificant as far as resisting the imposed loads. The magnitude of the primary stresses is generally scarcely affected by the secondary stresses because the moment resistance of the truss as whole, by means of tension and compression in opposite chords, is so much greater than the moment resistance of individual members.

If the material is ductile, then, neglecting the effect of fatigue due to repetition of load, secondary stresses will not affect the ultimate load capacity of the structure. When the yield stress is exceeded, plastic hinges will begin to form at the ends of the members and the truss will tend to act as the pin-connected structure on the basis of which primary stresses were determined. If fatigue is a factor, as it often is, secondary stress is quite important because the stress level is raised, thus affecting the endurance limit.

The greatly exaggerated deflected shape of a truss with rigid joints, but with rotation at the joints artificially restrained, is shown in Figure 12-10(a). The displacements, Δ, can be taken as those due to change in length of the members from axial force only. Changes in length due to bending are of second order and have a negligible effect on displacements. The fixed-end moments due to

[6] Column Research Council of Engineering Foundation, *Guide to Design Criteria for Metal Compression Members*, 1960.

displacement are proportional to $EI\Delta/L^2$. If the rigid joints are now permitted to rotate in their displaced position, the resulting moments will also be proportional to $EI\Delta/L^2$. These are the secondary moments. The accompanying secondary stresses, σ_s, have the following proportional relationships:

$$\sigma_s \propto \frac{M_s d}{I} \propto Ed\,\frac{\Delta}{L^2} \tag{a}$$

in which d is the depth of a member. The primary stresses, σ_p, are directly

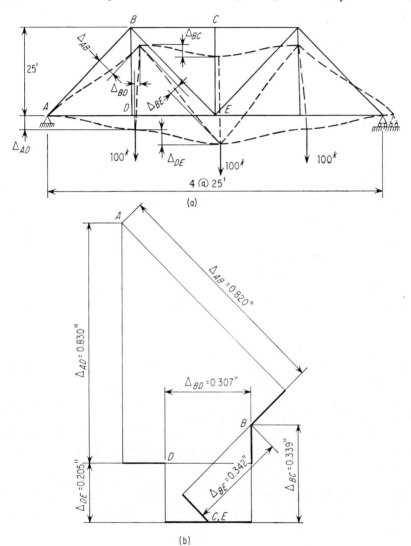

Figure 12-10.   Bar Displacements of Truss (no joint rotation)

TABLE 12-1 Truss Information

Member	F (kips)	L (in.)	A (gross) (in.^{2})	FL/AE (in.)	Δ (in.)	I (in.^{4})	I/L (in.^{3})	$6\,EI\,\Delta\,/L^2$ (in. kips)
AB	- 212	424	17.5	- 0.171	0.820	1,450	3.42	- 1190
BC	- 200	300	13.3	- 0.150	0.339	1,260	4.20	- 855
AD	150	300	9.6	0.156	0.830	840	2.80	- 1400
DE	150	300	9.6	0.156	0.205	840	2.80	- 345
BD	100	300	7.5	0.133	0.307	33	0.11	- 20
BE	71	424	7.5	0.133	0.342	600	1.43	- 208
CE	0	300	7.5	0	0	327	1.09	0

proportional to the changes in length of the members, and consequently to the lateral displacements, Δ. Therefore

$$\sigma_p \propto E\,\frac{\Delta}{L} \tag{b}$$

Using relationship (b) in (a),

$$\sigma_s \propto \sigma_p\!\left(\frac{d}{L}\right) \tag{12.22}$$

Thus, for a given level of primary stress, secondary stresses vary with the depth-to-span ratios of the members.

Values of the lateral displacements, Δ, of the ends of the members of the truss shown in Figure 12-10(a) are obtained in (b) of the same figure. The displacement diagram has been drawn using the changes in length, FL/AE, from Table 12-1. Because of symmetry, only one half of the truss is considered. Values of Δ and I are used to obtain the fixed-end moments, $6\ EI\Delta/L^2$, included in Table 12-1. The value of E has been taken as 30,000 ksi. Clockwise rotation of the end of a member is taken as positive. Therefore all fixed-end moments in the left half of the truss are negative. Since Δ varies inversely with E, and since fixed-end moment varies directly with $E\Delta$, values of fixed-end moment are actually independent of E.

Moment distribution is performed in Figure 12-11 to obtain the secondary moments, M_s. Distribution factors, shown boxed, were obtained by making use of the relative stiffnesses, I/L, shown in Table 12-1. Since member CE remains vertical and is subject to no bending, the truss is considered fixed along line CE and moment distribution is performed on only half the truss.

With the make-up of the members known, secondary stresses can be obtained from

$$\sigma_s = \frac{M_s c}{I} \tag{12.23}$$

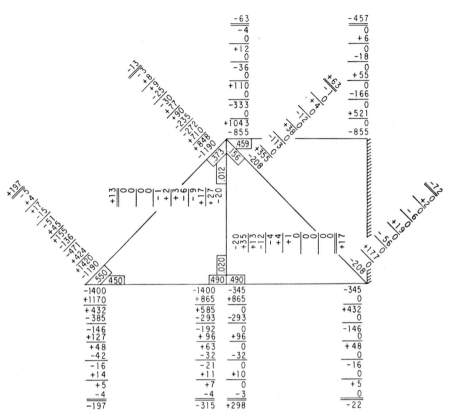

Figure 12-11. Secondary Moments by Moment Distribution

in which *c* is the distance from the centroidal axis of the cross section to an extreme fiber. Generally, we are interested in the extreme fiber for which the secondary stress is of the same type (tension or compression) as the primary stress.

The diagram of secondary moments, drawn on the tension side, is shown in Figure 12-12(a). The shear in each member was computed in (b) by adding end moments and dividing by the length of the member. These shears, but in opposite direction, are the additional "loads" applied to the joints because of the secondary moments. The resultant vertical and horizontal load at each joint is shown in (c). The student should use these loads to compute axial forces in the truss. These are the corrections to the primary axial forces. When combined with the original axial forces, the resulting axial forces are a little smaller. Such corrections to the primary forces are generally neglected.

In trusses with very short and deep members the change in axial force may be significant. New secondary stresses can be determined, using the corrected axial forces, and a third set of axial forces obtained by means of these secondary stresses.

Secondary stresses should be computed using end moments such as those in Figure 12-12(a) rather than moments at the ends of gusset plates. The reason

373

for this is that, because of the presence of the gussets, moments are actually greater than those obtained by treating the members as of constant cross section. See Michalos, *Theory of Structural Analysis and Design*, for a treatment of gusseted members.

The effect of axial force (with or without gusseted members) can be included by using appropriate values of fixed-end moment and stiffness and carry-over factors, as explained in Section 12.7. This effect is generally negligible except in extremely flexible trusses, such as might be used in aircraft or spacecraft, for which secondary stresses are, in any event, extremely small.

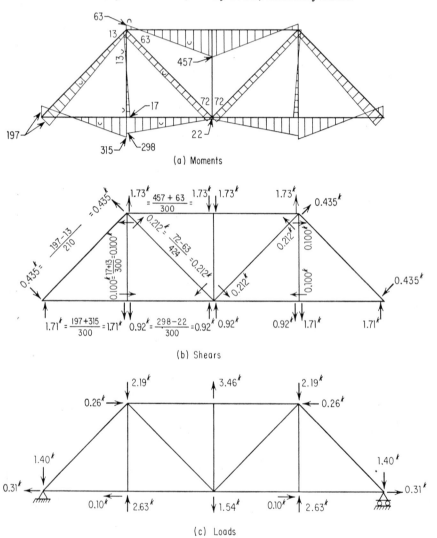

Figure 12-12. Secondary Moments, Shears, and Loads

A matrix analysis can be used in which secondary as well as primary stresses are obtained in one analysis. To do this, it is necessary to include in the stiffness matrix stiffness coefficients for rotation at the joints. The procedure is then identical to that used in Chapter 9. The stiffness matrix for even small trusses will be of an order such that the use of an electronic computer is mandatory.

Problems

12.1. Work the problem in Figure 12-4, but use four segments rather than ten. (*Ans.*: $P_{cr} = 1.055\pi^2 EI/L^2$.)

12.2. Work the problem in Figure 12-5, but with one half the total axial load applied at midlength.

12.3. Determine the first approximation to the buckling load for column AB, using a deflected shape of four straight line segments approximating a parabola. *Hint:* Compute equivalent concentrated angle change at B as $R_b = (\Delta L/6)(4b + a + c)$, using value of $c(=a)$ from extrapolated curve which is mirror image of assumed deflected shape. (*Ans.*: $P = 2.50\ EI/L^2$. What is exact answer?)

12.4. Determine the critical load. (*Ans.*: $P_{cr} = 4.18\ EI/L^2$.)

12.5. Repeat Problem 12.4, but with one half the load applied at midheight.

12.6. Compute the buckling load, using eight subdivisions. *Hint:* In using procedure outlined at end of Section 12.4, obtain slopes ϕ_1 and ϕ_a as reactions at A due to equivalent concentrated angle loads *including* the angle at A. (*Ans.*: 20.2 EI/L^2. How does this compare with answer obtained by using coefficient from Figure 12-1?)

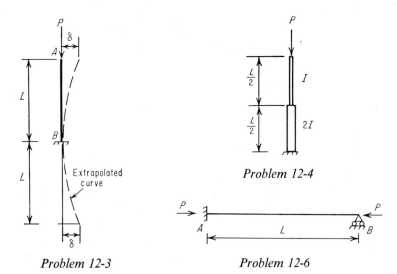

Problem 12-3

Problem 12-4

Problem 12-6

12.7.   Obtain the deflections of the beam column in Figure 12-9 if the distributed load is replaced by a concentrated load, W, at midlength.

12.8.   Determine the deflections of the member in Figure 12-5 if it is subjected to an axial load $P = 0.4 P_{cr} = 12.2 E I_0 / L^2$ and to a uniformly distributed lateral load of w per unit length.

12.9.   Subdivide L into six segments and compute the deflections. *Hint:* Include a constant moment, $0.2PL$, in determining values of y_0.

12.10.   The displacement diagram for the symmetrical truss is as shown. With the joint displacements indicated, determine the secondary moments and the resulting corrections to the axial stresses. (*Ans.:* For $L_0 L_1$, $M_s = -760$ in.-kips at L_0, and $F_s = -6.0$ kips.)

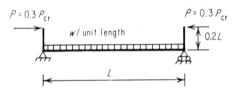

Problem 12-9

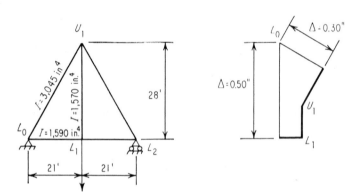

Problem 12-10

Chapter 13

Structural Dynamics

All loading considered to this point has been of a static nature. That is, it has not varied with time. In this chapter we consider various problems involving dynamic loading of structures. These loadings may be due to shock or blast, seismic forces, reciprocating machinery, non-steady wind, or impact resulting from moving loads. It will be seen that in all but the most elementary cases, solutions involve the use of numerical analysis and are usually obtained with the aid of a digital computer.

13.1   Single-Degree-of-Freedom Systems: Free Vibrations

If an elastic system is disturbed from its equilibrium position by the application and removal of an externally applied force, the system will oscillate about its static equilibrium position. Motions of this type are called *free*, or *natural*, *vibrations*.

In practice there are always certain forces, called damping forces, tending to oppose motion. These include air friction, resistance at supports, and so forth. If forces of this nature are present, the type of vibrations mentioned above are called *damped free vibrations*.

Most elastic systems can vibrate in any of several configurations, called mode shapes. For the simplest cases the position of all points of the vibrating system can be determined by one coordinate. Systems of this type are said to have a *single degree of freedom*.

Consider the spring-mass system shown in Figure 13-1(a). If only vertical displacements of the weight are possible and if the weight of the spring is negligible, the system has one degree of freedom. The spring constant, k, is equal to the force necessary to cause a unit change in the length of the spring. Its units may be kips/ft, lb/in., and so forth. The y-coordinate represents the displacement of the weight from its static equilibrium position, with a downward displacement called positive.

The relationship $F = ma$, which is a mathematical statement of Newton's second law of motion, is used to derive the differential equation defining the motion of the system. In the absence of damping or any permanent external forces, undamped free vibrations result if the weight in Figure 13-1(a) is displaced vertically and then released. At any time, t, the force, F, in the spring is

$$F = -(W + ky)$$

Since this force is opposed only by a static force of $+W$, oscillations will occur. The mass of the vibrating body is W/g, where g is the acceleration of gravity (32.2 ft/sec^2 or 386 in./sec^2). The acceleration of the body is equal to the second derivative of the displacement y with respect to t, $\dfrac{d^2y}{dt^2}$, and is

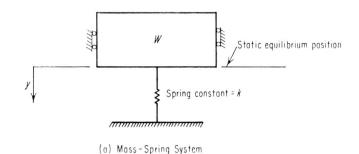

W

Static equilibrium position

Spring constant $= k$

(a) Mass-Spring System

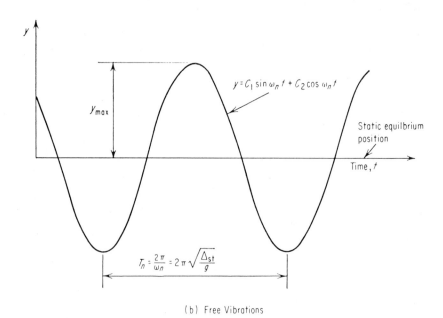

$y = C_1 \sin \omega_n t + C_2 \cos \omega_n t$

y_{max}

Static equilibrium position

Time, t

$T_n = \dfrac{2\pi}{\omega_n} = 2\pi \sqrt{\dfrac{\Delta_{st}}{g}}$

(b) Free Vibrations

Figure 13-1.   System with a Single Degree of Freedom

commonly denoted as $\ddot{y}$. Using Newton's principle, the differential equation of motion is

$$\frac{W}{g}\ddot{y} = W - (W + ky) \tag{13.1}$$

Let

$$\omega_n^2 = \frac{kg}{W} = \frac{g}{\Delta_{st}}$$

where $W/k = \Delta_{st}$, the static deflection of the weight. Then Equation (13.1) reduces to

$$\ddot{y} + \omega_n^2 y = 0 \tag{13.1a}$$

The solution of Equation (13.1a) is

$$y = C_1 \sin \omega_n t + C_2 \cos \omega_n t \tag{13.2}$$

which is an equation of harmonic motion. The term ω_n is called the *circular frequency* and has units of radians per second. The velocity of the vibrating mass is $\frac{dy}{dt}$, or $\dot{y}$, and is equal to

$$\dot{y} = C_1 \omega_n \cos \omega_n t - C_2 \omega_n \sin \omega_n t \tag{13.3}$$

Both $\sin \omega_n t$ and $\cos \omega_n t$ are periodic functions. As a result, the displacement y given in Equation (13.2) will have the same value at time t_2 as at time t_1 if the interval between t_2 and t_1, T_n, is such that

$$\omega_n(T_n + t_1) - \omega_n t_1 = 2\pi$$

or

$$T_n = \frac{2\pi}{\omega_n} = 2\pi\sqrt{\frac{W}{kg}} = 2\pi\sqrt{\frac{\Delta_{st}}{g}} \tag{13.4}$$

The time interval T_n is called the *natural period* of vibration and is independent of the amplitude of the oscillations. The reciprocal of the natural period is called the *natural frequency* of vibration, f_n. Thus

$$f_n = \frac{1}{T_n} = \frac{1}{2\pi}\sqrt{\frac{kg}{W}} = \frac{1}{2\pi}\sqrt{\frac{g}{\Delta_{st}}} \tag{13.5}$$

If the acceleration of gravity, g, is expressed in second units, f_n has units of cycles per second.

To define the displacement and velocity of the body in Figure 13-1(a) at a given time, the constants of integration C_1 and C_2 in Equations (13.2) and (13.3) must be evaluated based on known initial conditions. If at time equal zero the body has a displacement y_0 from the static equilibrium position and an initial velocity $\dot{y}_0$, then

$$C_1 = \frac{\dot{y}_0}{\omega_n}; \qquad C_2 = y_0$$

and Equations (13.2) and (13.3) become

$$y = \frac{\dot{y}_0}{\omega_n} \sin \omega_n t + y_0 \cos \omega_n t$$

$$\dot{y} = \dot{y}_0 \cos \omega_n t - y_0 \omega_n \sin \omega_n t \tag{13.6}$$

It can be shown that the maximum value of y, called the *amplitude* of vibration, is

$$y_{max} = \sqrt{y_0^2 + \left(\frac{\dot{y}_0}{\omega_n}\right)^2} \tag{13.7}$$

A plot of the periodic variation of the displacement of a vibrating system against time is shown in Figure 13-1(b).

The spring-mass system of Figure 13-1(a) was used to derive the various relationships for a single-degree-of-freedom system as a matter of convenience only. Another example of such a system is that of a weightless beam supporting a single concentrated mass, as shown in Figure 13-2(a). The equations defining the motion of the concentrated load are exactly the same as those for the spring-mass system. The static displacement of the load W is

$$\Delta_{st} = \frac{Wa^2b^2L^3}{3EI}$$

The natural period and natural frequency of the system are computed by substitution in Equation (13.4) and Equation (13.5). If $\Delta_{st} = 0.5$ in. and g is taken as 386 in./sec^2, then

$$T_n = 2\pi\sqrt{\frac{\Delta_{st}}{g}} = 2\pi\sqrt{\frac{0.5}{386}} = 0.226 \text{ sec}$$

$$f_n = \frac{1}{T_n} = 4.42 \text{ cycles/sec}$$

As previously stated, T_n and f_n are properties of the beam-load system only. If values of displacement and velocity of the body at time zero are known, the displacement and velocity at any other time can be computed from Equations (13.6) and the maximum displacement from Equation (13.7).

The beam in Figure 13-2(b) is similar to that in Figure 13-2(a) except that numerical values of W, L, E, I, a, and b are given. In addition, it is assumed that motion of the system is initiated by dropping the 1-kip load from a distance of 1 in. onto the beam. The weight is then assumed to remain in contact

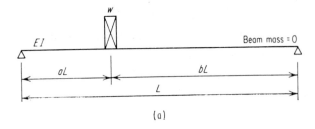

(a)

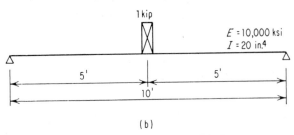

(b)

Figure 13-2. Beam-Mass Systems

with the beam at all times. It is required to determine the natural frequency of the system, the maximum vertical displacement, and the maximum dynamic moment in the beam.

The static displacement of the load is

$$\Delta_{st} = \frac{WL^3}{48EI} = \frac{1(120)^3}{48(10,000)(20)} = .0180 \text{ in.}$$

The circular frequency is

$$\omega_n = \sqrt{\tfrac{386}{0.180}} = 46.3 \text{ rad/sec}$$

and the natural frequency is

$$f_n = \frac{1}{2\pi}\sqrt{\frac{386}{0.180}} = 7.37 \text{ cycles/sec}$$

The velocity of the load, striking the beam from a height $s = 1$ in., is

$$\dot{y}_0 = \sqrt{2gs} = \sqrt{2(386)(1)} = +27.8 \text{ in./sec (downward)}$$

and since the dynamic displacement is measured from the static equilibrium position of the beam (0.180 in. below horizontal),

$$y_0 = -0.180 \text{ in. (upward)}$$

From Equation (13.7)

$$y_{max} = \sqrt{(-0.180)^2 + (\tfrac{27.8}{46.3})^2}$$

$$y_{max} = \pm 0.626 \text{ in.}$$

381

The maximum total deflection is equal to the sum of the static and the maximum dynamic displacements, or,

Maximum total displacement $= 0.180 + 0.626 = 0.806$ in. (downward)

and the maximum moment is

$$M_{max} = \frac{0.806}{0.180} M_{st} = 4.48(2.5) = 11.2 \text{ ft-kips}$$

where M_{st} is the static moment resulting from the 1-kip load. The dynamic analysis of the load-beam system is based on the elastic theory and is valid only if the moment of 11.2 ft-kips is less than the elastic resisting moment of the beam.

13.2 Application of Energy Methods

It is possible to derive the governing differential equation, Equation (13.1a), for the undamped single-degree-of-freedom system in Figure 13-1(a) by an energy approach. Since the mass of the spring is neglected, the kinetic energy of the system in Figure 13-1(a) is

$$K = \frac{1}{2} \frac{W}{g} \dot{y}^2$$

The potential energy of the system consists of two parts: the potential energy due to deformation of the spring and the potential energy of the weight W based on its position. The energy stored in the spring during a displacement y is $Wy + ky^2/2$. The potential energy of the weight decreases by an amount Wy. Therefore, the total change in the potential energy of the system is

$$U = \tfrac{1}{2}ky^2$$

As no damping is present, the total energy in the system must be the same at all times, or

$$K + U = \text{constant}$$

$$\frac{1}{2} \frac{W}{g} \dot{y}^2 + \frac{1}{2} ky^2 = \text{constant} \qquad\qquad \textbf{(13.8)}$$

The magnitude of the constant depends on the initial conditions for the system. The total energy must be the minimum possible. Therefore

$$\frac{\partial}{\partial t}(K + U) = \left(\frac{W}{g} \ddot{y} + ky\right) \frac{dy}{dt} = 0$$

and since no motion is possible if the velocity, $\dfrac{dy}{dt}$, is zero,

$$\frac{W}{g} \ddot{y} + ky = 0$$

which is equivalent to Equation (13.1a).

Figure 13-3 shows a beam with uniformly distributed mass, m per unit length, supporting a concentrated mass, M, at midspan. Actually, this system has an infinite number of degrees of freedom, but the value of the lowest natural frequency based on the assumption of a single degree of freedom is that which is usually desired. An energy approach attributed to Lord Rayleigh can be used to advantage in determining the effects of the mass of a spring or beam on the value of natural frequency of a single-degree-of-freedom system.

The Rayleigh method is based on two assumptions. First, the distributed mass of the beam is assumed so small compared to the concentrated mass that the potential energy of the distributed mass may be neglected. Second, it is assumed that a good approximation to the shape of the deflection curve can

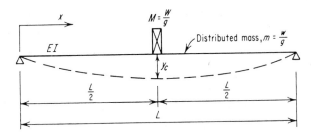

Figure 13-3. Beam with Distributed Mass

be made. Making the reasonable assumption that the dynamic deflection curve is of the same shape as that due to the concentrated load acting statically on the beam, the vertical displacement of a point at a distance x from the left support is

$$y = y_c \frac{3xL^2 - 4x^3}{L^3}$$

where y_c is the displacement under the concentrated load. The kinetic energy of the distributed mass is

$$2 \int_0^{L/2} \frac{w}{2g} \left(\dot{y}_c \frac{3xL^2 - 4x^3}{L^3} \right) dx = \frac{17}{35} wL \frac{\dot{y}_c^2}{2g}$$

The total energy of the system is $K + U$, or

$$\frac{1}{2} \dot{y}_c^2 \frac{(W + \frac{17}{35}wL)}{g} + \frac{1}{2} k y_c^2 = \text{constant}$$

Taking the partial derivative with respect to time,

$$\frac{(W + \frac{17}{35}wL)}{g} \ddot{y}_c + k y_c = 0$$

This expression is equivalent to Equation (13.1a) except that $\frac{17}{35}$ of the total mass of the beam is considered to act with the concentrated mass. The natural frequency is

$$f_n = \frac{1}{2\pi} \sqrt{\frac{kg}{W + \frac{17}{35}wL}} = \frac{1}{2\pi} \sqrt{\frac{g}{\Delta_{st}}} \tag{13.9}$$

In Equation (13.9), Δ_{st} is the static deflection under the concentrated load due to a total load of $W + \frac{17}{35}wL$ acting at the same point.

It was stated previously that the Rayleigh approach is based on the assumption that the distributed mass is small compared to the concentrated mass. Actually, Equation (13.9) is in error by only 1 per cent compared to an exact solution if $W = 0$. The assumption that the dynamic curve is of the same shape as the static curve has the effect of introducing restraining forces into the beam-mass system. Consequently, natural frequencies computed by use of the Rayleigh method are always slightly higher than the true frequencies.

13.3   Undamped Forced Vibrations

Most vibration problems encountered in structural engineering involve forced vibrations. In this section only the elementary case of undamped forced vibrations of single-degree-of-freedom systems will be considered. More complicated forced vibration systems will be studied in Sections 13.4 and 13.7.

Assume that the load W in the system of either Figure 13-1(a) or Figure 13-2(a) is subjected to a periodic vertical disturbing force $P \sin \omega t$. This force has a period $T_1 = 2\pi/\omega$ and a frequency $f_1 = \omega/2\pi$. Applying the equilibrium expression $F = ma$ to the system, the governing differential equation is

$$\frac{W}{g} \ddot{y} + ky = P \sin \omega t \tag{13.10}$$

If we set

$$\omega_n{}^2 = \frac{kg}{W}, \quad \text{and} \quad r = \frac{Pg}{W},$$

$$\ddot{y} + \omega_n{}^2 y = r \sin \omega t \tag{13.10a}$$

A solution of Equation (13.10a) is

$$y = C_1 \sin \omega_n t + C_2 \cos \omega_n t + r \frac{\sin \omega t}{\omega_n{}^2 - \omega^2} \tag{13.11}$$

Equation (13.11) consists of two parts. The first two terms represent free vibrations and were discussed in Section 13.1. The third term represents the forced vibration of the system and has the same period as the disturbing force.

It is apparent that the motion defined by Equation (13.11) is rather complex since two frequencies are involved. This type of motion is called transient motion and will not be discussed. In most instances, however, the forced vibration term dominates after a short period of time, and the effects of free vibrations may be neglected. Motion defined by the third term of Equation (13.11) is called a *steady-state* forced vibration and may be rewritten in the following form:

$$y = \frac{P}{k}\left(\frac{1}{1 - \omega^2/\omega_n^2}\right) \sin \omega t \qquad (13.12)$$

P/k is the displacement, y_{st}, if the maximum disturbing force P acts statically. The term $1/(1 - \omega^2/\omega_n^2)$ expresses the dynamic effect of the force and its *absolute value* is called the magnification factor, M.F. Therefore

$$y = y_{st}(\text{M.F.}) \sin \omega t \qquad (13.12a)$$

In Figure 13-4 the relationship between the magnification factor and the term ω/ω_n is shown. As the ratio of ω/ω_n approaches unity the magnification factor and, consequently, the amplitude of vibration increase rapidly and become infinite if $(\omega/\omega_n) = 1$. This condition, known as resonance, occurs when the frequency of the disturbing force is equal to the natural frequency of the system. In practical applications, a certain amount of damping is always present and, consequently, while the amplitude may become large it cannot become infinite.

For small values of ω/ω_n, say less than $\frac{1}{4}$, the magnification factor is approximately unity, and deflections are essentially the same as those produced by

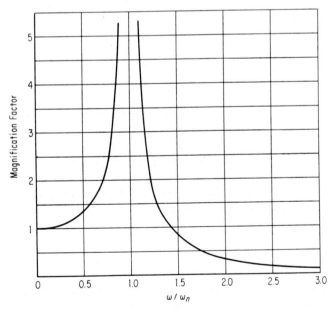

Figure 13-4.   Magnification Factor, Undamped Forced Vibrations

force $P \sin \omega t$ acting statically. If the ratio ω/ω_n is rather large, say greater than 2, the magnification factor is considerably less than unity, so that the vibrations have a small amplitude and in many instances the body can be considered immovable.

Forced vibrations will also result if the supports oscillate. In a real structure such a disturbance may be due to earthquake forces. Suppose that the support of the mass-spring system of Figure 13-1(a) moves vertically so that

$$y_1 = a \sin \omega t$$

where y_1 is the displacement of the support at time t, and a is the amplitude of the support movement. The resulting force in the spring at any time t will be $k(y - y_1) + W$, where y is the displacement of the weight from its static equilibrium position. The equation of motion becomes

$$\frac{W}{g}\ddot{y} + k(y - y_1) = 0$$

Substituting $a \sin \omega t$ for y_1, and letting

$$\omega_n{}^2 = \frac{kg}{W} \quad \text{and} \quad r = \frac{akg}{W}$$

we obtain

$$\ddot{y} + \omega_n{}^2 y = r \sin \omega t \qquad\qquad (13.13)$$

which is identical to Equation (13.10a). Therefore, a periodic vertical motion, $a \sin \omega t$, of the support is equivalent to the application of a disturbing force $(ak) \sin \omega t$ to the supported mass. The steady-state forced vibration of the weight is as defined by Equation (13.12):

$$y = a\left(\frac{1}{1 - \omega^2/\omega_n{}^2}\right) \sin \omega t$$

The material in this section is intended to be simply an introduction to the concept of forced vibrations. The expressions developed can be used only to determine the steady-state behavior of rather elementary systems with one degree of freedom and subjected to disturbing forces such as those associated with reciprocating machinery. It will be seen in subsequent sections that the problems encountered in structural dynamics are usually far too complicated to be dealt with in this simple manner.

13.4 Damping

In the previous sections any resisting forces acting on the dynamic systems have been neglected. Some damping forces are always present, and their effects should be included in computations for the behavior of mechanical

systems. Damping is also important when considering the response of structures to seismic forces. However, in many problems in structural dynamics,
such as the behavior of structures subjected to blast, or impact, the effects of
damping on maximum amplitudes and moments are small and are commonly
neglected. The following treatment of the effects of damping on the response
of single-degree-of-freedom systems is superficial and should be considered
to be essentially a definition of various terms.

If damping forces are a result of friction between dry surfaces, the friction
force, F, is proportional to the normal component, N, of the force acting
between the surfaces, or

$$F = \mu N \qquad\qquad (13.14)$$

in which μ is the coefficient of friction of the materials in contact. This type
of damping is commonly called Coulomb damping and might be developed
in the end bearings of a beam or bridge or in riveted connections.

The friction force between perfectly lubricated surfaces is a function of the
viscosity of the lubricant and of the velocity of motion. Resistance forces
proportional to velocity are associated with the movement of a body in air
at low speed and with the internal friction resistance of many solid materials.
The viscous damping force is

$$F = c\dot{y} \qquad\qquad (13.15)$$

in which c is a constant. Dash spots are often introduced into mechanical
systems to provide a known viscous damping force.

The solution of the differential equation of motion of elementary systems is
considerably simplified if the damping is of the viscous type. As a result, true
resisting forces are often replaced by so-called equivalent viscous damping
which dissipates the same amount of energy per cycle as that dissipated by the
actual resisting forces. In the following only viscous damping will be considered. It must be remembered that damping forces ordinarily act to oppose
any motion.

First consider the effects of damping on the free vibrations of the single-
degree-of-freedom system in Figure 13-1(a). With a viscous damping force, $c\dot{y}$,
opposing motion, Equation (13.1) becomes

$$\frac{W}{g}\ddot{y} = W - (W + ky) - c\dot{y} \qquad\qquad (13.16)$$

It can be shown that if

$$c = c_{cr} \geq 2\sqrt{\frac{kW}{g}} \geq 2m\omega_n \geq \frac{2k}{\omega_n}, \qquad\qquad (13.17)$$

no vibratory motion occurs. That is, the spring-supported mass will move
slowly back to its static position when it is displaced a vertical distance
and released. The value of the damping constant $c = c_{cr}$ is termed the critical

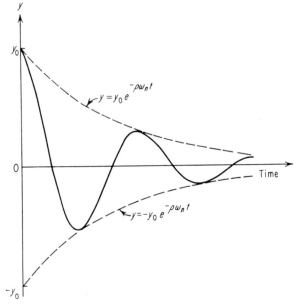

Figure 13-5. Damped Free Vibrations

value of damping. The dimensionless ratio c/c_{cr} is called the viscous damping factor and is given by

$$\rho = \frac{c}{c_{cr}} = \frac{c}{2\sqrt{km}} = \frac{c}{2m\omega_n} = \frac{c\omega_n}{2k} \tag{13.17a}$$

Letting

$$\omega_n{}^2 = \frac{kg}{W} \quad \text{and} \quad \frac{cg}{W} = 2\rho\omega_n$$

Equation (13.16) becomes

$$\ddot{y} + 2\rho\omega_n\dot{y} + \omega_n{}^2 y = 0 \tag{13.16a}$$

If the value of ρ is less than one, free vibratory motion will occur if the mass is displaced and released. A solution of Equation (13.16a) is

$$y = e^{-\rho\omega_n t}(C_1 \sin \omega_1 t + C_2 \cos \omega_1 t) \tag{13.18}$$

where $\omega_1 = \sqrt{1 - \rho^2}\omega_n$. As before, C_1 and C_2 are constants whose values depend on the initial conditions for the particular problem considered. The expression in parentheses in Equation (13.18) is of the same form as Equation (13.2) for undamped free vibrations. In the present case the period and frequency of the function are

$$T_1 = \frac{2\pi}{\omega} = T_n \frac{1}{\sqrt{1 - \rho^2}} ; \qquad f_1 = f_n\sqrt{1 - \rho^2} \tag{13.19}$$

388

As a result of damping, the period of vibration increases and the frequency decreases as compared to the undamped case.

The factor $e^{-\rho\omega_n t}$ in Equation (13.18) decreases with time. As a result the vibrations will be eventually damped out. It should be noted that if ρ is negative—that is, if energy is added to the system, $e^{-\rho\omega_n t}$ increases with time, and unstable motion occurs. A disturbing force which varies as the velocity would have the same effect and cause the vibration phenomenom known as flutter.

If the initial conditions for the damped free vibration system are $y = y_0$ and $\dot{y} = \dot{y}_0$ at time zero, Equation (13.18) becomes

$$y = e^{-\rho\omega_n t}\left(\frac{\dot{y}_0 + \rho\omega_n y_0}{\omega_1}\sin\omega_1 t + y_0 \cos\omega_1 t\right) \qquad (13.20)$$

Figure 13-5 shows a plot of part of Equation (13.20), $y = e^{-\rho\omega_n t} y_0 \cos\omega_1 t$. The curve is tangent to the curves $y = \pm y_0 e^{-\rho\omega_n t}$. The ratio of the displacement at any time t to that at time $t + T_1$ is constant.

$$\frac{y_t}{y_{t+T_1}} = \frac{e^{-\rho\omega_n t}}{e^{-\rho\omega_n(t+T_1)}} = e^{\rho\omega_n T_1} \qquad (13.21)$$

The natural logarithm of this ratio,

$$l_n\left(\frac{y_t}{y_{t+T1}}\right) = \rho\omega_n T_1 = \frac{2\pi\rho}{\sqrt{1-\rho^2}} \qquad (13.22)$$

is called the logarithmic decrement and is a measure of the viscous damping present in a system. In actual structures the value of the viscous damping coefficient, c, can be determined experimentally by measuring the amplitude of free vibrations at two intervals a time T_1 apart, solving for ρ in Equation (13.22), and recalling that $\rho = c/c_{cr}$.

The differential equation for the damped single-degree-of-freedom system in Figure 13-1(a) subjected to a disturbing force $P \sin \omega t$ when a viscous damping force is included becomes

$$\ddot{y} + 2\rho\omega_n\dot{y} + \omega_n^2 y = \frac{Pg}{W}\sin\omega t \qquad (13.23)$$

A solution of Equation (13.23) is

$$y = e^{-\rho\omega_n t}(C_1 \sin\omega_1 t + C_2 \cos\omega_1 t) + R \sin\omega t + S \cos\omega t$$

The first term represents the free damped vibrations. The last two terms have the same frequency as the disturbing force and represent the forced vibration. The quantities R and S are constants.

Neglecting the free vibration terms, the magnitude of forced vibration is

$$y = y_{st}(\text{M.F.})\sin(\omega t - \alpha) \tag{13.24}$$

where y_{st} is the static displacement, P/k, (M.F.) is the magnification factor,

$$\text{M.F.} = \frac{1}{\sqrt{(1 - \omega^2/\omega_n^2)^2 + [2\rho(\omega/\omega_n)]^2}}$$

and

$$\alpha = \text{arc tan} \frac{2\rho\omega/\omega_n}{1 - (\omega/\omega_n)^2}$$

In Figure 13-6 the magnification factor is plotted against ω/ω_n for various ratios of ρ. It is apparent that the value of M.F. is insensitive to the ratio ρ for all values of ω/ω_n except in the general vicinity of $\omega/\omega_n = 1$. For values of ρ less than 0.707 the maximum value of M.F. occurs at

$$\frac{\omega}{\omega_n} = \sqrt{1 - 2\rho^2}$$

When ρ is equal to or greater than 0.707, the magnification factor decreases

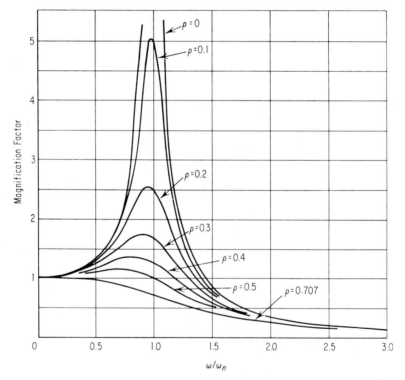

Figure 13-6.   Magnification Factor, Damped Forced Vibration

continuously from a value of one at ω/ω_n equal to zero. If ρ is small compared with ω_n, the maximum amplitude of the forced vibrations is very nearly that occurring at $\omega = \omega_n$, or

$$y_{max} = \frac{y_{st}}{2\rho}$$

If a piece of machinery is rigidly attached to a supporting structure, any vibrations originated by the machinery are transmitted directly to the support. This may result in undesirable dynamic response of the surrounding structure. Conversely, any oscillations of the supporting structure may be transmitted to the machinery. In either case the transmitted vibrations can be controlled to a considerable degree by the use of springs and damping devices inserted into the system between the machinery and the support.

Figure 13-7(a) shows a viscously damped single-degree-of-freedom system subjected to a periodic force $P \sin \omega t$. Any force P_{tr} transmitted to the base must pass through the springs and damping device. It can be shown that the transmissibility ratio, T.R., of the system is

$$T.R. = \frac{P_{tr}}{P} = \sqrt{\frac{1 + [2\rho(\omega/\omega_n)]^2}{[1 - (\omega/\omega_n)^2]^2 + [2\rho(\omega/\omega_n)]^2}} \qquad (13.25)$$

A plot of a family of curves of T.R. versus ω/ω_n for various values of ρ would reveal that all curves pass through T.R. = 1.0 when $\omega/\omega_n = \sqrt{2}$. The transmitted force P_{tr} is always greater than the applied force P when ω/ω_n is less than $\sqrt{2}$ and less than P when ω/ω_n is greater than $\sqrt{2}$. In other words, vibration isolation is possible only if ω/ω_n is greater than $\sqrt{2}$.

Probably the most common source of periodically varying applied forces is found in reciprocating or rotating machinery. In both cases the forces are of the inertia type—that is, they are equal to the mass of the moving parts multiplied by the angular acceleration. For such machinery the periodic force is

$$P \sin \omega t = (me\omega^2) \sin \omega t$$

where m, e, and ω are as shown in Figure 13-7(b) and (c). For the reciprocating

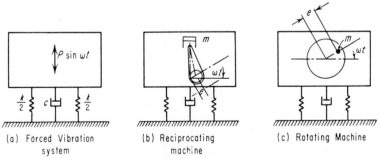

(a) Forced Vibration system   (b) Reciprocating machine   (c) Rotating Machine

Figure 13-7. Forced Vibrations

machine, m represents the mass of the vertically moving piston. In the case of the rotating machine, m is the mass of any unbalanced parts. Analyses for the dynamic amplitude and transmissibility of the machinery may be obtained by substitution of $P = me\omega^2$ in the appropriate expressions.

13.5   Multi-Degree-of-Freedom Systems: Free Vibrations

A beam having distributed mass has an infinite number of degrees of freedom. That is, it can undergo free vibrations in any of an infinite number of mode shapes. A different value of natural frequency accompanies each mode shape. Obviously, any structure containing members with distributed mass also has an infinite number of degrees of freedom.

To facilitate the solution of various dynamics problems, it is common practice to replace a member having distributed mass with one having mass concentrated at several points along its length. The degree of freedom of the lumped-mass member is then equal to the number of mass concentrations.

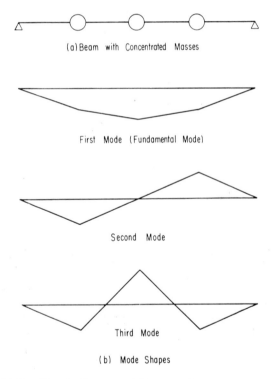

(a) Beam with Concentrated Masses

First Mode (Fundamental Mode)

Second Mode

Third Mode

(b) Mode Shapes

Figure 13-8.   Simply Supported Beam with Concentrated Masses

Figure 13-8 shows a simply supported beam with its mass concentrated at three points. This member has three degrees of freedom and can vibrate in any one of three mode shapes. If it is assumed that the member can undergo angle changes only at the mass points, all the mode shapes consist of straight line segments as shown.

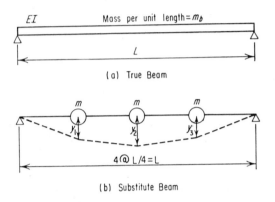

(a) True Beam

(b) Substitute Beam

Figure 13-9.   Lumped-Mass Beam

A different natural frequency is associated with each mode. The natural frequency of the first mode shape is the lowest frequency and is called the *fundamental frequency*. This frequency is usually the most important natural frequency involved in vibration analysis. Free-mode shapes other than the first usually occur only if the beam is restrained in some manner. These higher mode properties of beams are sometimes used in determining natural frequencies of more complex structures.

In Figure 13-9 a beam of constant cross section and uniformly distributed mass is replaced by a beam with equal parts of the total distributed mass concentrated at each of the quarter-points. The stiffness of the substitute beam is such that any pattern of loads applied at the lumped-mass points produce the same static displacements of these points as would occur at corresponding points in the true beam subjected to the same loading pattern. In other words, the flexibility matrix of the lumped-mass beam is equal to that of the real beam. The flexibility matrix for displacements of the quarter-points of the beam in Figure 13-9(a) has been given, in Figure 9-7, as

$$\frac{L^3}{768EI} \begin{bmatrix} 9 & 11 & 7 \\ 11 & 16 & 11 \\ 7 & 11 & 9 \end{bmatrix}$$

For the free vibration case the only forces acting on the beam are the inertia forces of the lumped masses, $m\ddot{y}$, acting in a direction opposite to the motion. The displacements of the mass points are therefore

$$\begin{bmatrix} y_1 \\ y_2 \\ y_3 \end{bmatrix} = \frac{L^3}{768EI} \begin{bmatrix} 9 & 11 & 7 \\ 11 & 16 & 11 \\ 7 & 11 & 9 \end{bmatrix} \begin{bmatrix} -m\ddot{y}_1 \\ -m\ddot{y}_2 \\ -m\ddot{y}_3 \end{bmatrix} \qquad \textbf{(13.26)}$$

If harmonic motion is assumed, then

$$y_i = a_i \sin \omega_n t \quad \text{and} \quad \ddot{y}_i = -a_i \omega_n^2 \sin \omega t$$

where $i = 1$, 2, or 3. Substituting in Equation (13.26), and letting $\lambda = 768EI/mL^3\omega_n^2$, we obtain

$$\begin{bmatrix} (9 - \lambda) & 11 & 7 \\ 11 & (16 - \lambda) & 11 \\ 7 & 11 & (9 - \lambda) \end{bmatrix} \begin{bmatrix} a_1 \\ a_2 \\ a_3 \end{bmatrix} = 0 \qquad \textbf{(13.27)}$$

Equation (13.27) represents a set of homogeneous simultaneous equations for which there is a solution other than the trivial $a_1 = a_2 = a_3 = 0$ only if the determinant of the matrix is equal to zero. This is an eigenvalue problem, as discussed in Section 9.3. The matrix in Equation (13.27) is the same as that used as an example in Section 9.3 where it was shown that setting the determinant of the matrix equal to zero yields the cubic equation

$$-\lambda^3 + 34\lambda^2 - 78\lambda + 28 = 0$$

for the eigenvalues, λ. The three values of λ are given in Section 9.3 as

$$\lambda_1 = 31.56; \qquad \lambda_2 = 2.00; \qquad \lambda_3 = 0.444$$

Since $\lambda = 768EI/mL^3\omega_n^2$,

$$\omega_n^2 = \frac{768EI}{mL^3\lambda}.$$

Referring to Figure 13-9, if the beam in (b) is to represent that in (a), each concentrated mass should be taken equal to the distributed mass in (a) multiplied by the distance between lumped masses, or $m = m_b L/4$. Substituting for m in the expression for ω_n^2,

$$\omega_1^2 = 97.33 \frac{EI}{m_b L^4}; \qquad \omega_2^2 = 1,536 \frac{EI}{m_b L^4}; \qquad \omega_3^2 = 6,919 \frac{EI}{m_b L^4}$$

The first two values are quite close to the exact values for a beam with distributed mass; ω_1^2 differs by 0.07%; ω_2^2 by 1.41%; and ω_3^2 by 12.30%. More lumped masses are required to get a better value of ω_3^2.

The mode shape for each frequency is found by substituting the corresponding values of λ in Equations (13.27) and solving. Only relative values of displacements can be found in this manner. The relative values of a_1, a_2, and a_3, for the three modes are

		a_1	a_2	a_3
first mode (fundamental)	$\lambda = 31.56$:	1.000	1.414	1.000
second mode	$\lambda = 2.00$:	1.000	0	-1.000
third mode	$\lambda = 0.444$:	1.000	-1.414	1.000

To determine absolute values of a_1, a_2, and a_3, the initial conditions at the beginning of the oscillations must be known.

It was shown in Section 9.3 that the highest eigenvalue and the corresponding eigenvector of a matrix can be obtained by iteration. The highest eigenvalue is directly related to the fundamental frequency of the lumped-mass system, and the corresponding eigenvector represents the shape of the fundamental mode. Since in most instances only the value of the fundamental (lowest) natural frequency is of interest in structural dynamics problems, the use of the iteration procedure obviates the necessity of evaluating the determinant of a matrix and solving for the roots of the resulting polynomial equation.

The matrix iteration scheme involves the assumption of an eigenvector. Since it is known that the eigenvector represents the shape of the fundamental mode, a good initial assumption for the eigenvector is one corresponding to the shape of the static deflection curve. In the beam of Figure 13-9(a) this shape is approximately 1.000 : 1.410 : 1.000. Using this vector as a first assumption and multiplying with the matrix consisting of the constant terms of Equation (13.27), we obtain

$$\begin{bmatrix} 9 & 11 & 7 \\ 11 & 16 & 11 \\ 7 & 11 & 9 \end{bmatrix} \begin{bmatrix} 1.000 \\ 1.410 \\ 1.000 \end{bmatrix} = \begin{bmatrix} 31.51 \\ 44.56 \\ 31.51 \end{bmatrix} = 31.51 \begin{bmatrix} 1.000 \\ 1.414 \\ 1.000 \end{bmatrix}$$

Taking the vector 1.000 : 1.414 : 1.000 as a second approximation,

$$\begin{bmatrix} 9 & 11 & 7 \\ 11 & 16 & 11 \\ 7 & 11 & 9 \end{bmatrix} \begin{bmatrix} 1.000 \\ 1.414 \\ 1.000 \end{bmatrix} = 31.56 \begin{bmatrix} 1.000 \\ 1.414 \\ 1.000 \end{bmatrix}$$

The eigenvalue $\lambda = 31.56$ is used to compute the fundamental frequency, and the vector 1.000 : 1.414 : 1.000 represents the shape of the fundamental mode. The results are identical to those previously determined.

13.6 Numerical Approximations

Many problems encountered in structural dynamics require the solution of differential equations too complex to be solved in an exact form. Such equations must be solved by means of numerical techniques. In this section certain of these techniques are discussed. In Section 13.7 these numerical procedures will be used to obtain solutions of some problems.

The differential equations governing the dynamic behavior of structures usually include displacement, velocity, and acceleration terms. Most numerical procedures for the solution of such equations involve replacing the differential equation with an equivalent difference equation. That is, all displacements, velocities, and accelerations at some time are expressed in terms of values of displacements, velocities, and accelerations at some earlier time $t - \Delta t$, where Δt is a small interval of time.

Knowing the initial conditions at time t_0 of a particular problem, the displacements and so forth are computed at time $t_0 + \Delta t$ and these values are used to obtain the solution to the governing equation at time $t_0 + 2\Delta t$. This scheme is repeated a number of times, always increasing the total elapsed time by Δt, until the total time interval is covered. Since Δt must be quite small, the procedure must usually be repeated a large number of times to obtain the solution to a particular problem.

Numerical solutions for most differential equations used in structural dynamics require a prohibitive amount of computational time when a desk calculator is used. When a digital computer is available, results can be obtained quite readily. A program is written for an increase in time, Δt, and the same program repeated a number of times to cover the required time period.

Only two of several available techniques that can be used in solving differential equations of motion will be given here. One widely used procedure is called linear acceleration. In this scheme the acceleration term is assumed to vary linearly in the small time interval Δt.

The assumption that the acceleration varies linearly can be expressed mathematically as $\ddot{y}_1 = \ddot{y}_0(1 + r\Delta t)$ where r is a constant. In the following equations the zero subscript 0 refers to values at the beginning of the time interval and the subscript 1 refers to values at the end of the time interval. Since the change in velocity in the interval Δt is $\int_t^{t+\Delta t} \ddot{y}\, dt$, the velocity at time $t + \Delta t$ is

$$\dot{y}_1 = \dot{y}_0 + \frac{\Delta t}{2}(\ddot{y}_0 + \ddot{y}_1) \tag{13.28}$$

Similarly, the change in displacement y is $\int_t^{t+\Delta t} \dot{y}\, dt$, and we obtain

$$y_1 = y_0 + \dot{y}_0\Delta t + \tfrac{1}{3}\ddot{y}_0(\Delta t)^2 + \tfrac{1}{6}\ddot{y}_1(\Delta t)^2$$

or

$$\ddot{y}_1 = \frac{6}{(\Delta t)^2}[y_1 - y_0 - \dot{y}_0\Delta t - \tfrac{1}{3}\ddot{y}_0(\Delta t)^2] \tag{13.29}$$

The following difference equation representation for velocity and acceleration, involving only displacements, has been proposed by C. Houbolt:

$$\dot{y}_n = \frac{11y_n - 18y_{n-1} + 9y_{n-2} - 2y_{n-3}}{6\Delta t} \qquad (13.30)$$

$$\ddot{y}_n = \frac{2y_n - 5y_{n-1} + 4y_{n-2} - y_{n-3}}{(\Delta t)^2} \qquad (13.31)$$

where the subscript n indicates values at some time t, $n - 1$ refers to values at time $t - \Delta t$, $n - 2$ refers to time $t - 2\Delta t$, and $n - 3$ refers to time $t - 3\Delta t$.

Both the linear acceleration approximations and Houbolt's relationships will be used in the solution of problems in Section 13.7.

13.7   Forced Vibrations of Structural Systems

Most systems of interest in structural dynamics involve structures having an infinite number of degrees of freedom and subjected to rather complicated loadings. In order to obtain solutions for the dynamic response of such systems, it is often necessary to simplify both the structure and the loading. This procedure was illustrated in Section 13.5 where a prismatic, simply supported beam was replaced by a lumped-mass system with three degrees of freedom in order to facilitate the calculation of natural frequencies.

Dynamic loading imposed by reciprocating or rotating machinery is usually of a sinusoidal nature. Solutions for the behavior of single-degree-of-freedom systems subjected to such loadings can usually be obtained by use of the relationships given in Section 13.3 and 13.4. However, the dynamic loading resulting from shock, blast, seismic forces, wind, or impact is often of such a complex nature that some idealized loading must be used to represent the true loading.

In Figure 13-10(a) is shown a rigid frame subjected to a concentrated, time-dependent lateral load P. The moment of inertia of each leg is designated as $I/2$. Therefore, the rigidity per unit length is $EI/2$. All mass is assumed concentrated in the girder. The frame translates laterally due to P, but the girder and the knees do not rotate because the girder has been assumed infinitely rigid. Since the position of the girder at any time can be specified by one coordinate, the system has a single degree of freedom.

The behavior of the substitute system in (b) is the same as that of the frame in (a). M is the total mass of the girder, P is the impulse force, x is the displacement at any time, and k is the spring constant of the system. Since a unit lateral movement of the mass produces a moment of $6EI/h^2$ at the top and at the bottom of the combined substitute column, the spring constant is $k = 12$ EI/h^3. The value of the elastic restoring force is kx, or $(12EI/h^3)x$. In general,

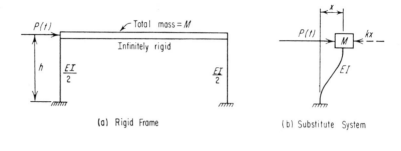

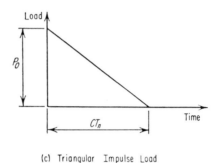

(c) Triangular Impulse Load

Figure 13-10.   Rigid Frame Subjected to Impulse Load

the spring constant for a column fixed top and bottom can be obtained from Equation (12.21), in which a reduction factor is included to account for the effect of axial force on the column.

As no frame is likely to have an infinitely stiff girder, the representation chosen may be taken to illustrate the replacement of a true structure by another with simpler properties. The type of impulse loading shown in Figure 13-10(c) has been used to represent the air pressure due to nuclear blast.

In what follows, numerical techniques developed in Section 13.6 are used in the determination of the elastic dynamic response of *any* single-degree-of-freedom system subjected to *any* impulse type of loading. All that is required is a knowledge of the value of the spring constant and of the variation of the applied loading with time. The relationships developed are based on Figure 13-10(b) as a matter of convenience only.

Writing the equilibrium expression for the mass in Figure 13-10(b), assuming no damping occurs,

$$P = kx + M\ddot{x} \tag{13.32}$$

or

$$\frac{P}{k} = x + \frac{M}{k}\ddot{x} = x + \frac{T_n^2}{4\pi^2}\ddot{x} \tag{13.32a}$$

where T_n is the natural period of the single-degree-of-freedom system.

The left side of Equation (13.32a), P/k, represents the static displacement of the mass. Since it is assumed that the value of P is known at any time, $P/k =$

398

Δ_{st} is also known. The acceleration term can be eliminated from Equation (13.32a) only if some numerical technique is used. If the linear acceleration procedure is used, then $\ddot{x}$ becomes, from Equation (13.29),

$$\ddot{x}_1 = \frac{6}{(\Delta t)^2} [x_1 - x_0 - \dot{x}_0 \Delta t - \tfrac{1}{3}\ddot{x}_0 (\Delta t)^2] \qquad \textbf{(13.29b)}$$

where the subscript zero refers to values of displacement, velocity, and acceleration at a time Δt previous to those referenced with the subscript 1. As discussed in Section 13.6, Δt is assumed to be a very small time interval. If all terms known from the previous time, $t - \Delta t$, are grouped together and called A_1, then

$$\ddot{x}_1 = \frac{6}{(\Delta t)^2} (x_1 - A_1) \qquad \textbf{(13.29c)}$$

Substituting this linear acceleration approximation in Equation (13.32a),

$$\Delta_{st_1} = x_1 + \frac{6 T_n^2}{4\pi^2 (\Delta t)^2} (x_1 - A_1)$$

If Δt is expressed in terms of the natural period as $\Delta T = C_1 T_n$,

$$\Delta_{st_1} = x_1 + \frac{6}{4\pi^2 C_1^2} (x_1 - A_1)$$

Letting $C_2 = 6/4\pi^2 C_1^2$, and rearranging,

$$x_1 = \frac{\Delta_{st_1} + C_2 A_1}{(1 + C_2)} \qquad \textbf{(13.33)}$$

Equation (13.33) expresses the displacement x_1 at time t in terms of known quantities at time $t - \Delta t$. Knowing initial values of x, $\dot{x}$, and $\ddot{x}$ at time equal zero, Equation (13.33) is used to compute the value of x at time $0 + \Delta t$. Equations (13.29c) and (13.28) are then used to compute the values of acceleration and velocity at time $0 + \Delta t$. The time is then advanced to $0 + 2\Delta t$ and the values of x, $\dot{x}$, and $\ddot{x}$ at time $0 + \Delta t$ are substituted into Equation (13.33) to obtain x at time $0 + 2\Delta t$, and so forth. The force in the spring at any time is simply kx.

Table 13-1 shows the values of dynamic displacement, velocity, acceleration, and static displacement for a single-degree-of-freedom system, with $T_n = 0.40$ sec, subjected to a declining triangular impulse similar to that in Figure 13-10 (c). The initial value of load, P_0, is such as to cause a static displacement of unity. The impulse load becomes zero after 0.6 sec—that is, $C = 1.5$. The time interval Δt is 0.1 T_n, or 0.04 sec, and the initial values of displacement, velocity, and acceleration are each equal to zero.

In Figure 13-11 the values for dynamic and static displacement given in Table 13-1 are plotted as well as the dynamic displacement for the same problem with Δt equal to $0.05 T_n$, or 0.02 sec. A discussion of the maximum

TABLE 13-1 Dynamic Response of a Single Degree-of-Freedom System Subjected to an Impulse Loading

Time	Relative Dynamic Displacement	Velocity	Acceleration	Relative Static Displacement
0.000	0.00000	0.00000	0.00000	1.00000
.040	.05761	4.32147	216.07369	.93333
.080	.37787	11.05501	120.60355	.86666
.120	.87919	13.07629	-19.53958	.80000
.160	1.35116	9.63660	-152.44503	.73333
.200	1.59429	2.01004	-228.88300	.66666
.240	1.49381	-6.97841	-220.53995	.60000
.280	1.06225	-13.99933	-130.50624	.53333
.320	.43477	-16.45209	7.86855	.46666
.360	-.18088	-13.42814	143.32874	.40000
.400	-.58138	-6.04760	225.69823	.33333
.440	-.64306	2.95568	224.46638	.26666
.480	-.36776	10.24680	140.08948	.20000
.520	.11784	13.12502	3.82174	.13333
.560	.60918	10.52423	-133.86161	.06666
.600	.89957	3.40777	-221.96101	0.00000
.640	.86086	-5.27963	-212.40954	0.00000
.680	.50327	-12.01140	-124.17902	0.00000
.720	-.04072	-14.29400	10.04890	0.00000
.760	-.56964	-11.28193	140.55460	0.00000
.800	-.88756	-4.09090	218.99717	0.00000
.840	-.87671	4.61545	216.32056	0.00000
.880	-.54112	11.61218	133.51619	0.00000
.920	-.00508	14.30762	1.25582	0.00000
.960	.53282	11.70335	-131.46971	0.00000
1.000	.87337	4.76401	-215.49729	0.00000
1.040	.89041	-3.93997	-219.70207	0.00000
1.080	.57763	-11.18454	-142.52656	0.00000
1.120	.05089	-14.28622	-12.55749	0.00000
1.160	-.49470	-12.09611	122.06302	0.00000
1.200	-.85705	-5.42546	211.46992	0.00000
1.240	-.90194	3.25485	222.54581	0.00000

permissible value of Δt is beyond the scope of this text. However, the close agreement between the values for dynamic displacement with $\Delta t = 0.1 T_n$ and $\Delta t = 0.05 T_n$ indicates that, in this particular instance, either increment is

400

satisfactory. Observe that free vibrations occur after the applied force becomes zero. The initial conditions for these free vibrations are those values of displacement and velocity at time equal 0.6 sec, when the impulse load goes to zero.

The results shown in Table 13-1 were obtained by solving Equation (13.33) a total of 31 times. The curve in Figure 13-11 for $\Delta t = 0.02$ sec was plotted using points determined by solving Equation (13.33) a total of 62 times. If studies were made to determine the response of single-degree-of-freedom systems having different values of T_n, duration of impulse, or Δt, a correspondingly large number of computations would be necessary.

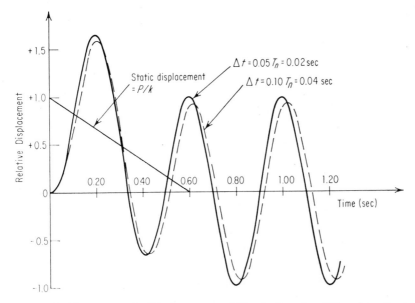

Figure 13-11. Dynamic Displacement of Single-Degree-of-Freedom System

The following material illustrates the computations involved in determining the values in the first three lines of Table 13-1. It will be seen that the numerical values determined do not agree exactly with those in Table 13-1 because those values were obtained by use of a digital computer, using twelve significant figures with the numerical answers rounded to the values shown in the table. At time equal zero, the initial conditions are $x = \dot{x} = \ddot{x} = 0$, and $\Delta_{st} = P_0/k = 1.00$. In addition we have $C_1 = \Delta t/T_n = 0.04/0.40 = 0.10$, and $C_2 = 6/4\pi^2 C_1^2 = 15.1982$. For any other time interval, Δ_{st} can be determined by ratio from Figure 13-10(c), noting that CT_n has been taken as 0.60. For time $= 0 + 0.04$,

$$\Delta_{st_1} = 1.00000(\tfrac{0.60 - 0.04}{0.60}) = 0.933333$$

$$A_1 = [x_0 + \dot{x}_0\Delta t + \tfrac{1}{3}\ddot{x}_0(\Delta t)^2]$$

The zero subscripts refer to values at the preceding time—that is, at time equal zero, so $A_1 = 0$. Equation (13.33) yields

$$x_1 = \frac{\Delta_{st_1} + C_2 A_1}{(1 + C_2)} = \frac{0.933333}{(1 + 15.1982)} = 0.0576196$$

From Equation (13.29c),

$$\ddot{x}_1 = \frac{6}{(\Delta t)^2}(x_1 - A_1)$$

$$\ddot{x}_1 = \frac{6}{(0.04)^2}(0.0576196 - 0) = 216.074$$

From Equation (13.28),

$$\dot{x}_1 = \dot{x}_0 + \frac{\Delta t}{2}(\ddot{x}_0 + \ddot{x}_1)$$

$$\dot{x}_1 = 0 + \frac{0.04}{2}(0 + 216.074) = 4.32148$$

Proceeding to time $0 + 2\Delta t$, or 0.08 sec, the values of x, $\dot{x}$, and $\ddot{x}$ computed at time equal to 0.04 sec now become those with zero subscripts in the expressions. Therefore

$$\Delta_{st_2} = 1.00000\left(\frac{0.60 - 0.08}{0.60}\right) = 0.866667$$

$$A_2 = [0.057620 + 4.32148(0.04) + \tfrac{1}{3}(216.074)(0.04)^2] = 0.346074$$

$$x_2 = \frac{0.866667 + 15.1982(0.346074)}{(1 + 15.1982)} = 0.378213$$

$$\ddot{x}_2 = \frac{6}{(0.04)^2}(0.378213 - 0.34604) = 120.521$$

$$\dot{x}_2 = 4.32148 + \frac{0.04}{2}(216.074 + 120.521) = 11.0534$$

As an error in any computed value would result in incorrect values for all variables at subsequent times, it is important that periodic numerical checks be made if hand computations are used. This can be done by verifying Equation (13.32a), substituting computed values for displacement and acceleration into the equation.

13.8   Systems with Multiple Degrees of Freedom

It is often necessary to use a multi-degree-of-freedom system to represent accurately a structure subjected to dynamic loading. The substitute structure usually consists of a lumped-mass system whose static behavior closely resembles that of the prototype. Such a representation for a simply supported beam has been discussed in Section 13.5.

In Figure 13-12(a) a three-degree-of-freedom cantilevered system is shown. This sort of lumped-mass beam may be used to represent a cantilever beam with distributed mass, a tower with mass concentrated at several levels, or a building with extremely stiff columns but very flexible floor system. Figure 13-12(a) could also represent the more usual "shear" type of building (relatively stiff floor system) if each of the concentrated masses were free to translate but not to rotate.

A general scheme for determining the dynamic response, in the elastic range, of multi-degree-of-freedom systems subjected to impulse loading will now be developed, making use of Figure 13-12. The inclusion of damping terms in numerical methods of analysis does not unduly complicate the solution. However, since the amount of damping involved in structures is ordinarily too small to influence appreciably the maximum dynamic effects, damping will be neglected. Matrix notation will be used throughout, with acceleration terms replaced by Houbolt's approximation, Equation (13.31).

Consider a system such as that shown in Figure 13-12(a), with the subscript i referring to any mass point. The forces acting on a mass m_i are shown in Figure 13.12(b). They consist of the impulse load P_i, the inertia force $m_i\ddot{x}_i$, and the elastic restoring force R_i which is a function of the displacements of all mass points. The relationship between restoring forces and displacements can be expressed in matrix form as follows (see Section 9.5):

$$\{x_i\} = \mathbf{F}\{R_i\}$$

where $\{x_i\}$ and $\{R_i\}$ are column vectors of displacement and restoring force

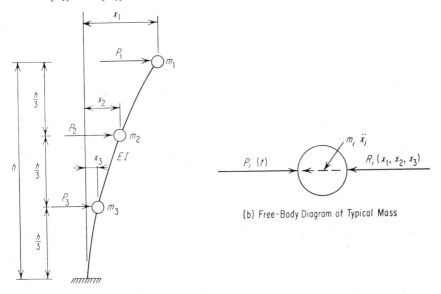

(a) Three-Degree-of-Freedom System

(b) Free-Body Diagram of Typical Mass

Figure 13-12.   Multi-Degree-of-Freedom System Subjected to Impulse Load

respectively, and **F** is the flexibility matrix of the system. We can solve for the restoring forces by inverting the flexibility matrix. Thus

$$\{R_i\} = \mathbf{F}^{-1}\{x_i\} \tag{13.34}$$

The equilibrium equations for the concentrated mass system are, in matrix form,

$$\{P_i\} = \{m_i\ddot{x}_i\} + \{R_i\} \tag{13.35}$$

Substituting for $\{R_i\}$ from Equation (13.34),

$$\{P_i\} = \{m_i\ddot{x}_i\} + \mathbf{F}^{-1}\{x_i\} \tag{13.35a}$$

Houbolt's approximation for acceleration, from Equation (13.31), is

$$\ddot{x}_{i_n} = \frac{1}{(\Delta t)^2}(2x_{i_n} - 5x_{i_{n-1}} + 4x_{i_{n-2}} - x_{i_{n-3}})$$

The subscript n refers to the value of x_i at the time under consideration, $n-1$ refers to the value at a time Δt before, $n-2$ refers to time $2\Delta t$ before, and so forth. Now rewrite Houbolt's approximation as

$$\ddot{x}_{i_n} = \frac{2}{(\Delta t)^2}x_{i_n} - \frac{1}{(\Delta t)^2}(D_{i_n})$$

where

$$D_{i_n} = (5x_{i_{n-1}} - 4x_{i_{n-2}} + x_{i_{n-3}})$$

Then, substituting in Equation (13.35a) and rearranging terms,

$$\mathbf{F}^{-1}\{x_i\} + \mathbf{I}\frac{2}{(\Delta t)^2}\{m_i x_i\} = \frac{1}{(\Delta t)^2}\{m_i D_i\} + \{P_i\}$$

or

$$\left[\mathbf{F}^{-1} + \mathbf{I}\frac{2}{(\Delta t)^2}m_i\right]\{x_i\} = \frac{1}{(\Delta t)^2}\{m_i D_i\} + \{P_i\} \tag{13.36}$$

where **I** is the unit matrix. Calling the matrix $\mathbf{F}^{-1} + \mathbf{I}[2m_i/(\Delta t)^2]$, **A**, and the column matrix $\{m_i D_i\}/(\Delta t)^2 + \{P_i\}$, $\{B\}$,

$$\{x_i\} = \mathbf{A}^{-1}\{B\} \tag{13.37}$$

At any time t, the matrix $\{B\}$ is obtained using values of displacements at time $t - \Delta t$, $t - 2\Delta t$, and $t - 3\Delta t$ and the known values of m_i, Δt, and P_i. The values of the elements of the matrix $\{x_i\}$ are then found at time t from Equation (13.37). Because the time interval must be small, this equation must be solved many times. The amount of time required for hand computations would be prohibitive, but solutions may be obtained readily by use of a digital computer.

The elastic dynamic displacement of the system shown in Figure 13-12(a) when subjected to a triangular impulse load at each mass point will now be determined. Constant EI and a uniformly distributed mass, m_b per unit length, or a total mass of M_b, are assumed. The flexibility matrix for the cantilever is obtained by applying unit horizontal loads successively at points 1, 2, and 3, and computing the lateral displacements at all three points for each such load. The resulting flexibility matrix is

$$F = \frac{h^3}{81EI} \begin{bmatrix} 27 & 14 & 4 \\ 14 & 8 & 2.5 \\ 4 & 2.5 & 1 \end{bmatrix}$$

The inverse is

$$F^{-1} = \frac{EI}{h^3} \begin{bmatrix} 43.615 & -99.693 & 74.770 \\ -99.693 & 274.154 & -286.615 \\ 74.770 & -286.615 & 498.462 \end{bmatrix}$$

The matrix A of Equation (13.37) becomes

$$A = \frac{EI}{h^3} \begin{bmatrix} \left(43.615 + \dfrac{2m_1 h^3}{(\Delta t)^2 EI}\right) & -99.693 & 74.770 \\ -99.693 & \left(274.154 + \dfrac{2m_2 h^3}{(\Delta t)^2 EI}\right) & -286.615 \\ 74.770 & -286.615 & \left(498.462 + \dfrac{2m_3 h^3}{(\Delta t)^2 EI}\right) \end{bmatrix}$$

and the column vector $\{B\}$ becomes

$$\{B\} = \begin{bmatrix} m_1 \dfrac{D_1}{(\Delta t)^2} + P_1 \\ m_2 \dfrac{D_2}{(\Delta t)^2} + P_2 \\ m_3 \dfrac{D_3}{(\Delta t)^2} + P_3 \end{bmatrix}$$

Since the total mass in Figure 13-12(a) is M_b, a reasonable assumption is that $m_1 = M_b/6$, and $m_2 = m_3 = M_b/3$. The analysis will be simplified if the time interval Δt is related to the fundamental period of the prismatic cantilevered member. This fundamental period is

$$T_n = 1.7857 \sqrt{\frac{M_b h^3}{EI}}$$

and

$$T_n^2 = 3.1887 \frac{M_b h^3}{EI}$$

Let $(\Delta t)^2 = cT_n^2$, in which c is a constant chosen to give a small value of Δt. Then, replacing $(\Delta t)^2$ by cT_n^2 and replacing m_1, m_2, and m_3 by $M_b/6$, $M_b/3$, and $M_b/3$, respectively, A and $\{B\}$ become

$$\mathbf{A} = \frac{EI}{h^3} \begin{bmatrix} \left(43.615 + \dfrac{0.10454}{c}\right) & -99.693 & 74.770 \\[2ex] -99.693 & \left(274.154 + \dfrac{0.20907}{c}\right) & -286.615 \\[2ex] 74.770 & -286.615 & \left(498.462 + \dfrac{0.20907}{c}\right) \end{bmatrix}$$

$$\{B\} = \begin{bmatrix} 0.05227D_1 \dfrac{EI}{ch^3} + P_1 \\[2ex] 0.10454D_2 \dfrac{EI}{ch^3} + P_2 \\[2ex] 0.10454D_3 \dfrac{EI}{ch^3} + P_3 \end{bmatrix}$$

Equation (13.37) can now be solved by a step-by-step procedure.

Figure 13-13 shows a plot of the dynamic displacement of mass m_1 in the system of Figure 13-12(a) when each of masses m_1, m_2, and m_3 is subjected to an equal triangular impulse loading. This loading is proportional to the static displacement curve in Figure 13-13, going from a maximum at time equal zero to a value of zero at time equal $1.2T_n$. Notice that the time scale is given in multiples of T_n and not in absolute (second) values.

To start the analysis at time equal $0 + \Delta t$ it is necessary to know values of all displacements at $t = 0$, $t = 0 - \Delta t$, and $t = 0 - 2\Delta t$. It was assumed that all these displacements were equal to zero. The step-by-step solution of Equation (13.37), using $c = 0.0025$, or $\Delta t = T_n/20$, gives results which vary considerably from those obtained using $c = 0.0100$, or $\Delta t = T_n/10$. However, the values obtained for $\Delta t = T_n/20$ agree closely with those using still smaller values for Δt and may be considered acceptable for this system.

Only values for the displacement of the top of the cantilever are plotted. Values of displacements of points 2 and 3 must also be computed for each time interval. With all displacements known, magnitudes of the elastic restoring forces R_1, R_2, and R_3 can be computed by multiplying the stiffness matrix of the structure with the vector of displacements. If R_1, R_2, and R_3 are known, values of dynamic shear and moment at any point can be determined by statics. The values of the dynamic loads P_1, P_2, and P_3 are *not* included in computations for shears and moments.

The computations required to evaluate the displacement ordinates given in Figure 13-13 would require many dozens of hours of computation time if an electric desk calculator were used. The importance of the role of the digital

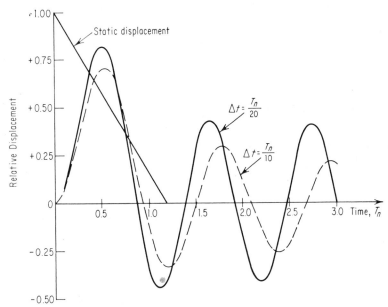

Figure 13-13. *Dynamic Displacement of Three-Degree-of-Freedom Cantilever*

computer in the solution of all but the most elementary structural dynamics problems cannot be overemphasized.

13.9 Elasto-Plastic Response

In all problems considered in this chapter it has been assumed that dynamic displacements are such that the material of the system is not stressed beyond the proportional limit. This is a logical assumption for many systems. One example of a system where displacements in the inelastic range may be expected is the case of a structure subjected to the air overpressure due to a nuclear explosion. It is common practice to represent such systems by a single degree of freedom structure such as that in Figure 13-10(b), subjected to a triangular impulse load, such as that shown in Figure 13-10(c). The restoring force is assumed to vary as in Figure 13-14. If the system in Figure 13-10(b) has an elasto-plastic restoring force such as that shown in Figure 13-14, Equation (13.32) should be written as

$$P = R + M\ddot{x} \tag{13.38}$$

where R is the restoring force. So long as x is less than x_{el}, $R = kx$ and Equation (13.38) is identical to Equation (13.32). When x exceeds x_{el}, the restoring force is $R = F_{el} = $ constant.

For problems of this nature, only the maximum displacement is generally of importance. Therefore, with the triangular impulse load, computations stop as soon as the computed value of x at time equal $t + \Delta t$ is less than at time t. Equation (13.38) can be solved by application of the linear acceleration

407

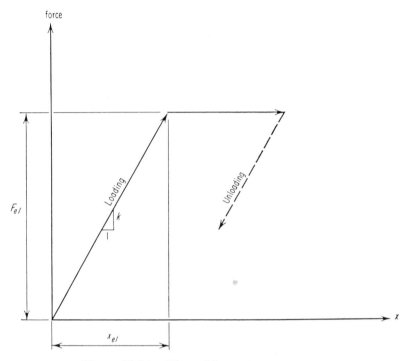

force

F_{el}

Loading

k

Unloading

x_{el}

x

Figure 13-14. Elasto-Plastic Restoring Force

method, as was done for Equation (13.32). However, in Equation (13.38) the maximum value of R is F_{el}. If values of dynamic displacement are required at times after the maximum is developed, some assumption must be made for the value of the restoring force when it falls below F_{el}. One possible assumption is that the unloading curve is a straight line parallel to the elastic loading curve. This possibility is indicated by the broken line in Figure 13-14.

Problems

13.1. What is the natural frequency of the cantilever system shown? The beam has a constant value of EI. The beam weight is negligible compared to the concentrated load.   (*Ans.:* $f_n = (1/2\pi)\sqrt{(3EIg/WL^3)}$.)

13.2. For the system of Problem 13.1, compute the natural frequency in cycles per second and the maximum displacement of the weight from the horizontal if the vibratory motion is initiated by displacing the weight W downward a distance of 0.5 in. from its static equilibrium position at time equal zero. $W = 5,000$ lb, $E = 30 \times 10^6$ psi, $I = 300$ in.^{4}, and $L = 12$ ft.

13.3. Referring to Problem 13.1, use the Rayleigh method to obtain an expression for the natural frequency of the system if the beam weighs w per unit length. Assume a deflected shape proportional to that due to the weight W acting on a weightless beam.

13.4. Determine the maximum displacement (in inches) of the weight from its static equilibrium position due to the pulsating load if $P = 500$ lb and $\omega = 15$ rad/sec. The values of E, I, L, and W are the same as those in Problem 2:
(a) no damping present;
(b) with viscous damping equal to 20 per cent of critical damping.

13.5. Determine the values of *both* natural frequencies and the corresponding mode shapes. EI is constant. The flexibility matrices are:

(a): $\dfrac{L^3}{486EI}\begin{bmatrix} 8 & 7 \\ 7 & 8 \end{bmatrix}$

(b) and (c): $\dfrac{L^3}{96EI}\begin{bmatrix} 4 & 10 \\ 10 & 32 \end{bmatrix}$

Ans. (b): $\omega_1{}^2 = 4.48EI/ML^3$;   mode shape, $1:3.05$
                 $\omega_2{}^2 = 132EI/ML^3$;   mode shape, $1:-0.66$

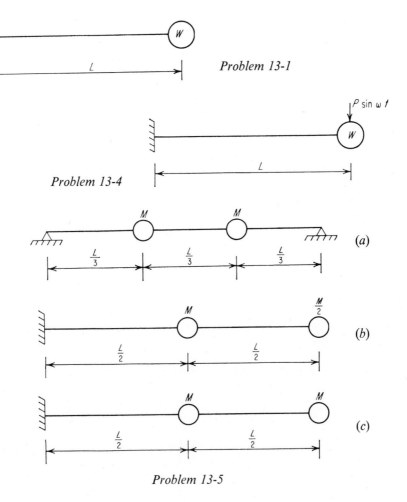

Problem 13-1

$P \sin \omega t$

Problem 13-4

(a)

(b)

(c)

Problem 13-5

13.6. Compute the fundamental frequency and corresponding mode shape for each of the systems in Problem 13.5(a), (b), and (c) by use of matrix iteration.

13.7. It has been shown in Section 13.8 that it is convenient to use a stiffness matrix multiplied by a vector to represent the elastic restoring forces involved in the dynamic equilibrium expressions for the forced vibrations of structural systems. The stiffness matrix may be obtained by inverting the corresponding flexibility matrix or the elements of the stiffness matrix may be evaluated independently as shown for several cases in Chapter 9. For the system of Problem 13.5(c), do the following:

(a) obtain the stiffness matrix by inversion of the flexibility matrix;
(b) compute the values of the elements of the stiffness matrix directly (*Hint:* See Figures 9-6 and 9-7.);
(c) use matrix iteration to obtain an eigenvalue and eigenvector for the stiffness matrix;
(d) explain the physical significance of the results in (c).

13.8. For the rigid frame with an infinitely rigid girder and massless columns shown in Figure 13-10(a):

(a) Compute the natural period of the substitute structure shown in Figure 13-10(b) if the total *weight* of the girder is 20 kips, $E = 30 \times 10^6$ psi, $I = 300$ in.^{4}, $h = 18$ ft. (*Ans.:* $T_n = 0.437$ sec.)

(b) Use Equation (13.33) to determine the lateral displacement of the mass of the substitute system at time equal two-tenths the natural period if a triangular impulse load of the form shown in Figure 13-10(c) acts on the mass. At time equal zero, the value of the impulse load P_o is 12 kips, the lateral displacement, velocity, and accerelation of the mass is each equal to zero. The value of C in Figure 13-10(c) is 2.0. Let $\Delta t =$ one tenth the natural period of the system. (*Ans.:* 0.432 in.)

Chapter 14

The Digital Computer

Digital computers are capable of performing from several hundred to hundreds of thousands of numerical operations per second. A computer can add, subtract, multiply, and divide, and compare numbers and store data.

A computer must be instructed to perform all operations necessary to solve any problem. A complete set of such instructions is called a program. Modern programming techniques can reduce computer programming to a rather routine procedure. Use of these techniques enables one to prepare complete computer programs for many types of problems in a reasonable amount of time.

Standard programs are generally available at computer installations for the solution of the more common numerical problems. These include programs for the solution of simultaneous equations, matrix inversion, and matrix multiplication and for the determination of eigenvalues of matrices.

The discussion of the digital computer and programming techniques in this chapter is intended to serve only as an elementary introduction to the field.

14.1 Problem Formulation and Block Diagrams

Figure 14-1 indicates the sequence of operations involved in originating and solving a problem by use of a digital computer.

Step one, the definition of the problem, requires somewhat more thought than ordinarily necessary for hand computations. Careful attention must be given to the format of the input data and output results. These decisions will be particularly affected by the type of computer used.

The most important steps in the preparation of a problem for computer solution lie in the second and third parts of Figure 14-1, the formulation of a numerical method of solution and the preparation of a block diagram.

A computer program consists of a series of logical steps which lead to problem solution. The logic of a program can be shown graphically by means of a block diagram. This diagram may be quite general or very detailed. It has nothing to do with the actual programming scheme and is only slightly, if at all, dependent on the type of computer to be used. A block diagram should be drawn before any programming is attempted.

411

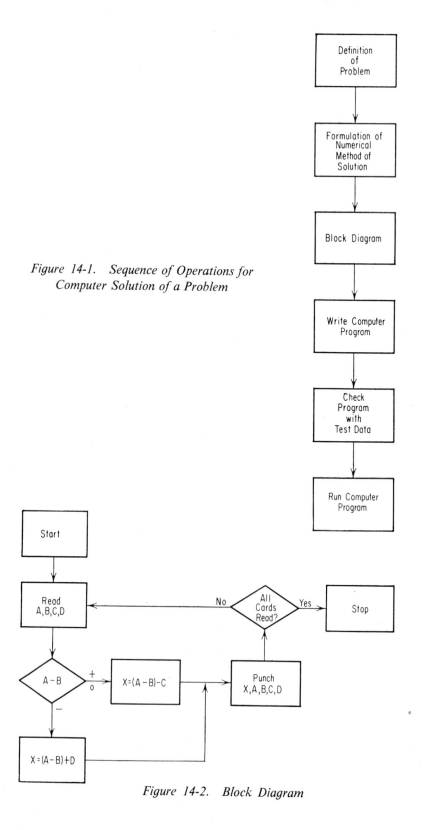

Figure 14-1. Sequence of Operations for
Computer Solution of a Problem

Figure 14-2. Block Diagram

Suppose four numbers are indicated on each of several punched cards. In each case these numbers are called A, B, C, and D. For each group it is desired to evaluate A minus B. If A − B is positive or equal to zero, then A − B − C is to be computed and the result punched on a card. If A − B is negative, A − B + D is to be punched. A block diagram for this problem is shown in Figure 14-2. It clearly shows all the logical steps necessary to prepare a computer program to solve the stated problem. Particular attention should be given to the two decision steps shown as diamonds. The first directs the flow of the diagram, based on the algebraic value of A − B. The second decision is based on whether all cards have been read. Such decisions are typical in computer computations but are usually taken for granted in hand operations.

Figure 14-3 shows a block diagram for the determination of the fixed-end

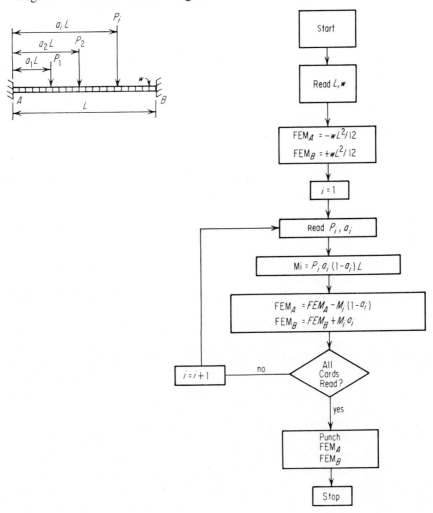

Figure 14-3.   Block Diagarm for Fixed-End Moments

moment at each end of a prismatic beam of length L subjected to any number of concentrated loads as well as a possible full-span uniform load. The expressions for fixed-end moment at A and B, with clockwise rotation at the ends of the member taken as positive, are the following:

(a) for uniform load :

$$\text{FEM}_A = -\tfrac{1}{12}wL^2; \quad \text{FEM}_B = +\tfrac{1}{12}wL^2$$

(b) for concentrated loads :

$$\text{FEM}_A = -\sum_{i=1}^{n} P_i a_i (1 - a_i)^2 L$$

$$\text{FEM}_B = \sum_{i=1}^{n} P_i a_i^2 (1 - a_i) L$$

Assuming that punched cards are used for input, the values of length L and uniform load w are punched in the first card. Each pair of values P and a are punched in succeeding cards. The output consists of the values of the total fixed-end moments.

The first computational step in the block diagram consists of the calculation of FEM_A and FEM_B due to the full-span uniform load. A value of $w = 0$ *must* be read into the computer if there is no uniform load on the beam.

The next several steps are an example of an important programming concept called *looping*, wherein a sequence of operations is repeated a number of times using different data. In the loop the magnitude and location of a concentrated load are represented by P_i and a_i, respectively. Initially, the subscript, i, is set equal to one so that P_1 and a_1 are the first values of data considered. The ordinary equal sign in the block diagram means "replace by" and not "equal to." For example, $\text{FEM}_A = \text{FEM}_A - M_i(1 - a_i)$ signifies that $\text{FEM}_A - M_i(1 - a_i)$ is to replace FEM_A. In other words, a previously computed value for FEM_A is to be modified by $-M_i(1 - a_i)$ to obtain a partial sum of the total value. After the indicated numerical operations are completed, a check is made to determine if all cards punched with values of P_i and a_i have been read. If not, i is advanced to $i + 1$, and the loop is repeated to obtain a new partial sum of FEM_A and FEM_B. If all cards have been read, the latest values of the fixed-end moments are punched on a card and the program stops.

A further example of block diagramming is given in Figure 14-4. The diagram indicates the steps necessary to compute the moments at the interior supports of a multispan continuous beam by means of the displacement method, using the matrix formulation of Section 9.8.

The beam may have any number of spans greater than two, but each span must be prismatic. The extreme ends are simply supported. The loading may consist of any number of concentrated loads as well as full-span uniform loads.

The construction of the block diagram has been considerably simplified by the use of three subroutines indicated by heavy box outlines. The inversion of the stiffness matrix and the matrix multiplications are performed through use of standard routines which should be available at any computer installation.

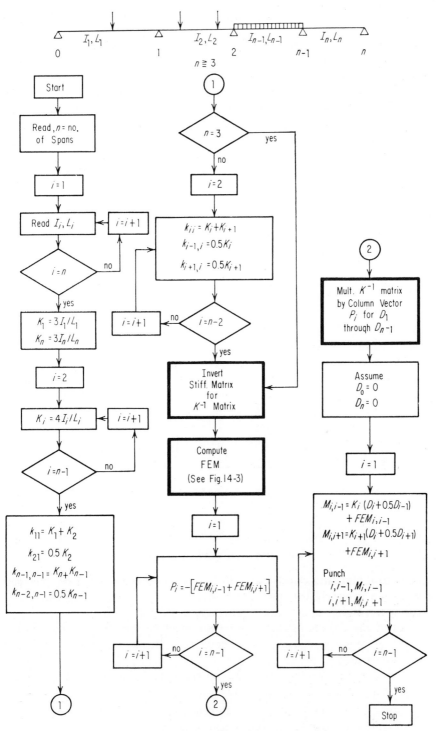

Figure 14-4. Block Diagram for Stiffness Matrix Analysis

415

The subroutine for the determination of fixed-end moments is similar to that shown in Figure 14-3. An important feature of the block diagram in Figure 14-4 is the repeated use of looping. Since the diagram is to represent the steps necessary for the analysis of a continuous beam with n spans, general subscripted expressions are written for computations involving interior spans or supports. After a set of computations is made for a particular interior span or support, the subscripts are advanced and similar computations made for the next span or support until all required computations are completed. Each looping scheme is terminated by relating a subscript to the total number of spans, n.

14.2 Digital Computer Organization

The major components of a digital computer are shown in Figure 14-5. Input devices read or sense coded data that are recorded on a prescribed medium and make this information available to the computer. Input devices used in engineering applications include punched cards, magnetic tape, paper

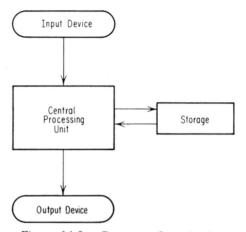

Figure 14-5.   Computer Organization

tape, disk files, and direct use of the computer console. Of these, punched cards are probably the most commonly used for small- and medium-size computers and magnetic tape is most common for large machines.

All of the devices listed for input are available for data output. Again, punched cards obtained directly or processed from magnetic tape are the most commonly used.

The central processing unit is the control center for the entire data processing system. It can be divided into two parts:

1. The arithmetic-logic unit.
2. The control section.

The arithmetic-logic unit performs such operations as addition, subtraction, multiplication, division, and comparing. It also is able to test various conditions encountered during processing.

The control section of the central processing unit directs and coordinates the entire computer system. These functions include control of the input/ output units, the arithmetic-logic operation of the central processing unit, and the transfer of data to and from the storage.

As previously mentioned, a computer can store and recall data. Storage is usually achieved by means of magnetized spots on a rotating drum or by use of a stationary magnetic core unit. All storage positions can be identified by number, and the data in storage are available almost instantaneously to the computer. All data must be placed in storage before they can be processed by the computer. Information is read into storage by an input unit; operations specified by a program in storage are performed and results are extracted from storage through an output unit.

14.3 Computer Coding

The various computer manufacturers have prepared manuals detailing the procedures for instructing particular computers to perform various arithmetic and logical operations. A computer is designed to perform only a specified number of operations, and it must be directed to perform each operation by an instruction. These instructions usually consist of two-digit numbers. For example, the number 21 may direct the computer to multiply. Furthermore, the storage location of any data must be indicated. A complete instruction to multiply might be 21 1253 1617, meaning that the data stored in storage location 1253 are to be multiplied by the data stored in location 1617. The entire series of instructions required to complete a given procedure is known as a program.

The example of the multiplication instruction presupposes that the multiplicand and multiplier have been previously read into storage. After the calculation has been performed, the product must be returned to a specified storage location from which it can be written out by an output device or used in subsequent calculations.

One of the most difficult problems in computer coding consists of locating decimal points. A discussion of this problem is beyond the scope of this presentation. Schemes involving numbers using a fixed decimal point location and ten raised to a power usually offer the best solution to the scaling problem.

Any problem must be reduced to a series of basic machine operations before a computer solution can be obtained. Each of these operations is coded as an instruction in a form which can be interpreted by the computer and is placed in storage. Data may be placed in storage directly or may be read into storage using appropriate program instructions.

The concept of machine-language coding will be illustrated by means of an imaginary computer having the following characteristics. All numerical computations will be performed in an accumulator located in storage position 00. Data can be read into and out of positions 01 through 05, only. It is assumed that all numbers encountered are such that no overflow occurs. That is, the proper location of the decimal point is assumed to present no problems. The computer can perform the following operations using the code indicated:

Code	Operation
31	Add to accumulator
32	Subtract from accumulator
33	Branch if accumulator is positive
34	Branch if accumulator is equal to zero
35	Branch
36	Multiply accumulator
37	Divide accumulator
38	Store accumulator
39	Read card
40	Punch card
41	Halt

The problem shown in the block diagram in Figure 14-2 is coded in Table 14-1. It is assumed that a set of values for A, B, C, and D are punched in each of several cards. The output is to consist of the value A − B − C or A − B + D, as indicated by the block diagram, as well as the values of A, B, C, and D. The problem differs from the block diagram in that all computer operations will stop when a read instruction is indicated and there are no cards in the read position. Consequently, no halt instruction is required. The first instruction will be stored in position 06 and all other instructions will be located sequentially.

The instructions in Table 14-1 are in the only form that the imaginary computer can interpret. However, for most computers it is possible to simplify machine-language coding somewhat by use of a symbolic programming system. In such a system, storage locations are not specified unless referred to in a branch instruction. Alphabetic characters are used for operation codes instead of numbers, and storage positions for data may or may not be specified. A compiler program prepared by the computer manufacturer is used to convert the program written symbolically into a program in machine language. That is, operation codes will be given numbers and all storage positions will be numbered. It must be remembered that symbolic programming can only be used when standard machine coding is thoroughly understood.

Because of the extreme simplicity of the problem and because it was assumed that no difficulties in locating decimal points would occur, it was possible to write the machine-language program for the problem of Figure 14-2 in a short amount of time. However, to write and check a machine-language program for a more complicated problem may require several days or even weeks of programming time for an experienced programmer.

In the next section a programming system is discussed that makes possible

TABLE 14-1 Machine Language Program

Storage Location	Oper. Code	Data Address	Description
06	39	01	Read A, B, C, D into locations 01 thru 04
07	32	00	Set accumulator = zero
08	31	01	Add value of A to accumulator
09	32	02	Subtract value of B from accumulator (A-B)
10	33	16	Branch to location 16 if accumulator is plus
11	34	16	Branch to location 16 if accumulator is zero
12	31	04	Add value of D to accumulator (A-B+D)
13	38	05	Store accumulator in 05 (A-B+D)
14	40	01	Punch locations 01 thru 05, A, B, C, D, A-B+D
15	35	06	Branch to 06, (Read next card)
16	32	03	Subtract value of C from accumulator (A-B-C)
17	38	05	Store accumulator in 05 (A-B-C)
18	40	01	Punch locations 01 thru 05, A, B, C, D, A-B-C
19	35	06	Branch to 06, (Read next card)

the preparation of computer programs in a fraction of the time required when machine language is used.

14.4   The Fortran Programming System

Several programming systems have been developed that are problem-oriented rather than computer-oriented. The system to be discussed in this article is Fortran, which has been developed by the International Business Machines Corporation. The use of Fortran is not limited to IBM equipment since most other manufacturers have adapted their computers to accept this method of programming. Only the barest concepts of Fortran will be given in this text. Teaching of programming would require a much more comprehensive treatment which is available in publications by IBM and others.

The use of a programming system such as Fortran requires absolutely no knowledge of the machine-language coding system of a computer. As a result, the same Fortran program can be used with several different computers if allowances are made for the possibly different input/output devices. Because of its simplicity, the basic rules of Fortran can be learned in several hours. After considerable practice fairly complicated programs can be written in a relatively short time. The only drawback is that the computer running time may be greater than that required to solve the same problem by use of a direct or symbolic machine-language program.

The Fortran programming system is illustrated in Figure 14-6. Fortran language is translated into machine language by means of a standard program called the Fortran processor. The resulting machine-language program is then used to obtain the solution to the problem. The original program (in Fortran language) is called the source program and the final program (in machine language) is called the object program.

Since a standard processor is used, all Fortran statements must follow rigid specifications. Fortunately, the Fortran language uses a statement format quite similar to that used in ordinary mathematics. In addition the necessary control statements are usually quite descriptive. The following are some Fortran symbols and statements:

Symbol	Description
+	Add
—	Subtract
*	Multiply
/	Divide
**	Exponentiation
READ	Read a card
PUNCH	Punch a card
FORMAT	Specifies form of input and output data
GO TO 7	Branch to statement 7
IF	Conditional branch
DO	Repeat a sequence of statements several times
( )	Open and closed parentheses
STOP	Stop computer
END	Last statement in all Fortran programs

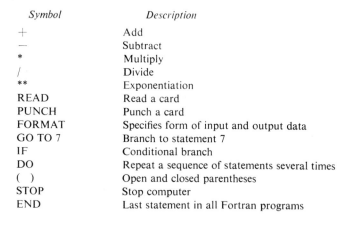

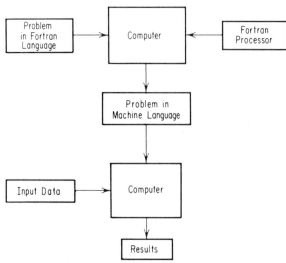

Figure 14-6.   Fortran Programming System

The problem shown in the block diagram of Figure 14-2 and programmed in machine language in Table 14-1 can be written in Fortran as follows:

```
 1   READ 10,A,B,C,D
10   FORMAT (4F10.0)
     IF (A − B)3,2,2
 2   X = A − B − C
     GO TO 4
 3   X = A − B + D
 4   PUNCH 11,A,B,C,D,X
11   FORMAT (5F10.4)
     GO TO 1
     END
```

The Fortran statements follow almost one for one from the block diagram of Figure 14-2 and are performed sequentially unless the program indicates otherwise. A statement is usually assigned a number only if it is referred to in another statement.

Statement 1, READ 10,A,B,C,D causes four numerical values to be read from a single punched card and assigns these values to A, B, C, and D, respectively. The number 10 in the statement refers to statement 10, which is FORMAT (4F10.0). In this instance the FORMAT statement specifies that the numerical value to be assigned to A is punched within the first ten columns of the card and includes a decimal point. Values of B, C, and D are located within successive ten column fields of the same card.

The IF (A − B)3,2,2 statement corresponds to the first decision box in Figure 14-2 and directs the program to either of two branches depending on the value of (A − B). If the value (A − B) is negative, the next statement in the program is statement 3. If the value (A − B) is zero or positive, the program goes to statement 2.

Assuming that the IF statement directs the program to statement 2, X is set equal to A − B − C. Note that the statement is exactly the same as the algebraic equation for the same condition. The statement GO TO 4 is inserted so that statement 3 can be skipped and the program directed to statement 4. PUNCH 11,A,B,C,D,X causes the values of A, B, C, D, and X to be punched in a single card with format indicated in statement 11, FORMAT (5F10.4). As a result, the values of A, B, C, D, and X will be punched in successive fields of ten columns, with four significant figures retained to the right of a decimal point.

If the value of (A − B) were negative, the IF statement would have directed the program to go directly to statement 3, where X = A − B + D would be evaluated. Since the next statement is then the PUNCH instruction, the values of A, B, C, D, and X would be punched using the format of statement 11. Regardless of the value of (A − B), the program eventually reaches statement 4 and proceeds to GO TO 1. This returns the program to the READ statement, causing a new set of values of A, B, C, and D to be read, and so forth. If all cards have been read, the computer will automatically stop. The last statement in all Fortran programs is END.

Index